Study Guide

Peterson and Estenson's

Income, Employment, and Economic Growth

EIGHTH EDITION

Harold R. Williams

Kent State University

W • W • NORTON & COMPANY

New York • London

Composition by Roberta Flechner Graphics
Manufactured by Capital City Press

ISBN 0-393-96855-3 (pbk.)

W. W. Norton & Company, Inc.
500 Fifth Avenue, New York, N.Y. 10110
W. W. Norton & Company Ltd.,
10 Coptic Street, London WC1A 1PU

567890

To my wife, Dorothy, and
two children, Theresa and
Mark.

Contents

Preface

This book of problems, concepts, and self-tests is designed to be used in courses pertaining to income and employment theory. The exercises correlate with Wallace C. Peterson's text *Income, Employment, and Economic Growth*, Eighth Edition. However, the material has been developed and organized so that it may be used in combination with any standard textbook in intermediate macroeconomic theory.

Each chapter has three parts: The first part contains key concepts relevant to the particular aspect of macroeconomic theory under consideration. Next there is a section presenting essay questions and problems. To facilitate rapid understanding as well as to guide the student, problems follow the sequence in which the subject matter normally appears in a textbook chapter. Nonetheless, the arrangement of problems may be altered to correlate with class lectures or the specific text being used. The last part is a self-test which includes sentences for completion, true and false statements, and multiple choice questions. It is unlikely that the student will be able to answer all the self-test questions from information given in the course textbook alone; some of the questions presume that the student has worked through the problems.

Brief answers to the problems and self-tests are provided in the back of the book. No attempt has been made to supply summary explanations for the essay questions since most of the answers can be found in the course text. In addition, answers to some of the essay topics depend on the individual's views; for these there are no simple responses. Definitions and explanations for the key concepts must be obtained from the course textbook and supplemental reading materials.

The purpose of this book is twofold. First and foremost, it is intended to guide and aid the student in understanding what is admittedly a difficult subject. By pointing out key concepts, important aspects, and problem areas, it may make easier the students' task. The author firmly believes that a book of this nature is not only useful but necessary for some students to master the subject. Second, it is hoped the instructor will be able to use this book to discover those aspects of the subject that the student has not fully comprehended. The book is self-contained so that students can utilize it on their own, whether the instructor makes specific references to it or not.

Several aspects of this book should be emphasized. First, it will aid the student in *understanding* macroeconomic analysis. Economic theory requires the student to think in an organized manner and continually to build upon knowledge previously gained in a step-by-step fashion. The problems developed here emphasize this step-by-step approach. Second, this book is *self-contained* with respect to the problems and self-tests; answers are provided at the end of the book. Third, it is *comprehensive*. With minor exceptions, all important aspects of intermediate macroeconomic analysis are considered. Furthermore, the essay topics and problems are designed to encourage the student to explore ramifications and subtleties of the theory which may not be stressed in class due to a lack of time—the student is encouraged to consider the views of other economists on particular aspects of the theory. Fourth, it emphasizes important *distinctions*.

The author owes a debt of gratitude to Professor Wallace C. Peterson of the University of Nebraska, who first suggested and subsequently encouraged this project. He contributed directly and indirectly some of the problems and discussion topics. Professors John Richard

Felton and Campbell R. McConnell, both of the University of Nebraska, made helpful suggestions and the author expresses his appreciation. Recognition must also be given to the many other professors and students who helped clarify and eliminate ambiguities in the analysis. Finally, a note of thanks goes to my wife, Dorothy, for her cooperation and encouragement. The author accepts, with much reluctance, full responsibility for any errors or ambiguities that remain in the following pages.

Harold R. Williams

To the Student

Macroeconomic analysis is not easy. A great deal of time and intensive study is required to comprehend fully its nature, significance, and intricate subtleties. This fact cannot be changed; you must accept it. But your study can be made more productive, and perhaps even shortened, if you have something to guide you, to point out the important concepts and aspects of the theory. It is in this respect that a book of concepts, essay questions, problems, and self-tests can be of invaluable assistance.

How should you approach each chapter? There is no one best approach for everyone, but perhaps the following comments will help you get started. Before commencing on the chapters in this book, read carefully the chapter assigned in your text. After doing so, turn to the corresponding chapter in this book. Study the key concepts first. Look in your textbook for the definition or meaning of those you cannot remember or did not note when reading the text. Once you understand the meaning of each, consider how one concept is related to another. You will be aided in this latter task when you subsequently work through the problems and self-tests.

You are now ready to tackle the problems and essay questions. They are not easy. Most of them require considerable thought on your part. Do not cheat yourself by looking at the answers at the end of the book before attempting to complete the problems. For an exercise you cannot do, study the answer provided, then work it through on your own. You will note that most of the problems are subdivided into several parts with many subquestions for each part. This is done to guide you in your analysis.

The answers at the end of the book are necessarily brief and should be considered only as a starting point for investigation. Longer explanations, with qualifications, should be developed on the basis of this book, the course text, supplemental readings, and lecture notes. It should also be realized that some of the answers, especially where an opinion is called for, may be controversial and not accepted by all economists. This has generally been indicated.

The self-test presumes that the problems have been completed. Most of the self-test questions, whether completion, true and false, or multiple choice, can be answered from the information provided in the course textbook, but you will find some questions that must be answered on the basis of information gained from the problems. Try to answer all questions. Use this self-test as a check to see if you are mastering the subject. If you can do well on the self-test, you will most likely do well on class exams.

The concepts, essay questions, problems, self-tests, and answers provided here can be used to great advantage when preparing for class quizzes and hour exams. A careful review will be beneficial in three major respects. First, it will provide you with most of the information, in a concise form, that you need for answering questions on the various subjects. Second, it will guide you in selecting the information that is most important and that hence will normally be emphasized on exams. Third, it will help you to determine which aspects you understand least and thus should devote the most time to in your review.

A basic objective of this course is to provide a body of knowledge that can be used to formulate and evaluate government policies designed to promote major socioeconomic goals. Since economic conditions, problems, and issues, change from one phase of the business cycle to another, and over the long run, you must work constantly to keep current on major domestic and international developments. Among the better sources of such information are the *Economist,* the *Financial Times,* and the *Wall Street Journal.*

CHAPTER 1   An Overview of Macroeconomics

Key Concepts

Macroeconomics
Microeconomics
Economics
Efficiency
Ceteris paribus
Methodology
Business Cycle
Stagflation
Employment Act of 1946
Full Employment and Balanced
   Growth Act of 1978
Gross domestic product (GDP)
Nominal GDP
Real GDP
Potential GDP
Implicit GDP deflator
Index number
Consumer price index (CPI)
Product price index (PPI)

GNP
Indexing
Employment
Labor force participation rate
Unemployment rate
Say's Law of markets
Quantity theory of money
John Maynard Keynes
Keynesian theory
Milton Friedman
Theory of rational expectations
Supply-side economics
"Disinflation"
Organization of Petroleum Exporting
   Countries (OPEC)
Balance of merchandise trade
Trade deficit
Net international investment position
   of the United States

Problems and Essays

1. It is important to understand a country's goals and the policies it has at its command to attain these goals.

  a. Identify the major U.S. macroeconomic goals.

  reach full employment ~4% unemployment

  b. What are the key aggregates that economists use to measure and evaluate how well a country is realizing these goals?

  GDP, unemployment rates,

  c. How well have these goals been realized since the Great Depression of the 1930s?

  We have only reached full employment a few times, although the flucuations of the economy have been tamed — the natural flucuations of the economy have been tamed to some extent since regulation began

1

 d. Is it possible to realize all these goals at the same time? Why or why not? (Note: This question will be asked several times in later chapters.)

No, you can't have full employment w/o inflation

2. During the 1980s the United States moved from a net international creditor nation to a net international debtor nation. Explain briefly what caused this change in the international position of the United States.

3. Identify and compare briefly the following major schools of thought:

 a. Keynesianism

 b. monetarianism

 c. new classical economics

 d. New Keynesian economics

 e. Post Keynesian economics

4. In your opinion, should economists be concerned with the "ultimate values of society"?

5. What place do "values" occupy in economic analysis? Can economics be completely free of value judgments? If so, should this be the approach of economists? If not, should economists be required to state their value judgments whenever they express their opinions?

6. Distinguish clearly between the method employed for testing theories in the social sciences (economics in particular) and the method used in the natural sciences.

A Self-Test

Completion Questions   Underline the appropriate word(s) and/or complete the sentence(s) by inserting the appropriate word(s) where necessary.

1. If someone is making a study concerned with the level of employment in the United States, he or she is dealing with a (macro, micro) economic problem.

2. The branch of economics that deals with the composition of the national output is called _____.

3. Economics is a social science because it deals with the

_____.

4. The four major macroeconomic goals of most countries are _____,

_____, _____, and _____.

True and False (Put *T* for true and *F* for false.)

_____ **T** 1. The level of output and changes in the level of output are macroeconomic problems.

_____ 2. A high degree of accuracy can be achieved in economic theories because economists can set up controlled experiments.

_____ 3. The recession of 1990–91 started, according to the National Bureau of Economic Research (NBER), in July 1990.

X _____ **F** 4. One way to measure the overall performance of the economy over time is to compare actual real GDP with potential GDP.

_____ **T** 5. The smaller the gap between actual and potential real GDP, the closer the country is to full employment.

_____ **T** 6. Over the past 25 years, the analysis of U.S. macroeconomic problems and the formulation of policies to remedy these problems have required more focus on the global economy.

X _____ **T** 7. *Ceteris paribus,* the best way to measure the impact of the Federal government deficit or surplus on the economy is as a percentage of GDP.
   Not True, but a sustainable deficit is 3% of GDP

Multiple Choice Circle the answer which makes the sentence correct, or most nearly correct.

1. Understanding economic analysis is important for several reasons, one of which is
   a. to state clearly why GDP does not measure the value of final goods and services.
   b. to understand why an individual does something.
   c. to provide an organized and orderly method of thinking about economic problems.
   d. to be able to explain how scarce resources can be conserved by expanding production.

2. Macroeconomics covers such matters as
   a. how total output is determined.
   b. what determines the amount of employment and unemployment.
   c. what determines the rate at which a country grows.
   d. what causes the general price level to rise and fall.
   e. all of the above

3. Microeconomics covers such important things as
   a. what determines the composition of output.
   b. how resources are allocated among different uses.
   c. what determines the distribution of income among the groups in society.
   d. how wages are determined in a particular firm.
   e. all of the above

4. The 1946 Employment Act makes the federal government responsible for
   a. subsidizing noncompetitive American industries.
   b. controlling and reducing the national debt.
   c. promoting maximum employment, production, and purchasing power.
   d. promoting equal employment opportunities.

5. GDP in nominal terms is the
   a. current monetary value of all goods and services produced by one nation during the relevant time period.
   b. real value of all production during one year.
   c. dollar value of all services.
   d. appropriate concept for measuring economic growth.

6. Real GDP is the value of goods and services produced during the relevant time period, normally one year, measured in
   a. nominal prices.
   b. gold certificates.
   c. constant prices.
   d. terms of total employment.

7. Potential GDP is a measure of the
   a. amount of goods and services that can be produced if the economy produces at full employment.
   b. amount of world production.
   c. gap between actual real GDP and what a nation can produce at full employment.
   d. amount of inflation.

8. Unlike the CPI, the PPI
   a. is in real terms.
   b. excludes durable goods.
   c. is not put in the form of an index.
   d. does not include services.

9. If the CPI (based on 1967 = 100) is 405 in 1991, then
   a. prices increased 305 percent.
   b. goods costing $100 in 1967 cost $405 in 1991.
   c. the purchasing power of the dollar has declined.
   d. all of the above
   e. none of the above

10. The implicit GDP deflator is
    a. the ratio of real to nominal GDP multiplied by 100.
    b. the sum of real and nominal GDP divided by 100.

    c. the ratio of nominal GDP to real GDP multiplied by 100.
    d. the product of nominal and real GDP multiplied by 100.

11. Which of the following is not included in the official U.S. unemployment rate?
    a. teenagers looking for work
    b. people who want jobs but are not actively seeking work
    c. women and minorities seeking work for the first time
    d. people working part-time who lose their job

12. The school of thought that is known for advocating demand management policies is the
    a. monetarist school.
    b. supply-side new classical school.
    c. Keynesian school.
    d. Post-Keynesian school.

13. The U.S. average annual rates of growth of real GDP during the 1960–69 decade and 1970–79 decade were about
    a. 4.0 percent and 2.3 percent, respectively.
    b. 4.2 percent and 3.2 percent, respectively.
    c. 4.2 percent and 2.0 percent, respectively.
    d. 5.0 percent and 4.5 percent, respectively.

14. From 1980 to 1990, the American economy
    a. grew at an average annual rate of about 2.5 percent.
    b. created 18 million new jobs.
    c. experienced CPI inflation of about 5.2 percent.
    d. became a net international debtor nation.
    e. all of the above

15. Major problems of the 1980s included
    a. a slowdown of productivity and an increase in inflation.
    b. a high saving rate and low productivity.
    c. unprecedented deficits in the federal budget and balance of merchandise trade.
    d. none of the above

16. Using the base of 1982–84 = 100, the CPI was 135.2 in April 1991. Hence,
    a. the PPI probably remained constant or fell between 1982 and April 1991.
    b. it cost $135.20 to purchase the same market basket of goods and services that cost $100 during 1982–84.
    c. prices were 135.2 percent higher in April 1991, than during the base period.
    d. the implicit GDP deflators must have declined.

17. The United States is linked to the rest of the world by
    a. exports and imports of goods and services.
    b. the rate of exchange.
    c. money and credit flows among nations.
    d. all of the above
    e. none of the above

18. Since 1960, the current-dollar net exports component of GDP has registered a deficit
    a. every year.
    b. never.
    c. in over 75 percent of the years.
    d. in less than 25 percent of the years.

19. Valuing international assets at their historical cost, the United States became a net international debtor nation in
    a. 1971.
    b. 1980.
    c. 1985.
    d. 1987.

20. Productivity growth is extremely important because it
    a. determines how fast the real standard of living increases.
    b. is closely and positively related to real wages.
    c. affects a nation's ability to compete internationally.
    d. all of the above

21. The new Keynesian economics does all the following except:
    a. combine Keynesian and new classical ideas.
    b. build macroeconomics on a microeconomic foundation.
    c. incorporate rational expectations to explain the formation of expectations.
    d. assume labor markets always clear because of the long-term contracts.
    e. assume imperfectly competitive firms.

22. The new classical economics
    a. assumes people frequently act irrationally.
    b. posits that there can be substantial unemployment.
    c. argues that macroeconomic policies are needed to promote full employment and growth.
    d. incorporates the theory of rational expectations into its model.

23. The basic difference between GNP and GDP is that GNP
    a. is always measured in nominal terms and GDP is always measured in real terms.
    b. includes income earned overseas by American businesses and American residents working and living abroad and excludes income earned in the U.S. by foreign businesses and foreign residents working and living in the U.S.
    c. does not include the factor income earned by American corporations and American workers in other countries.
    d. is *ex post* and GDP is *ex ante.*
    e. all of the above

24. According to most people, all of the following are serious problems experienced by the U.S. during the past decade except:
    a. large Federal budget deficits.
    b. large balance of trade deficits with Japan.
    c. rampant increase in consumer purchases of durable goods.
    d. lagging rate of growth of productivity.

25. All other things equal, the best way to measure the impact of a Federal government deficit on the economy is in terms of
    a. the absolute size of the deficit.
    b. its effect on interest rates.
    c. its size as a percent of GDP.
    d. how the deficit is funded.

CHAPTER 2   Measuring the Economy's Performance

Key Concepts

Income
National income accounts
Wealth
Flow concepts
Stock concepts
Human wealth
Consumption
Saving (and savings)
Gross investment
Net investment
Replacement investment
Gross domestic product (GDP)
Final goods and services
Intermediate goods and services
Monetary transactions
Imputations
Factor costs
Net domestic product (NDP)
National income (NI)
Personal income (PI)
Disposable income (DI)
Price index
Inventory valuation adjustment
  (IVA)
Capital consumption allowances
Indirect business taxes (IBT)
Constant (real) GDP
Current (nominal) GDP
Value added (VA)
Scientific method
Theory
Endogenous variables
Economic models
Predictions
Simulations
Functional relationship
Dependent variables
"if . . . then . . ." propositions
Chain-Weight GDP

Capital goods
Net exports
Ex post
Ex ante
Government purchases of goods and
  services
Transfer expenditures
Identity equations
Behavior equations
Net taxes
Circular flow of income
Measure of economic welfare (MEW)
MEW investment
Social costs
Social benefits
Consumer price index (CPI)
Producer price index (PPI)
GDP deflators (implicit price index)
Production function
Productivity (or labor)
Natural rate of unemployment
NAIRU
Productive capacity (potential GDP)
Short run vs. long run
GDP gap
Marginal productivity of labor
Average productivity of labor
Law of diminishing returns (principle of
  diminishing productivity)
Okun's law
Validity (of a theory)
Variables
Exogenous variables
Econometrics
Forecasting
Correlation (vs. causation)
Parameters
Independent variables

Problems and Essays

1. Discuss the purposes of having a set of national income accounts. Is there an analogy between the business executive's need for certain business accounts and the need for a set of national accounts?

2. Explain thoroughly the twin concepts of "income" and "wealth" and show how they are interrelated. Should human beings be included in the national wealth?

   Income is a flow phenomenon, while wealth is measured instantaneously. Both involve the quantity of money. Income is the exchange of money over a given time period. Wealth is the amount of income held.

3. Construct a simplified model of an economic system and explain the circular flow of income.

   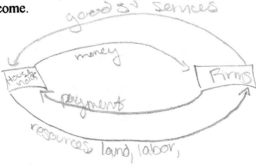

4. In the "mythical land of nowhere" there is no government nor do the residents enter into foreign trade. Prove that under these circumstances ex post saving (S) and investment (I) must be equal.

   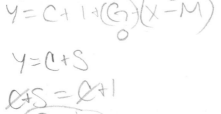

5. Suppose that because of frequent invasions by barbarians from outside its borders, the inhabitants of the mythical land of nowhere establish a government for the sole purpose of national defense. Assuming there is still no foreign trade, show (and explain) why investment (I) plus government purchases (G) must equal saving (S) plus taxes (TX) (all *ex post*).

$$Y = S + TX + C$$

$$Y = C + I + G + (X - M)$$ — we are saying there are no imports or exports

$$S + TX + C = C + I + G$$ consumption cancels out

$$\boxed{S + TX = I + G}$$

6. Let us forsake the mythical land of nowhere and consider a nation which has not only a government but also enters into some trade with other nations. Assuming no transfer payments, show that (*ex post*) the sum of domestic investment (I), exports of goods and services (X), and government purchases (G) must equal the sum of saving (S), taxes (TX), and imports of goods and services (M).

Show $I + X + G = S + TX + M$

$$Y = C + I + G + X - M$$
$$Y = C + S + TX$$
$$C + I + G + X - M = C + S + TX$$
$$\boxed{I + G + X = S + TX + M}$$

7. Statistics of the U.S. Department of Commerce indicate that *monetary* GDP was about $3,150 billion in 1982. Look in the *Survey of Current Business*, which is published monthly by the U.S. Department of Commerce, and find out how much of this GDP was derived from (a) consumption, (b) investment, (c) government purchases of goods and services, and (d) net exports. Compute the percentage contribution of each component to GDP. Do the same for 1995 and compare the results.

8. Define GDP. Explain fully the problem of double counting associated with computing GDP. How does it differ from GNP?

GDP = is the basic economic indicator it includes all goods and services made in the U.S. - You need to be careful about not counting intermediate goods. GNP is the measurement of all goods and services created in the US, and by firms and people located in other countries.

9. What is the distinction between intermediate products and investment goods? Why are they treated differently in national income accounting?

Intermediate goods are used in the production of other goods and services. They are not counted in National Income Accounting, only final goods and services are counted in National income accounting.

10. What problems are involved in determining GDP by adding all final monetary transactions during a specific income period? How does the U.S. Department of Commerce surmount these difficulties?

One problem is the vast number of goods and services that are created in the U.S. every year. As a result, the Department of Commerce surmounts this by estimating the GDP through the average prices and quantities of goods produced.

11. What is the difference between national income and personal income? What, if any, is the usefulness of such a distinction?

12. What is the difference between personal income and disposable income? Which of these concepts is more significant from the viewpoint of consumption expenditures?

13. Which of the following transactions (or items) would *not* be included in GDP during the year in which the transaction occurred? Why?

  a. The purchase of flour by a baker.

  Not, intermediate goods.

  b. The purchase of flour by a homemaker.

  No the flour will not be made into another good to be sold by the homemaker.

  c. The purchase of a huge deepwater oil drilling rig by Exxon.

  Yes

  d. The money paid to a neighbor for cleaning your house once a week.

  No, it is under the table

  e. The money given to your spouse for doing housework (you realize that he would be paid for his services if they were provided to someone other than yourself so you reimburse him to the same extent).

  No, under the table

  f. The purchase, in 1995, of a 1928 Model A Ford from a schoolteacher (who never drove it except to church on Sunday).

  No, it is a resale good, so not counted

  g. The purchase of a new 1994 Chevrolet sedan from a dealer on January 2, 1995.

  Yes, it is a new item

h. The purchase of 100 shares of IBM stock.

i. Dividends on the shares of IBM stock outstanding.

j. Interest paid by IBM on a $100,000 bond.

k. The repair by a carpenter of her own garage.

l. The money you would have to pay out in the form of rent if you did not own the house you are living in.

m. The receipt of $500 from the government, which constitutes part of the total interest paid to finance the national debt.

n. The purchase of two jugs of Kentucky moonshine (the production of which is illegal) for $15.

o. The payment of $100,000 by an underworld drug syndicate to have Mr. X "put out of the way."

p. A gift of $1,000 received January 23, 1996.

q. A $20,000 gain realized by selling for $130,000 a house which originally cost $110,000 in 1985.

r. A reduction in inventories held by the Ford Motor Company.

s. $3.25 billion paid out in expenses by a major oil company to clean up an oil spill from a supertanker that ran aground during a storm and broke in two.

t. Money received under the GI Bill (passed by Congress in 1966).

u. The receipt of milk and eggs by a farmhand as part payment for services rendered.

v. The purchase of a $19,000 car by a salesman which will be used for his sales activity.

No

w. The purchase of 1,000 tons of steel by one of the big automobile companies. [Would your answer be different if at the end of the year 100 tons of this steel remained unused?]

No

x. Sale of the *Mona Lisa* for $1.8 million.

No

y. The expenditure of $600 during the year by a wage earner to commute to work.

Yes

z. A monthly payment of $980 to Ms. Jamestown which is paid by the government under the social insurance program.

No

14. Price Indices

a. Using the following hypothetical information, compute the price index using 1958 as the base year.

Year	Price	Price Index
1950	50	( )
1954	42	( )
1958	55	( )
1962	68	( )
1966	70	( )
1970	80	( )
1974	110	( )
1978	150	( )
1982	175	( )
1986	185	( )
1990	205	( )
1995	240	( )

b. Using the following actual data given by the Department of Commerce, compute GDP in 1987 prices for the years indicated (in billions of dollars).

Year	GDP in Current Prices	Implicit Price Index 1987 = 100	GDP in 1987 Prices
1964	648.0	27.7	( )
1968	889.0	31.8	( )
1972	1,207.0	38.8	( )
1976	1,768.4	52.3	( )
1980	2,708.0	71.7	( )
1986	4,268.6	96.9	( )
1990	5,546.1	113.3	( )
1994	6,738.0	126.1	( )

c. Suppose you have all the information given in part b above (GDP in both current and 1987 prices) except the price index. How could you compute the price index?

15. In recent years there has been much discussion of possible ways to develop measures of output and well-being that are more inclusive and more refined than the measures based on GDP. One such approach develops a *measure of economic welfare* (MEW), whereas another attempts to perfect an accounting system that measures the social, as opposed to economic, health of the economy. Discuss these two lines of development in terms of:

a. what they hope to accomplish;

  b. the measurement approach suggested, and
  c. the difficulties involved in such a task.

16. Figure 2–1 displays two short-run aggregate production functions; that is, two
    relationships between output and employment in the short run. Study the
    relationship exhibited by production function $Y = f(N)_1$ and then answer the
    questions below. [Note: For ease of communication, assume throughout this
    chapter that an increase in the production function—that is, an upward shift of the
    production function—always increases the marginal product of labor at each level
    of employment. By the same token, assume a decrease in the production function
    always reduces the marginal product of labor at each level of employment. There
    is, of course, no necessity for this to be the situation in theory or practice.]

FIGURE 2–1

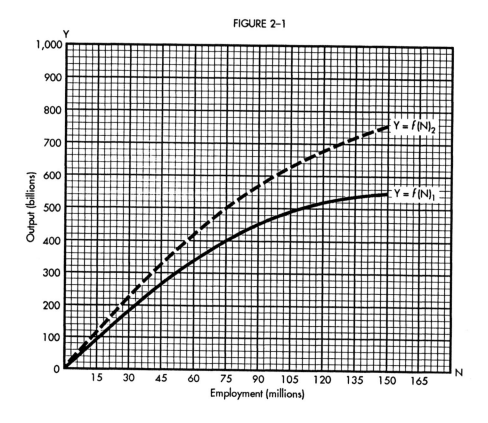

Output (billions)

Employment (millions)

a. What happens to the level of output (Y) as employment (N) increases and decreases? [Note: Output is measured in billions of constant dollars and employment in millions of workers.]

b. Suppose initially the production function is $Y = f(N)_1$ and that subsequently it shifts to $Y = f(N)_2$. What is implied by such a change? What factors could account for the change?

c. What impact would an increase or decrease in each of the following have on the production function and the marginal product of labor curve?

(1) The quality of natural resources.

(2) The quality of capital equipment.

(3) Technology.

(4) Population.

(5) The quantity (stock) of capital (plant and equipment).

(6) The average level of education.

A Self-Test

Completion Questions

1. The Great Lakes (*are, are not*) a part of the nation's wealth.

2. Income is a(n) _____ concept, whereas wealth is a(n) _____ concept.

3. When society consumes more than it produces in the form of goods and services, national wealth _____.

4. Saving is a(n) _____ variable.

5. When an economist states that saving and investment are necessarily equal, he or she is referring to (*ex ante, ex post*) saving and investment.

6. When the stock of capital goods employed by a business firm has been partially used up during an income period, _____ has taken place.

7. Disinvestment is conceptually identical with dissaving when values are in (*ex post, ex ante*) terms.

8. Net investment is equal to _____.

9. The portion of total investment which replaces capital goods used up or worn out during the current period is (*gross, replacement, net*) investment.

10. Economists utilize both identity and behavior equations. (*Identity, Behavior*) equations merely express an equality that is true by definition. (*Behavior, Identity*) equations normally express a total in terms of the sum of its parts. When an equation implies a hypothetical relationship between certain variables, it is referred to as a(n) (*identity, a behavior*) equation. Whereas the (*identity, behavior*) equation implies that a causal relationship exists, the (*identity, behavior*) equation does not.

11. GDP is "gross" because it includes _____.

12. Intermediate products are those which are _____.

13. Transfer payments are included in _____ and _____.

14. The term "indirect business taxes" is used to refer to _____.

15. Indirect business taxes are called such because it is assumed they will _____.

16. The difference between disposable income and personal income is that the latter

_____.

17. When comparing GDP figures over several years, it is necessary to adjust for

_____.

18. GDP data can be converted to real terms by (*multiplying, dividing*) the current

price data by the appropriate _____.

19. The capital consumption allowance is primarily a measure of _____.

20. The term "productive capacity" refers to the _____.

21. The economy's productive capacity basically depends on the following factors:

a. _____.

b. _____.

c. _____.

d. _____.

e. _____.

22. The three major factors upon which the productivity of labor is dependent are:

a. _____.

b. _____.

c. _____.

23. The actual level of output is determined by the _____ .

24. Scientific laws can be formulated as "if . . . then . . ." propositions. The

_____ part consists of the conclusion and the _____ part consists of the assumptions underlying the analysis.

25. In using the deductive method, the researcher must first _____. The second step is to _____. Third, it is necessary to

_____.

26. When using the inductive method, the researcher must first

_____. Second, he or she must

_____. And third, he or she must

_____.

True and False

X T 1. The National Bureau of Economic Research (NBER) is a governmental agency that determines what international transactions will be included in the national accounts.

X F 2. The Great Depression was a major factor leading to the establishment of national income accounting in the United States.

T 3. When measuring something that takes place over a specific period of time, we are dealing with a *flow* variable.

F 4. When concerned with the economy's performance over time, it makes no difference whether we consider money flows or real flows because both will always change by the same amount and in the same direction.

F 5. The circular flow of income refers to the idea that all income flows to the government in the form of taxes and these taxes flow back to consumers in the form of income when the government purchases goods and services.

F 6. Whereas income can be measured only at some point of time, wealth can be measured only with reference to a period of time.

X T 7. In order to determine the national wealth, it is first necessary to determine the value of all items which possess economic value and add to this figure the total value of all claims to wealth.

X F 8. While a bond may be classified as wealth for an individual, it is not wealth from the economy's point of view.

T 9. Saving requires that some part of current production not be consumed.

_____ T 10. The National Income Division of the U.S. Department of Commerce assumes that all consumer's durables, except houses, are completely used up during an income period.

_____ F 11. Residential construction, which is a consumer's durable product, is treated as a consumer expenditure in the national income accounts.

_____ F 12. If inventories are being depleted during a particular income period, we can conclude that the income of that period is understated unless some adjustment is made for the inventory change.

_____ F 13. In general, output of the public sector either would not be produced by the private sector or, if produced, would be produced in excessive amounts.

_____ T 14. Transfer payments are negative taxes because the Internal Revenue Service allows individuals and business firms to deduct the value of such transfers from their tax liability.

_____ 15. Net foreign investment has an impact on the economy similar to that of domestic consumption but unlike that of domestic investment.

_____ 16. Positive net foreign investment is similar to domestic investment because while the production of exports created domestic income, there is no increase in the amount of domestic goods and services available for purchase.

_____ 17. Expenditures on imports and saving have a similar economic impact precisely because both represent a nonconsumption of current output.

_____ 18. In general it can be said that exports use up national income, whereas imports create income.

_____ 19. The equation $h = f(i)$ is a behavioral relationship.

_____ 20. The Fisherian equation of exchange (that $MV = PY$) is a behavioral equation.

_____ 21. Although there are minor differences, most advanced nations employ similar techniques of national income accounting.

_____ 22. The U.S. Department of Commerce distinguishes between an intermediate and final transaction on the basis of whether the buyer intends to resell (or use for further processing) the product.

_____ 23. If a farmer produces all the food that is consumed on his farm, GDP is understated.

_____ 24. Regardless of whether the owner of a house rents it to someone or lives in it himself, the amount of rent that is received or could be received is included in GDP.

_____ 25. If a waitress at the Vacation Inn receives as part of her wages one meal a day, the value of this meal is not counted in GDP.

_____ 26. The total of C, I, G, and net exports equals the total of all factor costs plus capital consumption allowances.

_____ 27. The Department of Commerce excludes from factor costs both interest on the public debt and interest payments made by consumers.

_____ 28. If two neighbors decide to shovel the snow out of each other's driveway and pay each other for doing so, their actions will have no effect on GDP.

_____ 29. Interest on the public debt is not included in personal income.

_____ 30. One limitation of national income accounting aggregates is that they measure economic values which do not always reflect social values.

_____ 31. Theoretically, leisure should not be included in GDP because it does not result in an increase in goods and services.

_____ 32. Some price increases reflect improvements in the product rather than inflation.

_____ 33. The U.S. Department of Commerce makes no significant overall allowances for quality changes in products.

_____ 34. An increase in national output does not always mean that the standard of living of the individual has increased.

_____ 35. To determine the welfare implications of a change in GDP, it is necessary to know only whether GDP increased or decreased.

_____ 36. In establishing the appropriate price index, it is necessary to use a weighting system that takes into consideration the relative importance of different commodities.

_____ 37. In attempting to establish an economic theory, it is necessary to determine cause and effect relationships.

_____ 38. While it is true that all theories must explain something, an explanation by itself is not a theory.

_____ 39. It is not necessary for a deductive theory to be logically valid.

_____ 40. While the conclusion of a theory must necessarily flow from its premises, the usefulness of a theory will depend, as well, on the realism of its assumptions.

_____ 41. The distinction between the "practical man" and the "theorist" is not that one theorizes and the other does not, but rather in the quality of their theories.

_____ 42. The predictive value of economic theory applies to the individual as well as the group.

_____ 43. Economic theories tend to be more "unrealistic" than theories in the natural sciences because economists rely on abstraction, whereas scientists in the natural sciences try to duplicate precisely the real world.

_____ 44. There is a functional relationship between two variables when both of them fluctuate in the same manner as a result of changes in a third variable.

_____ 45. If two variables are functionally related, it can be said either one is the cause of the other.

_____ 46. If event B always follows event A, it can be said that A caused B.

_____ 47. If controlled experiments were possible in economics, the economists would not have to rely on the *ceteris paribus* assumption.

_____ 48. Several tests are required to "verify" an economic hypothesis.

Multiple Choice

1. National income accounts are especially useful for
   a. obtaining information on the availability of resources.
   b. measuring the impact of government economic policies on the economy as a whole and on parts of the economy.
   c. predicting the impact of specific government policies on employment and output.
   d. all of the above
   e. none of the above

2. Which of the following points is *not* illustrated by the simplified circular flow of income diagram?
   a. The production of goods and services involves two different markets.
   b. The price level depends on the forces underlying aggregate demand and aggregate supply.
   c. The flow of income and output are equal.
   d. Output can be considered in real or monetary terms.
   e. none of the above

3. When considering the total wealth of a nation, both nonhuman and human, which of the following should *not* be classified as wealth?
   a. national highways
   b. fish in the oceans
   c. ownership claim to shares of IBM stock
   d. a big generator used for producing electric power
   e. none of the above

4. When less output is consumed during a specific period than is produced, national wealth
   a. increases.
   b. remains unchanged as there is no relationship.
   c. decreases.
   d. may increase or decrease.
   e. none of the above.

5. Theoretically, the services rendered by any consumer-durable product during a specific period should be counted as productive activity of that period. However, the National Income Division does not employ this approach because
   a. it would make the figure for total income much larger than it is already.
   b. consumers would have to pay personal income taxes on the consequent statistical increase in their incomes.
   c. it would be almost impossible to determine a reasonably accurate figure for these services in each income period.
   d. it would result in double-counting.
   e. none of the above

6. Which of the following does *not* represent an investment expenditure?
   a. the purchase of a new house
   b. expenditures on producers-durable equipment
   c. an increase in inventories of a business firm
   d. the addition of a wing to the main plant of Cadre, Inc.
   e. none of the above

7. The best measure of the increase in the economy's productive wealth is
   a. net investment.
   b. gross investment.
   c. total investment in plant and equipment.
   d. replacement investment.
   e. none of the above

8. Output produced in the public sector
   a. enters into the national accounts according to the price at which it is sold.
   b. is valued at cost because most of it is distributed "free."
   c. is treated as if it were investment because it increases the productive wealth of the economy.
   d. is divisible and therefore can be sold on an individual basis.
   e. none of the above

9. Which of the following is *not* an identity equation?
   a. $Y = C + I + G$
   b. $C + I = C + S$
   c. $S + TX = I + G$
   d. $S = f(Y)$
   e. none of the above

10. The national income aggregate which measures the monetary value of all final goods and services produced during a particular period is
    a. national income.
    b. gross domestic product.
    c. net national product.
    d. total disposable income.
    e. none of the above

11. Which of the following is *not* a characteristic of current GDP?
    a. It is measured in real terms.
    b. It is a measure of final output only.

c. It applies only to a given period.

d. It makes no allowances for goods used up in the process of production.

e. none of the above

12. Which one of the following measures does *not* include final goods and services?

    a. gross domestic product

    b. net national product

    c. disposable income

    d. national income

    e. none of the above

13. Which one of the following is *not* an imputation?

    a. the payment of wages to a farmhand in kind, rather than in money

    b. food produced by a farmer and consumed by his family

    c. fuel obtained on the farm and used by the farmer to heat his own home

    d. the rental value of dwellings in which the owners live

    e. none of the above

14. Which one of the following items is *not* a factor cost?

    a. proprietor's income

    b. employees' compensation

    c. business transfer payments

    d. dividends

    e. rental income of persons

15. Which one of the following is *not* an indirect business tax?

    a. a sales tax

    b. a corporate profit tax

    c. an excise tax

    d. a business property tax

    e. none of the above

16. Which one of the following can be determined by adding all factor costs in the current period?

    a. national income

    b. gross domestic product

    c. disposable income

    d. net national product

    e. none of the above

17. Which of the following is *not* deducted from national income to obtain personal income?

    a. social security contributions

    b. interest on the public debt

    c. corporate income tax liability

    d. profits of the corporation which are not distributed

    e. none of the above

18. Which of the following is *not* a form of transfer payment which must be added to national income to arrive at personal income?

    a. G.I. Bill benefits to veterans

    b. unemployment compensation to the unemployed
    c. relief payments to those in need
    d. pensions to retired persons
    e. none of the above

19. Which of the following is *not* a limitation of national income accounting aggregates?
    a. They do not measure social costs.
    b. They measure economic but not social values.
    c. They do not include the value of leisure.
    d. They do not allow for changes in the quality of goods and services.
    e. none of the above

20. GDP in current dollars in 1955 was $398 billion; in 1965 it was $676 billion. The appropriate price index was 91 in 1955 and 111 in 1965. Real GDP between 1955 and 1965
    a. remained unchanged.
    b. advanced by about 40 percent.
    c. advanced by about 70 percent.
    d. advanced by about 90 percent.
    e. advanced by about 20 percent.

21. As a general rule the numerically smallest national income accounting aggregate is
    a. net national product.
    b. personal income.
    c. disposable income.
    d. national income.
    e. gross domestic product.

22. Which of the following would be included in current GDP?
    a. the purchase of flour by a baking firm
    b. the purchase of 40 shares of stock
    c. flour purchased by a homemaker
    d. the receipt of $43 in interest on government bonds
    e. none of the above

23. The basic shortcoming of GDP as a measure of economic welfare is that
    a. it is a measure of a nation's production and not of its consumption.
    b. it fails to measure the bulk of private output.
    c. it includes an excessive amount of social costs.
    d. it fails to measure production associated with expanding inventories.

24. Using the *measure of economic welfare* (MEW) developed by Professors Tobin and Nordhaus requires that the conventional GDP figure be adjusted. Which of the following adjustments would *not* be necessary?
    a. reclassifying the standard measures of investment, consumption, and intermediate products
    b. imputing a value for services derived from consumer capital, public capital, leisure, and household work
    c. making an adjustment for social costs (of urbanization)
    d. none of the above

25. Professors Tobin and Nordhaus define *MEW investment* as the
    a. expenditures of business firms on plant and equipment, residential construction, and business inventories.
    b. total of all investment that has taken place in the past decade.
    c. additional investment required to sustain per capita consumption with an expanding population and improvements in technology.
    d. investment undertaken by the federal government to ensure sufficient social capital to satisfy the needs of an expanding economy.

26. In moving from GDP to MEW, Tobin and Nordhaus must make all the following adjustments except
    a. adjust the figure for capital consumption allowances to reflect changes in private consumer durables, government capital, and educational and medical capital that is embodied in human resources.
    b. adjust the GDP data by classifying public expenditures on police services, road maintenance, sanitation, and national defense as intermediate expenditures.
    c. incorporate estimates for the value of leisure and all nonmarket productive activities.
    d. adjust the GDP figure so it includes estimates of some of the more important social costs—pollution, litter, congestion, noise, insecurity, offensive buildings and advertisements, etc.—and the value of governmental services and private capital of consumers.
    e. none of the above

27. After making all adjustments to GDP, Tobin and Nordhaus discover that MEW
    a. is much larger than GDP but has been growing at a slower rate than GDP.
    b. is substantially smaller than GDP.
    c. is actually an inferior measure of economic welfare.
    d. does not differ significantly from GDP and thus there is little need to bother with the adjustments.

28. The "natural rate of unemployment" is that rate at which
    a. the quantity of labor supplied and demanded are equal and below which any attempt to reduce unemployment will cause inflation.
    b. the growth of production and employment are equal.
    c. unemployment and inflation are equal in percentage terms.
    d. employment and unemployment grow at the same pace.

29. At the depth of the Great Depression unemployment was approximately
    a. 7 percent.
    b. 15 percent.
    c. 50 percent.
    d. 25 percent.
    e. 5 percent.

30. The productive capacity of the economy can be determined by
    a. multiplying the labor force by the average annual productivity of labor.
    b. multiplying the stock of capital by the average annual productivity of labor.
    c. dividing the labor force by the average annual productivity of capital.
    d. dividing the labor force by the average annual productivity of labor.

    e. multiplying the average productivity of labor by the average product of capital.

31. As a general rule unemployment in the United States is highest for the category
    a. women 20 years and older.
    b. men 20 years and older.
    c. teenagers and minorities.
    d. adult men and women.

32. Which of the following is *not* an important characteristic of economic theory?
    a. Economic theory explains something.
    b. Economic theory establishes cause-effect relationships.
    c. Economic theory deals only with a given set of data.
    d. Economic theory applies under all conditions.
    e. none of the above

33. Which one of the following is *not* a purpose of economic theory?
    a. to understand why things happen as they do
    b. to enable prediction under certain circumstances
    c. to exercise control, to some degree, over the environment
    d. none of the above

34. When dealing with a functional relationship, it is important to remember that
    a. it is difficult to say one variable caused the other.
    b. one variable may be dependent upon several variables.
    c. when relating one variable to another variable, it is necessary to hold all other factors constant.
    d. all of the above are important considerations.

35. When employing the deductive method *per se*, the investigator
    a. never has to worry about the assumptions underlying his analysis.
    b. goes from the particular to the general.
    c. must gather empirical information and formulate his hypothesis on the basis of such information.
    d. works to a conclusion on the basis of certain predetermined premises.
    e. none of the above.

36. When using inductive analysis *per se*, the economist must
    a. establish the assumptions upon which his or her analysis will rest.
    b. move from the general to the particular.
    c. investigate several specific instances or facts to arrive at a theory.
    d. combine the assumptions and raw data to arrive at a theory.
    e. none of the above.

37. The difference between "exogenous variables" and "endogenous variables" is that the values of
    a. each must be determined by relationships not covered in the model.
    b. exogenous variables are determined outside the model, whereas those of endogenous variables are determined inside the model.
    c. exogenous variables are determined inside the model and endogenous variables outside the model.

    d. endogenous variables are known with certainty, whereas those of exogenous variables are not.

38. A mathematical model may be misleading for all the following reasons *except* that
    a. it may imply a continuity of economic events that does not hold true.
    b. it may imply that there is a constant relationship among variables.
    c. it may not be valid as time passes.
    d. such models cannot be used to formulate government economic policy.

39. In 1995, U.S. per capital current dollar GDP was
    a. under $10,000.
    b. between $15,000 and $20,000.
    c. between $20,000 and $25,000.
    d. over $25,000.

The Classical System

SUMMARY SKETCH OF BASIC CLASSICAL THEORY

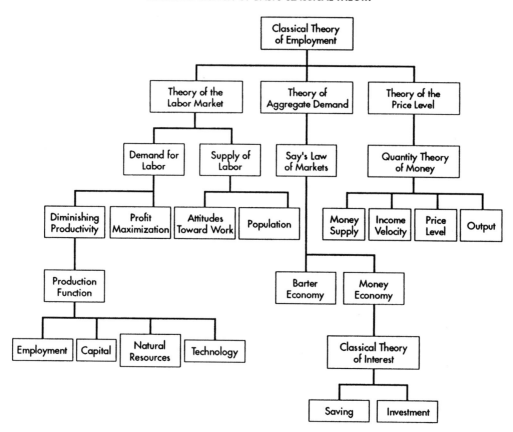

Key Concepts

Classical theory (economics)
"Fine tuning"
Involuntary unemployment
  (vs. voluntary unemployment)
Frictional unemployment
Dynamic economy (vs. static
  economy)

Classical supply of labor
Money illusion
Say's Law (of markets)
Classical theory of interest
Equation of exchange
Quantity theory of money
Laissez faire

Phillips curve
Production function
Productivity (or labor)
Utilitarianism
Invisible hand (of Adam Smith)
Real wage
Money wage
Classical demand for labor

Atomistic competition
Principle (law) of diminishing productivity
  (returns)
Marginal productivity (physical product) of
  labor
Average productivity of labor
Equilibrium
Static equilibrium

Problems and Essays

1. Understanding the classical (and Keynesian) model requires a thorough
   appreciation of the nature and properties of the short-run aggregate production
   function. That is the purpose of this question. You may skip it if you have already
   answered all parts of question 16 in Chapter 2.
      Figure 3–1 displays two short-run aggregate production functions, that is, two
   relationships between output and employment in the short run. Study the
   relationship exhibited by production $Y = f(N)_1$ and then answer the questions
   below.

FIGURE 3–1

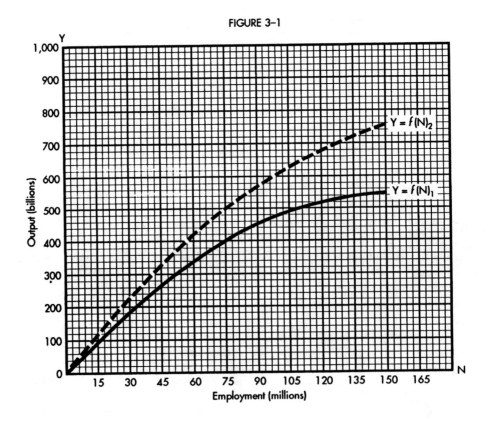

a. **What happens to the level of output (Y) as employment (N) increases and decreases? [Note: Output is measured in billions of constant dollars and employment in millions of workers.]**

As employment increases, output increases, but it increases more slowly as employment gets higher. Output decreases as employment decreases.

b. **Suppose initially the production function is $Y = f(N)_1$ and that subsequently it shifts to $Y = f(N)_2$. What is implied by such a change? What factors could account for the change?**

There could be a decrease in Capital inputs. A wage cut, worsening of education level
NVM, wrong lines? Wage increase, better education better Capital and technology.

c. **What impact would an increase or decrease in each of the following have on the production function and the marginal product of labor curve?**

(1) **The quality of natural resources.**

increase - shift up

decrease - shift ↓

(2) **The quality of capital equipment.**

increase - more output → shift upward

decrease - shift down

(3) **Technology.**

increase - shift ↑

decrease - shift ↓

(4) **Population.**

population increase or decrease will have no effect on the production function and so will do nothing to the graph.

increase - shift up - more competition for jobs = more productivity
decrease - wouldn't be able to hire as many people for workers = hire wage always, can find a new job. more competition and less productivity -

(5) **The quantity (stock) of capital (plant and equipment).**

increase - helps eliminate/reduce diminishing productivity shift↑

decrease - shift down > greater diminishing marginal returns

(6) **Educational attainments of the labor force.**

increase - shift↑   decrease - shift down

2. **Classical economists maintained that the demand for labor (N_d) is a function of the real wage (w/p) and is negatively sloped, as portrayed in Figure 3–2.**

FIGURE 3-2

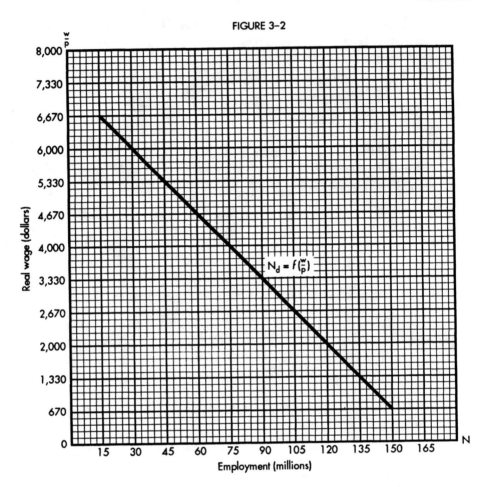

Employment (millions)

a. Explain why the classical demand curve for labor has a negative slope. How do the twin concepts of (1) diminishing productivity and (2) profit maximization fit into the analysis?

As a firm hires more workers, they're going to get less out of them due to the Rate of diminishing marginal returns, so they are going to pay each worker less. Also, because the firm wants to maximize profit, it will pay each worker as little as it can

b. Study Figure 3-2. What factors could cause a change in the real wage from $3,300 to $4,000? What happens to the quantity of labor demanded if there is an increase or decrease in (1) the money wage or (2) the general price level?

If there is a smaller labor pool, than the firm will pay their workers more for the same jobs in order to keep them there. An increase in the money wage = less demand for labor. A decrease = more demand for labor.
If the general price level increases, there will be less demand for workers.
An increase in $ wage or decrease in price level will raise the real wage and decrease labor demanded by the firm.

c. The demand curve for labor illustrated in Figure 3–2 is related to the production function $Y = f(N)_1$ in Figure 3–1. Suppose the production function shifts upward to $Y = f(N)_2$.

(1) What effect will this change in the production function have on the demand curve for labor?

there will be less demand for workers b/c the firm can get the same output w/ fewer people and less cost. However, they may pay people/employees more. (But in the real world it will probably go to the CEOs).

(2) What happens to the volume of labor demanded at any given real wage, say $4,000?

(3) Explain and illustrate the impact on the demand curve of a downward shift in the production function.

increase in money wage = less demand for labor and more demand for jobs.

d. The foregoing questions center around an *aggregate* production function and an *aggregate* labor demand curve. Explain how these two aggregates are derived from the firm's production function and the demand curve for labor.

The aggregate demand curves are basically a summation of each individual firm's demand for labor and production function.

However, aggregate problems still exist.

3. According to classical economists the supply of labor (N_s) is a function of the real wage. Figure 3–3 portrays this relationship graphically.

FIGURE 3-3

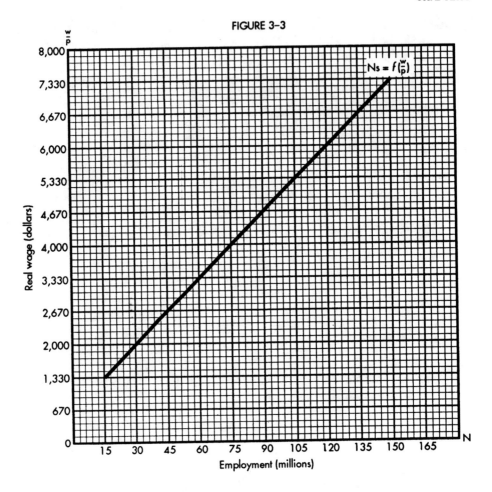

a. Explain fully both the theoretical foundation for the belief that the supply of labor is a function of the real wage and how it results in a positively, sloped supply curve of labor.

b. What happens to the quantity of labor supplied as the real wage increases from $3,330 to $4,000? Why?

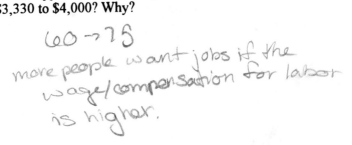

60→75
more people want jobs if the wage/compensation for labor is higher.

c. What happens to the quantity of labor supplied if there is an increase or decrease in (1) the general level of prices or (2) the money wage?

d. There is a direct relationship between shifts in the production function and shifts in the demand curve for labor. Is there a direct relationship between the production function and the supply curve of labor?

e. What factors could account for shifts in the supply curve of labor?

4. Problems 2 and 3 (above) relate to the classical theory of the demand for the supply of labor. Plot the statistical information provided in those two problems in Figure 3–4.

FIGURE 3–4

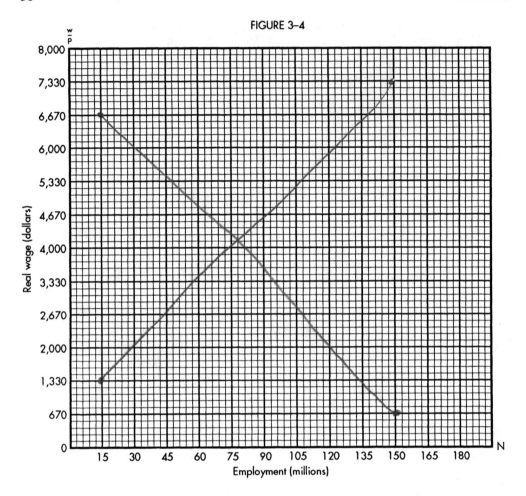

Employment (millions)

a. What is the volume of employment and the real wage at equilibrium? Is it possible for any *involuntary* unemployment to exist at equilibrium? Could any *voluntary* unemployment exist?

, No

involuntary unemployment is caused by a minimum wage-
if the minimum wage is above the equilibrium wage,
then there will be involuntary unemployment

A maximum wage rate set below equilibrium could
cause involuntary unemployment,

b. Assume the real wage is $6,000. Will the real wage remain indefinitely at this level? If so, why? If not, what is the process of adjustment to equilibrium?

No

c. Suppose the real wage is $2,000. Could the real wage remain at this level or is there something in the classical system to cause it to change? Why, or why not?

d. Assume the production function shifts from $Y = f(N)_1$ to $Y = f(N)_2$ in Figure 3–1. What impact will this change have on the equilibrium real wage, employment level, and output? If the production function declines, will the results be the opposite?

e. Assume the demand curve remains at its initial level, thus the production function must be $Y = f(N)_1$, and the supply curve shifts to the right. What is the effect on the equilibrium real wage, volume of employment, and level of output?

5. The theory of aggregate demand is the second major building block of classical economics.

a. Explain the classical theory of aggregate demand. What is the role played by Say's Law of markets?

Supply creates its own demand

b. Plot the following hypothetical saving (S) and investment (I) data in Figure 3–5. [The interest rate is a percentage, whereas saving and investment are in billions of dollars.]

Interest Rate (i)	Investment (I)	Saving (S)
10	20	100
9	30	90
8	40	80
7	50	70
6	60	60
5	70	50
4	80	40
3	90	30
2	100	20
1	110	10

FIGURE 3–5

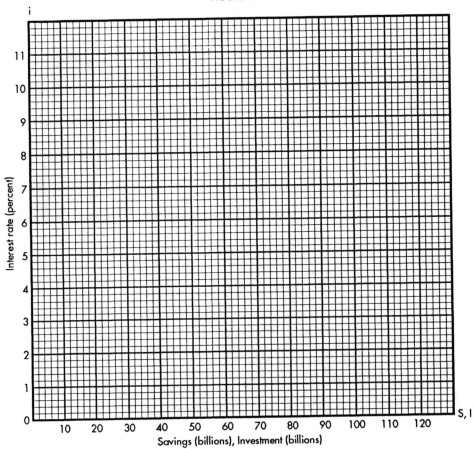

(1) What is the equilibrium level of i, S, and I?

(2) Why must equilibrium necessarily be at the point where saving and investment are equal? Choose a rate of interest above the equilibrium rate, say 9 percent, and one below the equilibrium rate, say 3 percent, and explain the process of adjustment to equilibrium.

(3) Suppose consumers decide to save more (less) at all interest rates. What effect will this decision have on the saving curve, and equilibrium of i, S, and I?

(4) Assume there is a reduction (increase) in the quantity of investment demanded at each interest rate. What is the effect of this change on the investment demand schedule and equilibrium of i, S, and I?

c. Why is the classical theory of interest necessary to make Say's Law valid in a monetary economy?

d. How does the classical theory of aggregate demand relate to the classical theory of the labor market?

6. The last major building block of classical theory is the classical theory of the price level. Figure 3–6 illustrates this theory geometrically. [Note: M is the money supply, V is the income velocity of money, p is the price level of final goods and services. The curve labelled MV represents the aggregate demand for goods and services expressed in money—as opposed to real—terms.]

FIGURE 3–6

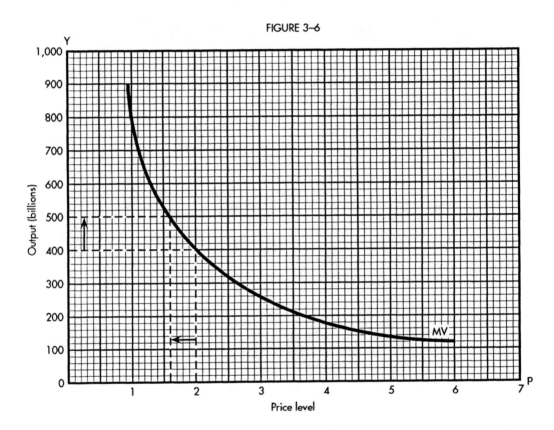

a. Explain the classical theory of the price level. What role does the quantity theory of money play in the classicists' price level theory?

b. Study Figure 3–6. Why can money income (*MV*) be represented as a rectangular hyperbola? What is the value of money income?

c. Note that when real income increases from $400 to $500, the price level declines (and vice versa). Explain the reason for this relationship.

d. Construct a new *MV* curve in Figure 3–6 showing what happens when the monetary authorities increase (decrease) the money supply. Assume output remains constant and show the effect on the price level.

e. Construct a new *MV* curve in Figure 3–6 to show the impact of an increase (decrease) in velocity on the price level for any given output.

7. Figure 3–7 combines into one diagram the production function, labor market, and price level components of classical theory. In addition a fourth quadrant, part D (in the lower right part of the figure), is incorporated into Figure 3–7 to show the money wage associated with the relevant real wage and price level. We shall have more to say about part D shortly. [Note: With respect to Figure 3–7, recognize that (a) the horizontal axes, *N*, of parts A and B are identical, (b) the vertical axes, *Y*, of parts A and C are identical, and (c) the horizontal axes, *p*, of parts C and D are identical. Warning: The vertical axes of parts B and D are *not* the same since the former measures the real wage, *w/p*, and the latter measures the money wage, *w*.]

a. Study the diagram to determine the relationship among the parts. Assume the relevant production function is $Y = f(N)_1$ (which automatically indicates the appropriate demand curve for labor).

   (1) What is the equilibrium real wage and volume of employment in the labor market (part B)?

   (2) After determining the equilibrium volume of employment, move up to part A—the production function—and find the level of output that will be produced by the equilibrium amount of employment. What is *Y*?

(3) With the level of output known, it is possible to determine the equilibrium
     price level from part C. What is p? [Note: The equilibrium price level must
     be the one at which the aggregate demand for goods and services is just
     equal to the aggregate supply of goods and services being produced. Since
     aggregate supply has already been determined from the production
     function and labor market quadrants, finding the equilibrium price level
     merely entails finding that price level which generates an amount of
     aggregate demand (in money terms) just equal to the known aggregate
     supply.]

FIGURE 3–7

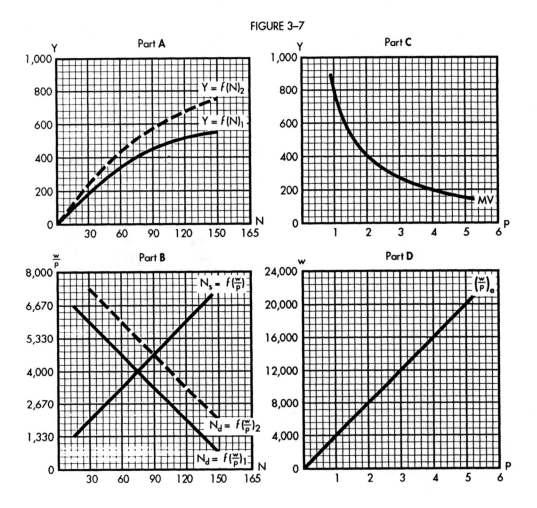

(4) The final step in this chain of analysis is to find the equilibrium money wage. One way to find this value is to multiply the real wage by the price level; that is, $w = (w/p) \times p$. Since we already know the real wage (from quadrant B) and the price level (from quadrant C), it is apparent that we have all the information needed to find the numerical value of the money wage. Alternatively, we can find the money wage graphically by using quadrant D of Figure 3–7. It is merely a matter of moving downward from the equilibrium price level given in part C to the real-wage line of part D and then reading the equilibrium money wage off the vertical axis of part D. What is the numerical value of the equilibrium money wage? [Note: In part D of Figure 3–7 the money wage is measured on the vertical axis and the price level on the horizontal axis. Any straight line in this quadrant that runs through the origin represents one specific real wage—such a line gives all combinations of the money wage and price level that equal a given real wage. For example, in part D the real-wage line designated $(w/p)_e$ represents a real wage of $4000. If we take various price levels and money wages along this line, we can easily see that this is the case. Thus,

$$\frac{w}{p} = \frac{\$4,000}{1} = \frac{\$8,000}{2} = \frac{\$14,000}{3.5} = \frac{\$20,000}{5} = \$4,000.$$

For real wages above $4000, the constant real-wage line of part D would be steeper; the higher the real wage, the greater the slope of the real-wage line. What real-wage line should be constructed in part D? The answer is the one representing the equilibrium real wage determined in the labor market (part B).]

b. Assume that technological improvements, or an increase in the supply of capital, cause the production function to shift upward from $Y = f(N)_1$ to $Y = f(N)_2$.

(1) When the production function shifts upward, the demand curve for labor shifts to the right. Why? How can you determine the magnitude of shift in the demand curve?

(2) What is the new equilibrium real wage, employment level, output level, price level, and money wage?

c. Assume the production function is $Y = f(N)_1$ (again this indicates which demand curve is relevant). What impact will a shift in the supply curve (inward and outward) have on the real wage, employment, output, and price level? Work out the results.

d. Assume the system is initially in equilibrium with the appropriate production function being $Y = f(N)_1$. Suppose further that the money supply is increased by 50.

   (1) If $V = 4$, what is the level of money income (MV)? Construct the new curve in part C. (Note that the initial money supply was 200.)

   (2) What are the new equilibrium price level and money wage?

   (3) Did this increase in the money supply (and thus money income) have any lasting effect on equilibrium output and employment? Why?

8. The data below pertain to the production function, labor market, and price level components of classical theory. Using the information, complete Figure 3–8 as indicated.

FIGURE 3–8

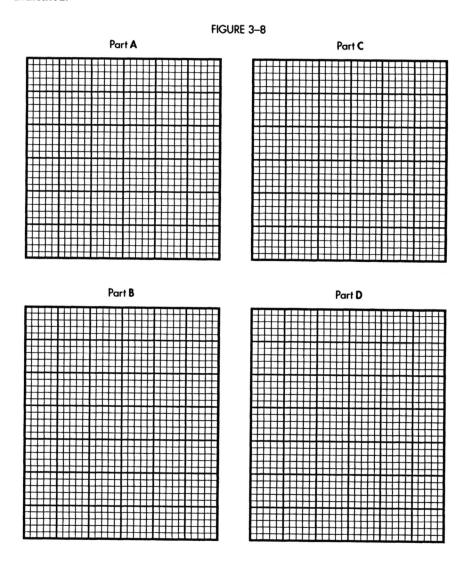

Part A

Part C

Part B

Part D

a. The following hypothetical data represent the aggregate production function for the economy. (For simplification assume that Y is expressed in billions of constant dollars and N in millions of workers). Compute the marginal product of labor (MP_L) for the various employment levels.

N (millions)	Y (billions)	MP$_L$
10	$ 90	
20	170	
30	240	
40	300	
50	350	
60	390	
70	420	
80	440	
90	450	

(1) Plot the production function in part A of Figure 3–8.
(2) Plot the demand curve for labor in part B of Figure 3–8.

b. The following hypothetical data gives the classical supply curve of labor. Plot this data in part B of Figure 3–8.

N (millions)	w/p
10	$1,000
20	$2,000
30	$3,000
40	$4,000
50	$5,000
60	$6,000
70	$7,000
80	$8,000
90	$9,000

c. Output (Y) can now be related to money income (MV) and the price level (p). Assume the money supply (M) is $200 billion and velocity (V) is 3. On the basis of this information, complete the table below (for p and MV) and plot the appropriate data in part C of Figure 3–8.

p	Y	MV
	$100	
	200	
	300	
	400	
	500	
	600	
	700	
	800	
	900	

d. The relationship between the parts can now be analyzed.

   (1) What are the equilibrium values of N, w/p, Y, p, and the money wage (w)?

   (2) What is the effect on the equilibrium values of N, w/p, Y, p, and w of a shift in (a) the production function, (b) the supply curve of labor, and (c) the money income curve?

   (3) How do Say's Law and the classical theory of interest relate to this analysis?

9. *Departures from the Classical Model.* One of the major assumptions upon which the classical model is constructed is that money wages and product prices are completely free to adjust upward and downward according to changes in supply and demand. Although this assumption may have been fairly realistic during the classical era (say the eighteenth and nineteenth centuries), it is not a good description of price behavior in the industrialized countries today. Whereas money wages and prices may be flexible upward (with some qualifications), they are inflexible in the downward direction. What happens to the classical conclusions—especially the one that says full employment is the normal state of the economy—if the price-wage flexibility assumption is modified? To answer this question, study Figure 3–9 and answer the questions below.

  a. Rigid money wages. Continue to assume perfect competition (and hence perfect flexibility of product prices) reigns in the product market (represented in part C) but that now, perhaps because workers are organized into powerful labor unions, money wage rates do not decline with a contraction of aggregate demand. Let us work through Figure 3–9 to determine how this assumption alters the classical conclusion.

   (1) If we assume the original aggregate demand curve in part C is AD_1 (the solid curve), what are the equilibrium values of w/p, N, Y, p, and w? [Note: Recall that the MV curve is essentially the aggregate demand curve expressed in money terms. The aggregate supply is in real terms and thus is not functionally related to the price level—it is the amount of goods and services produced at the full-employment level (in this case).]

FIGURE 3–9

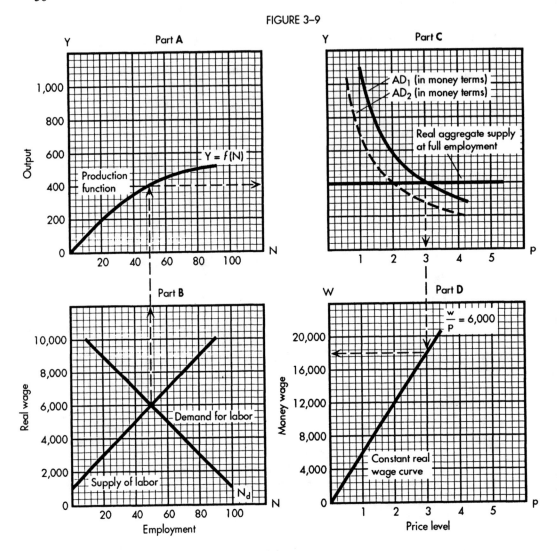

(2) Assume the aggregate demand curve declines from AD_1 (the solid curve) to AD_2 (the dashed curve)—see part C of Figure 3–9. Keep in mind that we are now assuming that labor unions keep the money wage at its initial level of $18,000.

(a) What effect does this have on the price level?

(b) Given that the money wage is held at $18,000 and p is now $p = 2$, what is the new real wage? Is the new real wage higher or lower than the original real wage?

(c) Go to part B of Figure 3–9 and find the real wage of $9,000. Is there any unemployment at this real wage?

(d) Can the real wage remain at approximately $9,000? Why?

(e) With the real wage at $9,000, what happens to the level of output?

(3) Compare the conclusion arrived at here under the assumption of rigid money wages with that derived earlier on the assumption that money wages are fully flexible.

b. *Rigid product prices.* Now consider the case in which money wages are fully flexible in the downward and upward direction (thus pure competition in the labor market) but product prices are flexible downward. We can use Figure 3–9 to demonstrate how rigid product prices may affect output and employment. Assume aggregate demand in part C falls from AD_1 to AD_2 as we did above. Assume further that instead of lowering prices, decision makers hold them at the original level. Thus, the price level remains at $p = 3$.

(1) At the price level $p = 3$, what is the quantity of output that producers will be able to sell—that is, the quantity of output demanded (see AD_2)?

(2) What level of employment is necessary to produce the amount of goods and services demanded at $p = 3$?

(3) What then is the amount of unemployment? Thus, here again, the classical conclusion of full employment no longer holds.

10. Keynes refuted the classical theory of employment. Explain fully his reasons for doing so. (The student is advised to consult Chapter 2 of *The General Theory of Employment, Interest and Money* by Keynes.)

A Self-Test

Completion Questions

1. Keynes (*agreed, disagreed*) with the classical view that the demand for labor is inversely related to the real wage.

2. The equation $\Delta Yp = \Delta Nw$ means that at equilibrium employment for the economic system the _____ is equal to the

   _____.

3. Keynes reconstructed the classical demand for labor and supply of labor in terms of the following two postulates:

   a. _____.

   b. _____.

4. The classical theory of the supply of and demand for labor implies that (*voluntary, involuntary*) unemployment cannot exist.

5. In classical employment theory, if the real wage is temporarily below the equilibrium rate, the real wage will increase because _____ _____.

6. If the production function shifts downward, the level of employment will tend to (*rise, fall*) because the demand curve for labor will _____. Under these circumstances, the real wage will (*rise, fall, remain unchanged*).

7. The classical theory of aggregate demand rests on _____, which in a monetary economy depends on the validity of _____ _____.

8. A simple statement of Say's Law is _____ _____.

9. If the rate of interest is temporarily below the equilibrium rate, classical economists maintained that it will rise because _____ _____.

10. The equation of exchange, $MV = pY$, is a tautology because it merely says _____ _____ _____.

11. Classical economists said the only function of money, other than as a standard of value, is as a(n) _____.

12. A rigid interpretation of the quantity theory of money implies that the price level varies directly and _____.

13. Classical economists argued that the way to eliminate any temporary unemployment is to _____ _____.

14. The two major forces leading to the downfall of classical employment theory were:

    a. _____.

    b. _____.

15. Classical economists believed that _____ is the normal condition of the economy, whereas Keynes argued that the normal condition of the economy is at _____.

16. Although Keynes accepted the classical demand curve for labor, he attacked the belief that the supply of labor depended on the real wage on the basis that:

    a. _____,

    b. _____.

True and False

_____ 1. Keynes, unlike the classical economists, used inductive analysis.

_____ 2. The classical theory of the demand for and supply of labor is based on microeconomics.

_____ 3. Classical employment theory posits that output is inversely related to the level of employment.

_____ 4. The real wage is the amount of goods and services that the money wage will buy.

_____ 5. If someone suffers from the "money illusion," he is concerned with the real value of his wage (or assets) and pays no attention to changes in monetary terms.

_____ 6. In classical employment theory, profit maximization requires that each firm continue to hire laborers until the money wage rate equals the value of the output produced by the last worker.

_____ 7. Equilibrium in the labor market also determines the level of output.

_____ 8. Say's Law implies that there can never be overproduction, whether overproduction of all products or overproduction of a particular product.

_____ 9. A major criticism of Say's Law is that it makes no allowance for the act of saving.

_____ 10. The validity of Say's Law in a monetary economy is insured by the classical theory of interest.

_____ 11. Few economists today believe that there is any natural tendency for the economy to operate continuously at full employment.

_____ 12. Keynes refuted the classical theory not so much on the basis of experience, but primarily on the basis that several major points were untenable.

_____ 13. Keynes argued that a reduction in the money wage would cause prices to fall in roughly the same proportion and thus leave the real wage unchanged.

Multiple Choice

1. At the depth of the Great Depression unemployment was approximately
   a. 7 percent.
   b. 15 percent.
   c. 50 percent.
   d. 25 percent.
   e. 5 percent.

2. The productive capacity of the economy can be determined by
   a. multiplying the labor force by the average annual productivity of labor.
   b. multiplying the stock of capital by the average annual productivity of labor.
   c. dividing the labor force by the average annual productivity of capital.
   d. dividing the labor force by the average annual productivity of labor.
   e. multiplying the average productivity of labor by the average productivity of capital.

3. Classical economists believed that the demand for labor is a function of the
   a. money wage rate.
   b. total money wages.
   c. total real wages.
   d. real wage rate.
   e. none of the above

4. In classical theory, an increase in the money wage, if we assume all other factors constant, will
   a. increase the quantity of labor demanded by the firm.
   b. reduce the quantity of labor demanded by the firm.
   c. have no effect on the quantity of labor demanded.
   d. cause the demand curve for labor to shift to the right.
   e. cause the demand curve for labor to shift to the left.

5. In classical employment theory, an increase in the price level, *ceteris paribus*, will
   a. cause the demand curve for labor to shift leftward.
   b. cause the demand curve for labor to shift rightward.
   c. result in an increase in the quantity of labor demanded.
   d. have no effect on the demand for labor.

6. In classical theory, the basic reason why the demand curve for labor is negatively sloped is that the
   a. additional output from successive units of labor declines.
   b. incremental output of successive workers increases too slowly.
   c. demand curve for labor keeps shifting to the right.
   d. demand curve for labor keeps shifting to the left.
   e. the price level is falling.

7. The classical demand for labor and the supply of labor schedules
   a. necessarily intersect at full employment.
   b. determine the volume of employment.
   c. automatically determine the real wage.

d. all of the above

e. none of the above

8. If there is an advance in the level of technology, *ceteris paribus*, the classical demand curve for labor will
   a. remain unchanged as the marginal product of labor is unchanged.
   b. shift to the right as the advance implies an increase in the marginal productivity of labor.
   c. shift to the left as the marginal product of labor declines.
   d. remain unchanged but the supply curve will fall.
   e. remain unchanged but the supply curve will rise.

9. Say's Law holds that
   a. the money value of total production must be equal to total money income.
   b. voluntary unemployment cannot exist.
   c. unemployment due to inadequate aggregate demand is not possible.
   d. even though overproduction is possible, full employment will prevail.
   e. none of the above.

10. If consumption is $100 million and saving is $15 million, then according to Say's Law (if we assume a closed economy with no government), aggregate demand will be
    a. $100 million.
    b. $85 million.
    c. $115 million.
    d. $15 million.
    e. impossible to determine.

11. According to classical economists, saving
    a. would never occur because the end of all economic activity is consumption.
    b. would automatically be converted into investment.
    c. is dependent upon the level of income.
    d. is defined exactly the same as investment.
    e. none of the above.

12. In the classical system
    a. saving is a function of income and investment is a function of the rate of interest.
    b. both saving and investment are a function of income.
    c. investment depends on income and saving depends on the rate of interest.
    d. both saving and investment are a function of the rate of interest.
    e. the rate of interest is determined by the level of investment.

13. On the basis of classical theory, if there is an increase in the supply of saving,
    a. the rate of interest will fall.
    b. investment will increase.
    c. the supply of saving curve will shift to the right.
    d. the investment demand schedule will not change.
    e. all of the above.

14. According to classical economics, if the money supply is fixed, an increase in real income must cause the price level to
    a. fall.
    b. remain unchanged.
    c. rise.
    d. there is no relationship.
    e. none of the above.

15. Which of the following is *not* necessary under the classical theory of employment?
    a. Wage reductions are continuously necessary to ensure full employment.
    b. There must be flexible wages and prices.
    c. The rate of interest must be responsive to the slightest discrepancy between saving and investment.
    d. Workers must compete among themselves for available jobs.
    e. none of the above

16. Which of the following was *not* assumed by the classical economists?
    a. Wages adjust freely upward and downward.
    b. Prices of final goods adjust freely upward and downward.
    c. Business executives try to maximize profits.
    d. Diminishing returns exists.
    e. Workers suffer from a money illusion.

17. Suppose we accept all aspects of the classical model *except* the assumption that money wages are completely flexible and assume instead that money wages are rigid in the downward direction. Under these circumstances, a fall in money aggregate demand
    a. may result in unemployment but only for a relatively short period since the real wage will fall via price-level adjustments.
    b. may result in permanent unemployment because the real wage will be held up above the equilibrium real wage.
    c. may result in permanent unemployment because the real wage will be held up below the equilibrium real wage.
    d. can result in only temporary unemployment because the price level will ensure that full employment is maintained.

18. Suppose we accept all aspects of the classical model *except* the assumption that the prices of final goods and services are fully flexible and assume instead that product prices are rigid. If money aggregate demand falls, then
    a. the classical model continues to yield the conclusion that full employment is the normal situation.
    b. there may be unemployment since the price level will fall and increase the real wage.
    c. there may be a permanent unemployment since the price level will not fall and thus the quantity of output demanded will be less than that needed to ensure full employment.
    d. equilibrium must ultimately be obtained at the full-employment level since, even though the price level may not change, money wages can decline.
    e. none of the above

The Keynesian System

SUMMARY SKETCH OF BASIC KEYNESIAN MACROECONOMIC MODEL

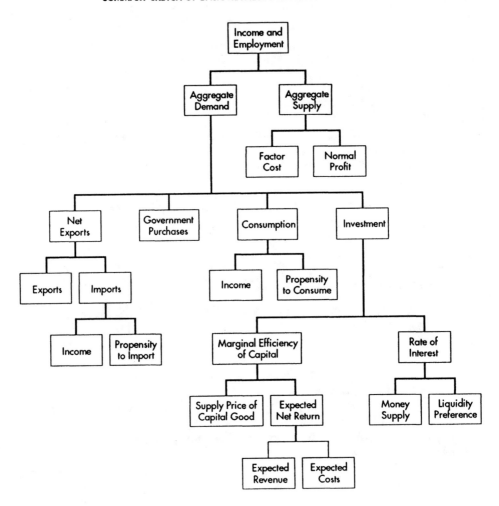

Key Concepts

Aggregate supply schedule
Expectations
Aggregate demand schedule
Equilibrium
Static analysis
Comparative statics
Real balance effect
Interest rate effect
Trade balance effect

Dynamic analysis
Disequilibrium
Disinvestment
Inflationary gap
Deflationary gap
Keynesian cross model
Keynesian-classical aggregate demand
  curve
Keynesian-classical aggregate supply curve

Problems and Essays

1. What determines the level at which an economy's productive capacity is utilized?

2. Explain why the aggregate supply schedule can be depicted as a straight line running through the origin on the Keynesian cross aggregate demand-aggregate supply diagram. Suppose increases in the price level are allowed to affect the aggregate supply. How will the supply schedule change?

3. Must the equilibrium level of income and employment be that which is economically and socially desirable? Why?

4. *Basic Keynesian Model.* Use the hypothetical data (for a closed economy) provided in the following table to complete the questions below (all in billions of constant dollars).

Aggregate Supply	Aggregate Demand	Direction of Change in Output
$200	$800	( )
400	900	( )
600	1,000	( )
800	1,100	( )
1,000	1,200	( )
1,200	1,300	( )
1,400	1,400	( )
1,600	1,500	( )
1,800	1,600	( )
2,000	1,700	( )
2,200	1,800	( )
2,400	1,900	( )
2,600	2,000	( )

a. Complete the column "Direction of Change in Output" by indicating whether output will increase or decrease.
b. Plot the aggregate demand and aggregate supply data in Figure 4–1. What is the equilibrium level of output? (Note: The equation for aggregate demand, AD, is assumed to be $AD = 700 + .5Y$.)

FIGURE 4–1

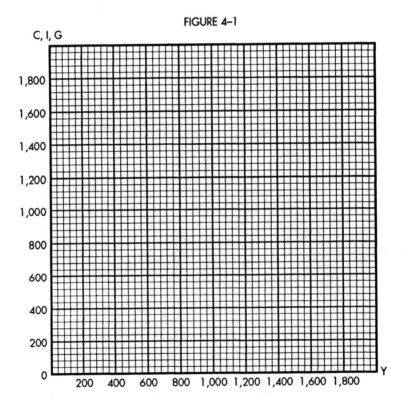

c. Assume output is $1,800 billion. Explain the process whereby equilibrium is restored.

d. Assume output is $800 billion. What is the process whereby equilibrium is restored?

e. Assume aggregate demand increases $100 billion at each level of output (that is, the aggregate demand curve shifts upward by $100 billion). Construct the new aggregate demand function on your diagram and note what happens to the equilibrium output level. Did output increase by the same amount as the autonomous shift in aggregate demand?

f. Now assume the aggregate demand curve shifts downward by $100 billion and note the impact on the equilibrium output level. Here again, did the output level fall by the same amount as the autonomous downward shift of the aggregate demand curve? [Assume the initial position is given by the original AD curve.]

g. Why is it not possible for the aggregate supply curve to shift up or down in this model (often called the Keynesian cross model)?

h. Assume the full-employment level of output is $1,000 billion. Is there an inflationary or deflationary gap? Point out the gap in Figure 4–1 and indicate its magnitude. (Use the original AD curve as your starting point.)

i. Now assume the full-employment output level is $1,600 billion. Indicate whether this entails an inflationary or deflationary gap. What is the size of the gap?

5. *Keynesian-Classical Aggregate Demand and Aggregate Supply Equilibrium.*
This problem develops an *AD-AS* model to determine output and the price level.
Once developed, the model can be used to explain how different government
policies affect inflation, output, and employment. Moreover, the model can be
used to compare the arguments and policy implications of the different schools of
macroeconomic thought. Note that the framework of the model relates directly to
the price level theory implicit in the upper-right quadrant of the classical model
developed in Chapter 3. The data for aggregate demand and aggregate supply are
summarized below.

| *Aggregate Supply* | | | *Aggregate Demand* | |
Price Level (p)	Y_{np}		Price Level (p)	Y_{np}
0.556	$180		2.5	$400
0.625	340		2.0	515
0.714	480		1.5	625
0.833	600		1.0	725
1.000	700		0.5	820
1.250	780			
1.670	840			
2.500	840			

FIGURE 4-2

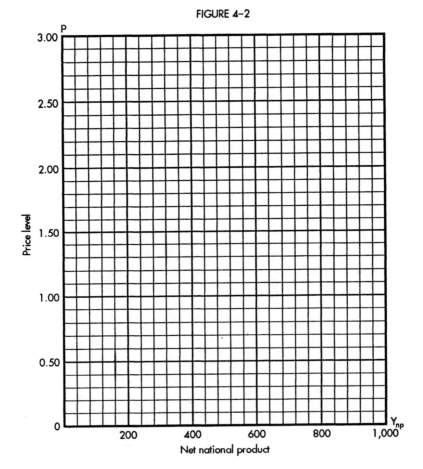

Price level

Net national product

a. *Keynesian-Classical Aggregate Demand Curve.* Now plot the data for aggregate demand in Figure 4–2, connect the points with a smooth curve, and label it AD_1.

(1) What is the meaning of the aggregate demand curve given in Figure 4–2?

(2) Why is the aggregate demand curve negatively sloped? That is, why does the quantity of aggregate demand increase as the price level falls?

(3) What factors cause the aggregate demand curve to shift in and out parallel to itself?

b. *Keynesian-Classical Aggregate Supply Curve.* Using the above data, construct the aggregate supply curve in Figure 4–2. Label it AS_1.

(1) Explain fully the meaning of the aggregate supply curve and why it is shaped as represented in Figure 4–2.

(2) What factors may cause shifts of the aggregate supply curve?

(3) Construct a classical AS curve, as would be obtained from the classical model in Chapter 3, assuming the full-employment output level is 840. Why is the classical model AS curve straight up and down on a p-Y graph?

c. What is the equilibrium price level p and output level Y_{np}? That is, what is the price level and output level at which AD intersects AS and thus ensures that everything produced can be sold?

(1) Why can the equilibrium price level not be at, say, $p = 1.5$? (Assume prices are flexible upward and downward.)

(2) Why can the equilibrium price level not be at, say, $p = 0.75$? (Again, assume prices are fully flexible both upward and downward.)

(3) Must equilibrium necessarily be at full employment?

d. Suppose there is an increase in government purchases of goods and services. Show this change in Figure 4–2 and explain how it will affect prices, output, and employment.

e. Now suppose there is an increase in money wages. Show this change graphically in Figure 4–2 and explain how it will affect prices and output.

f. Explain how an increase in the money supply will affect Figure 4–2 and thereby the price level and output.

A Self-Test

Completion Questions

1. The key question of modern employment theory is what determines the extent to which _____.

2. Keynesian income theory, is short run in the sense that _____

_____.

3. A long-run theory of employment must explain not only how aggregate demand adjusts over time, but also how _____

_____.

4. The aggregate demand and aggregate supply schedules are both (*ex ante, ex post*) terms.

5. Three sources of spending power for nongovernmental spending units are

_____, _____, and _____. In addition to the sources of spending power available to consumers and business firms, the federal

government can pay for part of its expenditures by _____.

6. If the actual income level falls short of the equilibrium level, the economy will adjust to equilibrium because the (*deficiency, excess*) of aggregate demand relative to aggregate supply will induce business executives to (*draw down, increase*) their (*investments, inventories*) and subsequently (*reduce, increase*) production. Production will be (*cut back, expanded*) not only to (*replace, reduce*) (*investments, inventories*) but also because of the (*lower, higher*) level of demand. Production (*is, is not*) very profitable.

7. If the actual income level exceeds the equilibrium level, adjustment to equilibrium will occur as the (*deficiency, excess*) of aggregate demand relative to aggregate supply causes (*investments, inventories*) to (*decline, accumulate*). Because it (*is, is not*) profitable, business executives will (*increase, cut back*) production and continue to do so until equilibrium is attained.

8. Keynes argued that there (*is, is not*) a necessary reason why aggregate demand and aggregate supply should intersect at full employment. It is because

_____ and _____ are made by (*different, the same*) groups in society and for (*different, the same*) reasons.

9. The deflationary gap refers to a condition in which there is a(n) (*excess, deficiency*) of aggregate demand. The inflationary gap refers to a condition in which aggregate demand (*exceeds, falls short of*) aggregate supply.

10. Immediately following World War II the American economy experienced conditions represented by a(n) (*inflationary, deflationary*) gap.

11. In speaking of aggregate demand and aggregate supply, it is necessary to recognize the difference between two types of change. One type of change originates from _____ of the aggregate demand curve which alter the equilibrium income level. The other type of change refers to

_____ the aggregate curves; in this case the equilibrium level of income (*changes rapidly, remains unchanged.*)

12. If there is a shift in the aggregate demand schedule, then the impetus for change originates with the (*spending units, producing units*) in the economy. However, if the change is merely a movement to equilibrium with given supply and demand curves, the impetus for change comes from the (*spending, producing*) units in the economy.

True and False

_____ 1. Keynes refuted the classical theory of interest primarily on the basis that saving and investment are undertaken by two different groups in society and for different reasons.

_____ 2. Keynes explicitly rejected the entire body of classical analysis.

_____ 3. In a market economy, the extent to which productive capacity is utilized depends primarily on the expectations of business executives that they will be able to sell what they produce at a profit.

_____ 4. The major theme of *The General Theory* is that aggregate demand determines the level of income and employment.

_____ 5. The "supply price" of a product is the price that will just induce the supplier to continue producing a certain amount of that commodity.

_____ 6. The aggregate supply schedule is the same as the supply price.

_____ 7. The 45-degree supply line tells us that the business executive must expect to receive an amount of money equal to what it costs him to produce various amounts of goods and services before he will provide them.

_____ 8. If the aggregate supply curve is illustrated by a 45-degree line, and prices are rising, one can conclude that the analysis is in monetary terms.

_____ 9. When the economic system is in disequilibrium, *ex ante* and *ex post* aggregate demand and aggregate supply are equal.

_____ 10. The concept of equilibrium implies that no change is taking place, whereas disequilibrium implies that changes are occurring.

_____ 11. There is little reason to expect that an economic system will experience much disequilibrium because actual and intended values always tend to be equal.

_____ 12. If full employment is not insured at the intersection of aggregate supply and aggregate demand, then the economic system must be at disequilibrium.

_____ 13. The equilibrium income level is necessarily the socially desirable level.

Multiple Choice

1. In the modern economy, income and employment depend mainly on
   a. aggregate supply.
   b. aggregate demand.
   c. government action.
   d. the volume of exports and imports.
   e. none of the above

2. In *The General Theory*, Keynes linked employment with
   a. income.
   b. output.
   c. expected proceeds.
   d. the average workweek.
   e. none of the above

3. If aggregate demand exceeds aggregate supply,
   a. inventories will be increased.
   b. inventories will remain constant and production will increase.
   c. inventories will remain constant and production will decrease.
   d. inventories will be reduced.
   e. none of the above

4. If aggregate supply exceeds aggregate demand, business executives will experience
   a. an unintended decrease in their inventories.
   b. an unintended increase in their inventories.
   c. a rise in their profits.
   d. an increase in their total sales.
   e. none of the above

5. If the current output level is $700 billion and aggregate demand is $690 billion, one can conclude that if the economy is not at full employment, the
   a. amount of employment will fall.
   b. amount of income will rise.
   c. amount of income and employment will be in equilibrium.
   d. amount of employment will rise.
   e. level of employment will rise and income will fall.

6. Keynes concluded that the intersection of aggregate demand and aggregate supply
   a. would always be at the level of full employment.
   b. would never be at the level of full employment.

    c. could never be an equilibrium position.
    d. may or may not be at the level of full employment.
    e. none of the above

7. If business inventories are unintentionally being depleted, then
    a. aggregate demand should be reduced.
    b. aggregate supply is inadequate to satisfy the existing level of demand.
    c. aggregate demand is less than aggregate supply.
    d. business executives will reduce production.
    e. none of the above

8. In the Keynesian income-expenditure model, the multiplier effect
    a. applies to shifts in the consumption function but not shifts in the investment function.
    b. equals the shift in autonomous aggregate demand.
    c. occurs when the aggregate demand function shifts up or down.
    d. does not apply to shifts in the export function.
    e. none of the above

9. The Keynesian-classical aggregate demand curve manifests an inverse relationship between the price level (p) and output (Y) when all of the following are true except
    a. expected profits from investment are constant.
    b. the money supply is constant.
    c. real government spending and taxation are constant.
    d. real GDP is constant.
    e. the income velocity of money is constant.

10. All of the following help to explain why the aggregate demand curve is negatively sloped (in a p-Y quadrant) except the
    a. effect of changes in the capital stock on production.
    b. the real balance effect.
    c. the interest rate effect.
    d. the balance of trade effect.
    e. none of the above

11. According to the real balance effect, an increase in the price level
    a. will reduce the real money supply, increase interest rates, and lower investment and consumption.
    b. will increase interest rates but not reduce investment.
    c. will cause consumers to increase their consumption of durable goods so they can acquire such goods before prices rise any further.
    d. will encourage the government to expand its purchases of goods and services.
    e. none of the above

12. The short run Keynesian-classical aggregate supply curve, constructed in a p-Y quadrant,
    a. slopes upward as the level of output (Y) increases.
    b. is parallel to the horizontal axis.
    c. is vertical at a level of output below full employment.
    d. shifts outward as the output level increases.
    e. is a vertical straight line at the full-employment level of output (Y).

13. In the Keynesian-classical aggregate demand-aggregate supply (p-Y) model, if money wages and price increase by more than expected,
    a. there will be an increase in the quantity of labor supplied.
    b. there will be no effect on the quantity of labor supplied.
    c. there will be a reduction in the quantity of labor supplied.
    d. none of the above

14. In the Keynesian-classical aggregate demand-aggregate supply (p-Y) model, if money wages and prices increase by less than expected,
    a. there will be a decrease in the quantity of labor supplied.
    b. there will be no change in the quantity of labor supplied.
    c. there will be an increase in the quantity of labor supplied.
    d. the labor supply will remain constant.
    e. none of the above

15. Parts of aggregate demand are autonomous with respect to real income because:
    a. aggregate demand is an *ex ante* not an *ex post* relationship.
    b. spending can also be financed by drawing upon assets or by borrowing.
    c. the government has the power to tax and print money.
    d. real income is not an important determinant of spending.
    e. none of the above

16. Assume aggregate supply and demand are equal at less than full employment. Now let there be a change in consumer behavior such that aggregate demand increased at all levels of output. The effect of this will be to:
    a. cause initially unintended decreases in business inventories.
    b. lower the equilibrium level of output.
    c. lower the rate of growth of the economy.
    d. raise the full employment equilibrium.
    e. none of the above

17. The Keynesian-classical *AD-AS* model postulates that
    a. workers have a money illusion because they end up responding to an increase in the money wage as if it were an increase in the real wage.
    b. workers look only at the price level in determining how many hours they will work.
    c. producers do not suffer from a money illusion.
    d. workers do not suffer from a money illusion.
    e. workers and producers respond only to changes in the real wage and relative prices.

18. The Keynesian-classical aggregate supply curve is positively sloped (on a p-Y graph) because when prices are rising
    a. producers and workers intentionally make their decision based on the price level and money wage only.
    b. the real balance effect, interest rate effect, and trade balance effect are positive.
    c. producers believe the relative price of their product has increased and hence expand production, while workers believe the real wage has increased and supply more hours.
    d. less than expected, producers increase production to make up for lower prices.

Money and Interest in the Keynesian System

Key Concepts

Money
M1 definition of money
M2 definition of money
M3 definition of money
L definition of money
Currency (C_u)
Money supply (M^o)
Liquidity
Debt instruments
Equity instruments
Standard-of-value function of money
Store-of-value function of money
Medium-of-exchange function
   of money
Treasury bills (and notes)
Treasury bonds
Consol (bonds)
Opportunity cost of holding money
Coupon rate of interest
Capitalization of income
Capital loss (gain)
Eurodollars
Required reserve ratio
Interest rate (i)
Open market operations (of Fed)
Legal reserve requirement
Total reserves
Required reserves
Excess reserves
Free reserves
Principle of fractional reserves
Money multiplier (k_m)
Lender of last resort
Discount rate
Hoarding (and dishoarding)
Money market
Bond market
Bearish market

Bullish market
Standard-of-deferred-payments function
   of money
Demand deposits (D_d)
Monetary base (high-powered money) (M_b)
Circulating media
Depository Institutions Deregulation
   and Monetary Control Act of 1980
Depository Institutions Deregulation
   Committee (DIDC)
Marginal efficiency of capital (MEC)
Foreign exchange
Foreign exchange rate
Foreign exchange market
Liquidity preference theory of interest
Loanable funds theory of interest
Classical theory of interest
Risk premium
Interest-elastic money supply function
Capital market
Commercial banks
Savings and loan associations
Mutual savings banks
Credit union share drafts (CUSDs)
Automatic transfer service accounts (ATSs)
Negotiable orders of withdrawal accounts
   (NOWs)
Payment order of withdrawal accounts
   (POWs)
"Money matters" controversy
Overnight repurchase agreements (RPs)
Individual retirement accounts (IRAs)
Money market deposit accounts (MMDAs)
Money market mutual funds (MMMFs)
Savings deposits
Traveler's checks
Certificates of deposit (CDs)
Federal funds rate of interest

Problems and Essays

1. Discuss the nature and significance of money with respect to the following points:

   a. Meaning of money (definition).

   b. Identify the following components of the alternative money stock measures and then distinguish between M1, M2, M3, and L. (See a recent issue of the Federal Reserve Bulletin for data on the dollar amount of each measure.)

   (1)   currency
   (2)   traveler's checks
   (3)   demand deposits at commercial banks
   (4)   negotiable order of withdrawal (NOWs)
   (5)   automatic transfer service accounts (ATSs)
   (6)   credit union share drafts (CUSDs)
   (7)   demand deposits at mutual savings banks
   (8)   money market deposit accounts (MMDAs)
   (9)   savings deposits
   (10) small denomination time deposits
   (11) overnight RPs and Eurodollars
   (12) money market mutual funds—general purpose and broker/dealer
   (13) money market mutual funds—institution only
   (14) large denomination time deposits
   (15) term RPs at commercial banks and savings and loan associations
   (16) other liquid assets

   c. What are the functions of money? Is it necessary that money always satisfy each of these functions? Might the degree to which money satisfies each function vary over time?

   d. Alternatives to money. Identify and distinguish clearly between money, debt instruments, and equity instruments.

e. Explain the relationship between bond prices and interest rates. Be specific. Why do interest rates go down when bond prices rise and vice versa?

2. Monetary equilibrium requires that the demand for money equal the supply of money.

   a. Explain the process by which money is created in the United States.

   b. What is the money multiplier and what role does it play in determining the supply of money?

   c. Explain how the Federal Reserve controls the money supply.

   d. How is monetary equilibrium restored if the supply of money exceeds the demand for money?

3. Explain and illustrate the role of money in modern employment theory. Emphasize the following:

   a. Whether money is neutral or non-neutral with respect to its effect on employment and output.

b. How the role of money differs in modern theory from that of classical theory.

c. How the Keynesian motives for holding money differ from those of the classical theory.

4. *Loanable Funds Theory of Interest.* There are essentially four theories explaining the determination of interest rates: the classical theory of interest, the loanable funds theory of interest, the Keynesian liquidity preference theory of interest, and the *IS-LM* model explanation. The classical theory was covered in Chapter 3. This chapter covers the loanable funds and liquidity preference theories. The *IS-LM* explanation is given in a subsequent chapter.

a. Define and illustrate graphically (in Figure 5–1) the demand for loanable funds. What are its components?

   (1) Why is the demand for loanable funds inversely related to the interest rate?

   (2) How is the demand curve for loanable funds related to the supply curve of bonds?

   (3) What factors will cause the demand curve for loanable funds to shift in or out?

b. Define and illustrate graphically (in Figure 5–1) the supply of loanable funds. What are its components?

    (1) Why is the supply of loanable funds positively related to the interest rate?

    (2) How is the supply curve of loanable funds related to the demand curve for bonds?

    (3) What factors will cause the supply curve of loanable funds to shift in or out?

c. Equilibrium. Explain and illustrate graphically (in Figure 5–1) the process of adjustment when the quantity of funds supplied exceeds (or falls short of) the quantity of funds demanded.

d. Explain and illustrate graphically (in Figure 5–1) how a change in the determinants of the demand and supply functions will affect the rate of interest and amount of funds borrowed.

FIGURE 5–1

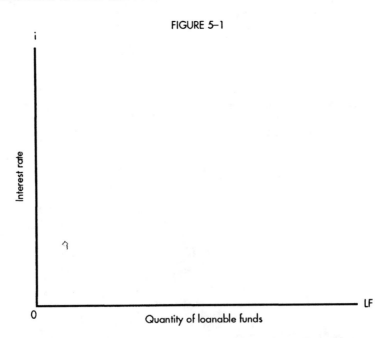

Interest rate

0

Quantity of loanable funds

LF

5. *Keynes' Liquidity Preference Theory of Interest.* The liquidity preference theory argues that the rate of interest is determined by the demand for money as an asset and the supply of money available for asset purposes, the equilibrium interest rate being determined by the intersection of these two functions. Figure 5–2 contains a graph showing the speculative demand for money curve. The interest rate is measured on the vertical axis while both the asset demand for money (L_a) and asset supply of money (M_a^0) are measured on the horizontal axis. Use this diagram as a basis for answering the questions below.

FIGURE 5–2

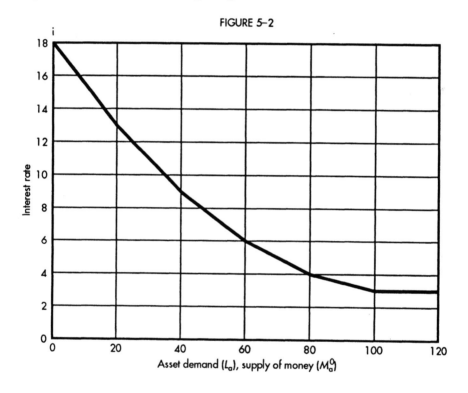

Asset demand (L_a), supply of money (M_a^0)

a. Assume that the amount of money available to hold as an asset is $60 billion. Construct a curve in the above figure showing the asset supply of money at $60 billion and assuming that the money supply for asset purposes is completely interest inelastic.

   (1) What is the equilibrium rate of interest?

   (2) How is equilibrium restored if the interest rate is temporarily at 9 percent?

(3) How is equilibrium restored if the interest rate is temporarily at 4 percent?

(4) Is it realistic to portray the money supply as being completely autonomous with respect to the rate of interest; that is, completely interest inelastic? Why or why not?

b. The equilibrium rate of interest will change if there is an alteration in the asset supply of money or if the speculative demand for money curve shifts up or down.

(1) Assume the interest rate is at equilibrium with the asset money supply equal to $60 billion. Now let the asset supply of money increase to $80 billion. What is the process whereby equilibrium is restored, and what is the new equilibrium rate of interest?

(2) Start over with the initial asset money supply being $60 billion and asset demand being as graphed. Now assume that there is an overall change in the climate of opinion so that all individuals think the normal interest rate is higher than previously. This shifts the asset demand curve upward. What is the process whereby equilibrium is restored? Is it realistic to assume shifts in the L_a curve? Why or why not?

c. Given the speculative demand for money curve, what determines the extent to which a given change in the money supply for asset purposes will alter the interest rate?

d. How realistic is the horizontal portion of the asset demand curve (i.e., the liquidity trap?

e. Keynes criticized the classical economists for not recognizing that income is an important determinant of their interest theory. This same criticism can be made of Keynes' interest theory. Changes in the income level will alter the interest rate. Explain what happens to the rate of interest, *ceteris paribus,* when the level of income rises. [Note: The relationships involved in this question will become more apparent subsequently when we analyze equilibrium for the economy as a whole.]

f. What is the significance of the Keynesian theory of interest?

g. Which theory best explains how interest rates are determined?

6. From both a domestic and international perspective, it is extremely important to know how changes in interest rates affect aggregate demand, aggregate demand being equal to $C + I + G + (X - M)$.

a. Explain how changes in interest rates may affect consumer expenditures (C).

b. Explain how changes in interest rates may affect government purchases (G).

    c. Explain how changes in interest rates may affect investment spending (*I*).

    d. Explain how changes in interest rates may affect net exports (*X* − *M*). Be sure to include, among other things, an explanation of the foreign exchange market and interest rate differentials.

A Self-Test

Completion Questions

1. The classical theory of interest relates to (*flows, stocks*), the Keynesian theory of interest relates to (*flows, stocks*), and the loanable funds theory of interest relates to (*flows, stocks*).

2. In the Keynesian theory of interest, if the interest rate is temporarily above the equilibrium rate, there is a (*surplus, shortage*) of money to hold as an asset. Individuals will (*buy, sell*) securities, thereby causing security prices to (*rise, fall*) and the interest rate to (*rise, fall*).

3. For outstanding bonds the higher the interest rate, the (*higher, lower*) the prices of bonds; the lower the interest rate, the (*higher, lower*) the prices of bonds.

4. If the majority sentiment in the market is "bearish," most people think the price of bonds will (*rise, fall*); if it is "bullish" most people think the price of bonds will (*rise, fall*).

5. Keynes said that the rate of interest is determined by the supply of and demand for

    _____. Classical economists said it was determined

    by the supply of and demand for _____. A third interest rate theory

    says the rate of interest is determined by the supply and demand for

    _____.

6. In the loanable funds theory, the supply of loanable funds consists of

    _____, _____, and

    _____. The demand for loanable funds is made up

    of the demands of _____, _____, and _____.

True and False

_____ 1. A major criticism of Keynesian interest theory is its assumption that, for outstanding bonds, the interest rate and bond prices are inversely related; this, of course, is not correct.

_____ 2. If we assume the money supply is unchanged and that the economy is not in the liquidity trap, increases in income will cause the interest rate to rise.

_____ 3. The M1 definition of money does not include MMDAs.

_____ 4. The M2 definition of money does not include demand deposits.

_____ 5. The M2 money stock always exceeds M1 and M3.

_____ 6. The income velocity of money tends to increase as monetary policy becomes more and more restrictive.

_____ 7. The monetary base is essentially equal to total reserves minus currency in circulation.

_____ 8. If the demand for asset balances exceeds the supply of asset money in the liquidity preference theory of interest, then the quantity of bonds supplied exceeds the quantity of bonds demanded.

_____ 9. A CD is a fixed-interest note that may be negotiable or nonnegotiable.

_____ 10. High-powered money is essentially the total of member bank reserves plus currency in circulation.

_____ 11. The Fed can force a contraction of the money supply but cannot *force* an expansion of the money supply.

_____ 12. If the legal reserve requirement is 12 percent, the *simple* money multiplier is about 8.33.

Multiple Choice

1. According to the loanable funds theory of interest, the total supply of loanable funds is composed of
   a. saving and the money supply.
   b. saving, changes in the money supply, and net dishoarding or hoarding.
   c. the amount of the loan that can be obtained from commercial banks.
   d. net dishoarding or hoarding, and saving.
   e. none of the above

2. It is not too unrealistic to assume that the money supply is autonomously determined by the Federal Reserve because
   a. the Federal Reserve sets the exact amount of money that can circulate on a day-to-day basis.

   b. Congress gave the Federal Reserve the power to regulate interest rates at which the commercial banks borrow from the Fed.

   c. the Federal Reserve has "ultimate" control over the level of bank reserves.

   d. banks always create as much money as possible regardless of the interest rate.

3. If, because of rising interest rates, people revise their *normal* level of the interest rate upward, the speculative demand for money curve will
   a. shift downward.
   b. shift upward.
   c. not be affected.
   d. be affected but cannot say if it would shift up or down.

4. Although we have not yet analyzed how inflation affects interest rates, we can be fairly certain that it causes
   a. interest rates to rise.
   b. interest rates to fall.
   c. interest rates to fluctuate sharply.
   d. the normal level of interest rates to fall slowly over time.

5. A consol is a bond
   a. issued by the U.S. consulate.
   b. with a 10-year maturity.
   c. with no maturity date.
   d. paid to get someone out of jail.

6. The Federal Reserve M2 definition of money is basically equal to
   a. currency, demand deposits, other checkable deposits, and traveler's checks.
   b. savings and time deposits in mutual savings banks, savings and loans associations, credit unions, and money market mutual funds.
   c. M1 plus savings deposits and large denomination time deposits.
   d. M1 plus savings deposits, MMDAs, small-denomination time deposits, and noninstitutional MMMFs.

7. The belief that any assets that are a "temporary abode for purchasing power" should be considered money is associated with the name of
   a. Arthur Burns.
   b. Irving Fisher.
   c. Alfred Marshall.
   d. Milton Friedman.
   e. J. R. Hicks.

8. Excess reserves of member banks equals
   a. total reserves minus required reserves minus member bank borrowing at the Fed.
   b. required reserves minus member bank borrowings at the Fed.
   c. total reserves minus free reserves.
   d. total reserves minus required reserves.

9. Assume total reserves are $35 billion, required reserves are $34.4 billion, and borrowing at the Fed by member banks is $0.4 billion. Excess reserves and free reserves are (respectively)

a. $34.6 billion and $34 billion.
b. $0.6 billion and $0.2 billion.
c. $0.2 billion and $0.6 billion.
d. $34.8 billion and $34 billion.
e. cannot be determined from data given

10. Assume the banking system is fully loaned up and that the average legal reserve ratio is .16. Now let the Fed undertake actions that increase excess reserves by $2 billion. The maximum amount by which the money supply can increase, using the simple money multiplier, is
a. $20 billion.
b. $0.2 billion.
c. $0.3 billion.
d. $0.1 billion.

11. Which of the following is *not* a means by which the Fed can alter the money supply?
a. buying and selling government securities via open market operations
b. changing the legal reserve requirement pertaining to demand and savings deposits
c. raising or lowering the discount rate—that is, the rate of interest the Fed charges on loans made to commercial banks
d. ordering commercial banks to increase or decrease their checking deposits

12. If the fixed annual income on a consol is $75 and the relevant interest rate is 6 percent, the present value of the consol is
a. $1,000.
b. $1,250.
c. $71 (approximately).
d. cannot be determined without more information

13. What is the current market value of a $5,000 bond paying $500 per year until maturity if the current interest rate is 12 percent?
a. $5,000
b. $500
c. $4,500
d. $4,167

14. The "monetary base" consists basically of all
a. reserves of the financial institutions plus currency in circulation.
b. the money represented by the M1 definition of money.
c. bank reserves at the Fed.
d. the currency in circulation.

15. A primary purpose of the Monetary Control Act of 1980 was to
a. impose additional controls on the commercial banks.
b. give the Fed better control over the money supply.
c. bring the Fed under control of the President.
d. lower interest rates on bonds.

16. The money multiplier used by the Fed is equal to
    a. M1 times the monetary base.
    b. M1 divided by the monetary base.
    c. M1 minus the monetary base.
    d. M2 divided by the monetary base.
    e. M2 multiplied by the monetary base.

17. A major difference between the classical economists and Keynes is that Keynes
    a. believed people would want to hold money only to facilitate the exchange of goods and services.
    b. said people would want to hold money as a store of wealth.
    c. believed there was no relationship between the demand for money and interest rates.
    d. said changes in the money supply would result in direct and proportional changes in the price level.

18. Keynesian interest theory:
    a. argues that investment and the demand for money determines interest rates.
    b. is based on flow concepts, whereas classical interest theory is based on stocks.
    c. is essentially the same as that of the classical theory.
    d. implies that holding financial assets in cash balances, as opposed to bonds, increases future uncertainty.
    e. makes money an important determinant of output and employment.

19. When bond prices increase
    a. interest rates will also increase.
    b. interest rates will not be affected.
    c. interest rates will fall.
    d. none of the above

20. Keynes argued that an increase in the money supply
    a. could result in changes in real GDP and the level of employment.
    b. could not be offset by Federal Reserve open market operations.
    c. would typically result in a more or less proportional amount of inflation.
    d. would have no effect on income and employment.
    e. none of the above

21. The average money multiplier for each year can be determined by
    a. adding the money supply to the monetary base and dividing by the total.
    b. multiplying the money supply by the monetary base.
    c. dividing the money supply by the monetary base.
    d. dividing the monetary base by the money supply.
    e. adding the amount of currency in circulation to total reserves.

22. For the United States, the average money multiplier in 1990 was in the range of
    a. 1.5 to 2.0.
    b. 2.0 to 2.5.
    c. 2.5 to 3.0.
    d. 3.0 to 3.5.
    e. 3.5 to 4.0.

23. According to the loanable funds theory of interest, the supply of loanable funds is composed of
    a. saving and investment.
    b. the money supply and dishoarding.
    c. saving, additions to the money supply, and dishoarding.
    d. all the money banks are willing to lend to businesses.
    e. the total money supply.

24. Which of the following will not cause a shift of the loanable funds supply curve?
    a. Fed monetary policy
    b. an increase in the economy's real wealth
    c. expectations about future interest rates
    d. the public's attitude toward risk
    e. an increase in interest rates

25. Which of the following will *not* cause a shift of the loanable funds demand curve?
    a. federal government fiscal policy
    b. the expected profitability of potential investment projects
    c. the expected rate of inflation
    d. a change in the rate of interest

26. If the quantity supplied of loanable funds exceeds the quantity demanded,
    a. the rate of interest will fall.
    b. the rate of interest will rise.
    c. it will not be affected.
    d. the demand curve for loanable funds will increase.
    e. the demand curve for loanable funds will decrease.

27. Keynes' liquidity preference theory of interest based on the asset demand for money
    a. includes less variables than the classical theory of interest.
    b. is based on flows instead of stocks.
    c. is not sufficient by itself to explain how interest rates are determined.
    d. is sufficient by itself to explain the determination of the rate of interest.

28. An increase in the rate of interest may affect a country's trade balance by
    a. strengthening its currency on the foreign exchange market and thereby reducing exports and increasing imports.
    b. strengthening its currency on the foreign exchange market and thereby increasing exports and imports.
    c. strengthening its currency on the foreign exchange market and thereby reducing exports and imports.
    d. weakening its currency on the foreign exchange market and thereby increasing exports and reducing imports.

29. An increase in the U.S. demand for Swiss francs to pay for imports will, *ceteris paribus,* cause
    a. the U.S. dollar to increase in value on the foreign exchange market.
    b. the U.S. dollar to decrease in value on the foreign exchange market.
    c. will have no affect on the U.S. dollar's international value.

  d. will affect the international value of the dollar, but it is not possible to predict whether the value will increase or decrease.

30. Which of the following is *not* a source of loanable funds?
    a. saving by individuals, businesses, and government
    b. capital inflows form other countries
    c. increases in the domestic money supply
    d. capital outflow from the United States
    e. none of the above

31. The federal funds rate of interest is the rate of interest
    a. the Fed charges the Federal government.
    b. banks charge each other for over-night intra-bank borrowings.
    c. the U.S. Treasury charges banks on loans made to banks.
    d. consumers have to pay banks on credit card borrowing.
    e. business firms have to pay to borrow from the Federal government.

CHAPTER 6   A General Macroeconomic Model

DETERMINANTS OF HICKS-HANSEN GENERAL EQUILIBRIUM

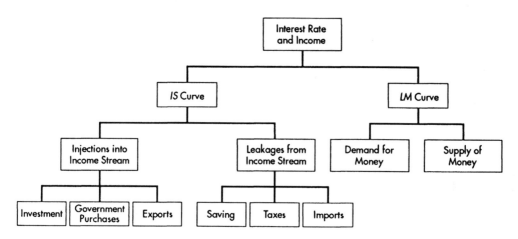

Key Concepts

Goods sphere
Monetary sphere
LM curve
IS curve
Money supply as function of
   interest rate
Real money supply
Hicksian general equilibrium
Keynes effect

"Neoclassical" synthesis
IS-LM model
Pigou effect
"Money doesn't matter"
"Only money matters"
Keynesian vs. monetarist position
Aggregate demand related to price level
Aggregate supply related to price level
Money wage curve

Problems and Essays

1. *Derivation of the* LM *Curve.* The first three problems of this chapter pull together
the two major parts of the Hicks-Hansen *IS-LM* model of general equilibrium, the
LM curve and the *IS* curve. This problem derives and analyzes the *LM* curve,
which shows multiple equilibria in the monetary sector of the economy, assuming
first that the money supply is completely autonomous and second that the money
supply is a function of the interest rate (although not highly interest elastic). The

second problem derives and analyzes the simple *IS* curve, which shows multiple equilibria in the real sector of the economy. The *LM* curve and simple *IS* curve are then brought together in problem 3 to find general equilibrium for the economy. Later problems refine the *IS-LM* model presented in problem 3 and use it for public policy purposes.

The table below gives hypothetical data for the speculative and total demand for money at various interest rates and income levels. All data except those for interest rates are in billions of constant dollars. The "plus" at the end of each column signifies that at the interest rate of 3 percent the demand for money becomes "infinitely" elastic.

i	L_a	L when Y=$200	L when Y=$400	L when Y=$600	L when Y=$800	L when Y=$1,000	L when Y=$1,200	L when Y=$1,400	L when Y=$1,600
18%	$0	$60	$120	$180	$240	$300	$360	$420	$480
13	20	80	140	200	260	320	380	440	500
9	40	100	160	220	280	340	400	460	520
6	60	120	180	240	300	360	420	480	540
4	80	140	200	260	320	380	440	500	560
3	100+	160+	220+	280+	340+	400+	460+	520+	580+

a. Plot the data for the speculative demand for money L_a and total demand for money, when income is $200, $400, $600, $800, $1,000, $1,200, $1,400, and $1,600 billion, in part A of Figure 6–1. Note that both the demand for money and money supply M^s are measured on the horizontal axis.

b. Assume the total real money supply is $300 billion and that it remains this amount regardless of the level of the interest rate—thus we are assuming the *money supply is completely autonomous* and given by the Federal Reserve. [Note: This assumption will be used until indicated otherwise.] Construct a completely interest-inelastic curve in part A showing the money supply at this level. What are the equilibrium rates of interest for each *feasible* income level; that is, what are the rates of interest that make the money demanded equal to the supply of money at each of the first five income levels?

c. Using the income levels from $200 billion to $1,600 billion and the corresponding equilibrium interest rates, construct the *LM* curve ($L = M$) in part B of Figure 6–1. Note that the interest rate is measured on the vertical axis and the various income levels, which before were represented by different total demand for money curves, are now measured along the horizontal axis.

(1) What is the meaning of the *LM* curve?

FIGURE 6–1
Part A

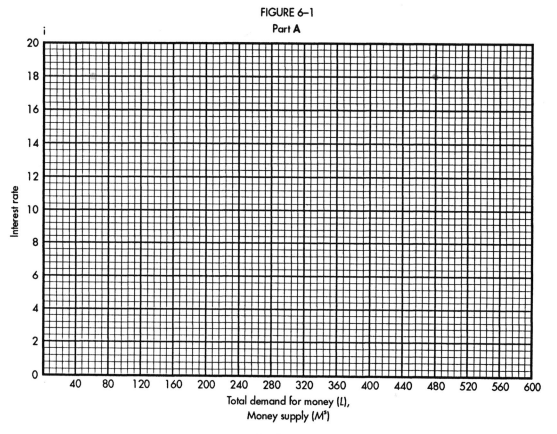

Total demand for money (L),
Money supply (M^s)

Part B

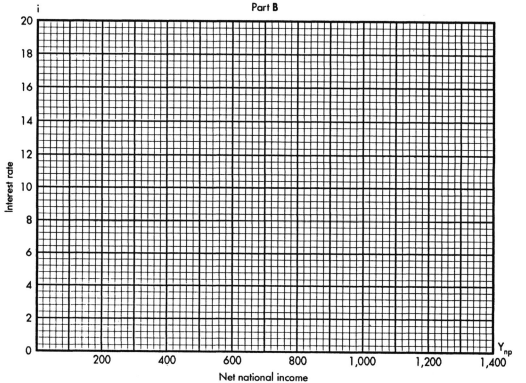

Net national income

(2) Explain why any point to the right of the *LM* curve, say at $i = 9$ percent
and $Y_{np} = \$1,000$, is one of disequilibrium. How will equilibrium be
restored?

(3) Explain why any point to the left of the *LM* curve, say at $i = 9$ percent and
$Y_{np} = \$600$, is one of disequilibrium. How will equilibrium be restored?

(4) Why is the *LM* curve positively sloped throughout a wide range of interest
rates? Note carefully that up to this point we are still assuming that the
money supply is autonomously determined by the Federal Reserve.

d. Shifts in the *LM* curve may be caused by either a change in the autonomous
money supply or an overall change (shift) in the demand for money.

(1) Suppose the Federal Reserve authorities increase the money supply to
$320 billion. Shift the money supply curve in part A to $320 billion and
show how this action affects the money equilibrium (that is, the *LM*) curve
in part B. In which direction and by how much does the *LM* curve shift at
each rate of interest? Would a reduction in the money supply have the
opposite effect?

(2) Explain and illustrate (in parts A and B) how an overall increase in the
demand for money by consumers and business firms will affect the *LM*
curve. Do the same thing for an overall reduction in the demand for money.

e. Up to this point, the price level has been held constant. Suppose the price level
is now allowed to change. How would a reduction or increase in the price level
alter the *LM* curve?

f. Money Supply Functionally Related to Interest Rate. Up to this point, it has been assumed that the money supply is completely autonomous and thus not at all responsive to the interest rate. In view of the Federal Reserve's ultimate control over the money supply, this is not a highly unrealistic assumption. However, it does appear that there is some responsiveness of the money supply— although not a high responsiveness—to rising interest rates and hence, even though it does not alter the analysis nor the conclusions of the prior part of this problem, it will be incorporated in the above analysis. Note that the demand for money is the same as above.

Plot the following hypothetical data showing the money supply at various interest rates in Figure 6–2. Be careful! Note that the *LM* curve in part B has been derived from the various demand-for-money curves and the *autonomous* money supply in part A. [Note: The equation for the money supply when the stock of money is assumed to be completely autonomous is $M^s = M^0$. When we make the money supply a function of the interest rate, that is, $M^s = f(i)$, we may specify the money supply function in a linear form to be $M^s = M^0 + hi$, where M^0 is the amount of money when the interest rate is zero and h is the parameter relating changes in the money supply to changes in the interest rate—thus $h = \Delta M^s / \Delta i$. The letter h is used instead of m because we have already used m to stand for the marginal propensity to import. Inserting the assumed parameters in this equation, we have $M^s = \$300 + 3.75i$. Note further that the money supply will be responsive to interest rates only so long as commercial banks have free reserves with which to expand demand deposits. Once the interest rate reaches a level at which all free reserves are used up—that is, free reserves are zero—the money supply is no longer responsive to the interest rate. Further increases in the money supply require action of the monetary authorities. Let us assume the interest rate at which all free reserves are zero is 16 percent. Thus, the above equation applies only as long as the rate of interest is *equal to or less than* 16 percent; at rates above 16 percent the money supply again becomes completely autonomous. All these assumptions are incorporated in the data below.]

Interest Rate (i)	Money Supply (M^s)
0%	$300 billion
4	315 billion
8	330 billion
12	345 billion
16	360 billion
20	360 billion

(1) Plot the money supply data in Figure 6–2 and connect the points with straight line segments. What are the equilibrium rates of interest—the interest rates that make money demanded equal to money supplied—for each of the income levels?

(2) Using the new equilibrium interest rates and various income levels, plot the new *LM* curve in part B of Figure 6–2. Does the new *LM* curve have the same meaning as the original curve based on a completely autonomous money supply?

FIGURE 6–2

Part A

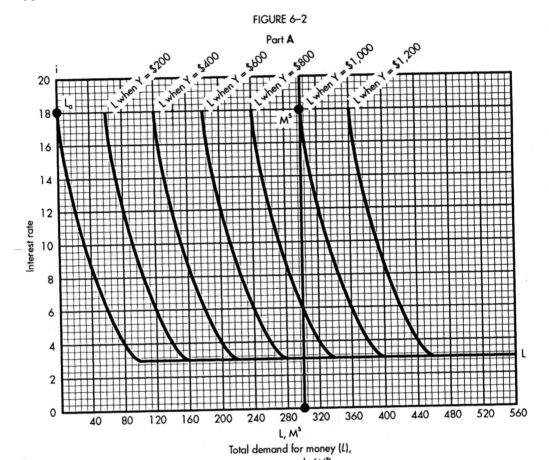

L, M^s

Total demand for money (L),
Money supply (M^s)

Part B

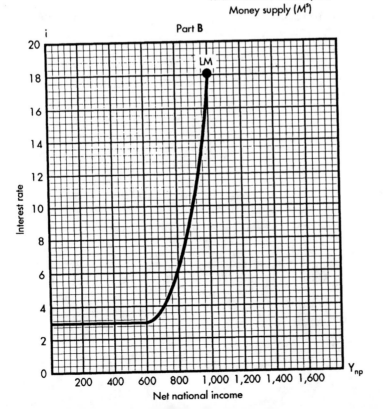

Net national income

(3) Will the new *LM* curve—that is, the one incorporating an interest-sensitive money supply function—always lie to the right of the *LM* curve based on an autonomous money supply? Why?

(4) Does the new *LM* curve still have a segment at some high income level that is parallel to the vertical axis? That is, a segment which implies that a further expansion of the economy is not possible because the entire money supply is being used solely for transactions purposes. Will this always be the case?

(5) At this point, it might be wise to consider how the actions of the Federal Reserve change the money supply. What are the major means whereby the Fed can increase or reduce the money supply?

2. *Derivation of the* IS *Curve.* The *LM* curve gives various equilibria in the monetary sphere of the economy. It is now necessary to derive a curve, called the *IS* curve for short (or sometimes the $I = S$ curve), giving various possible equilibria positions for the real (or commodity) sphere of the economy. As with derivation of the *LM* curve, there are many graphical techniques for deriving the *IS* curve. In this problem a technique is used that helps insure that you understand the nature of the derivation. [In a subsequent problem both the *IS* and *LM* curves will be derived in a fashion which is more "mechanical."]

Assume the following hypothetical data for investment and saving are given (in billions of constant dollars).

Investment Function		Saving Function	
Interest Rate (i)	Investment (I)	Income (Y_{np})	Saving (S)
18%	$10	$ 0	$-60
16%	40	200	20
14%	70	400	100
11%	100	600	180
8%	130	800	260
5%	160	1,000	340
2%	190	1,200	420
		1,400	500
		1,600	580
		1,800	660

a. Figure 6–3 is divided into three parts to facilitate deriving the *IS* curve. Plot the investment data in part A and the data for saving in part B. (The *IS* curve will be constructed in part C from this information.)

b. To derive the *IS* curve from the saving and investment functions, proceed in the following manner.

(1) Part A shows that when the interest rate is 18 percent, investment is $10 billion. Move to part B and measure off 10 on the vertical axis. Now slide over to the saving function and find the income level which will generate saving equal to $10 billion; in this case it is the income level of $175 billion. Thus when $i = 18$ percent and $Y_{np} = \$175$ billion, saving and investment are equal.

(2) Move to part C and plot in the point for $i = 18$ percent and $Y_{np} = \$175$ billion. This is a point on the *IS* curve as it represents equality between saving and investment.

(3) Now start over with the interest rate at 16 percent and find a second point on the *IS* curve (that is, a second point where saving equals investment) in part C. Do the same thing for interest rates of 14, 11, 8, 5, and 2 percent, respectively, and plot each new point in part C of Figure 6–3. What are the equilibrium income levels for these different interest rates?

(4) Connect all the equilibrium points in part C and you have the *IS* curve.

c. What is the meaning of the *IS* curve, and why is it negatively sloped?

d. Choose a point to the right of the *IS* curve (for example, $i = 10$ percent and $Y_{np} = \$600$ billion) and explain why it represents disequilibrium. How is equilibrium restored?

FIGURE 6–3

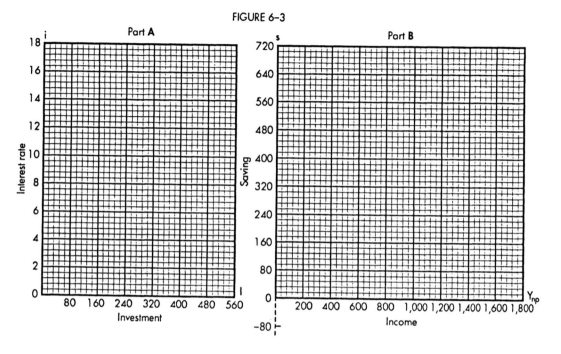

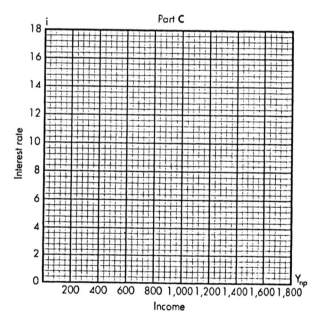

e. Changes in the position and slope of the *IS* curve, for a situation in which government and the foreign sector are excluded, may be caused by an alteration in any of the factors which determine the position and slope of the investment function or the saving function.

   (1) Assume the investment function shifts rightward (from the origin) by 10 at each interest rate. Illustrate this shift in part A of Figure 6–3 and derive the new *IS* curve in part C. In which direction and by how much did the *IS* curve shift? Explain. Did the slope of the *IS* curve change?

   (2) The equation for the saving function given above is $S = \$-60$ billion + $0.4Y_{np}$. What will be the effect on the *IS* curve if the consumption function equation changes to $C = \$40$ billion + $0.6Y_{np}$? Think carefully before answering.

   (3) Suppose the marginal propensity to consume increases from 0.6 to 0.8. What is the effect on the position and slope of the *IS* curve? (Show the change in part B and see how it alters the *IS* curve.)

3. IS-LM *Equilibrium.* The *IS* and *LM* curves may now be combined to determine general equilibrium for the economy as a whole. The following table summarizes the foregoing data with respect to the equilibrium interest rates and income levels for the commodity and money markets (determined in problems 1 and 2 above). [Recall that the model does not yet include government or foreign trade. Once these sectors are added, the equilibrium income level will be much higher.]

IS Curve		LM Curve	
i	Y_{np}	i	Y_{np}
18%	$175	3%	$ 200
16%	250	3%	400
14%	325	3%	600
11%	400	6%	800
8%	475	18%	1,000
5%	550		
2%	625		

a. **Construct the *IS* and *LM* curves in Figure 6–4 from the above data.**

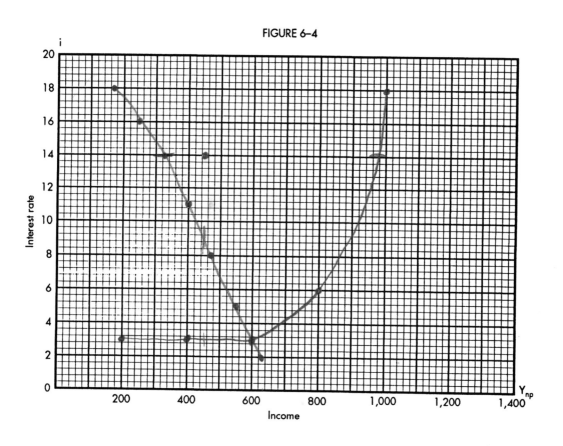

FIGURE 6–4

b. **What is the equilibrium interest rate and income level?**

> interest rate $i_e = 3\%$
> income level $Y_e = 600$

c. **Prove that equilibrium can be only at the point where the *IS* and *LM* curves intersect. Your proof should consist of taking several disequilibrium points (on the diagram) and demonstrating that at each point forces will be set into motion which drive the system to equilibrium. For example, take the point where the interest rate and income level are 14 percent and $450 billion, respectively. At this point how is equilibrium restored?**

> On IS Curve $I_p < S_p$
> inventories pile up, so
> production will slowdown,
> decreasing i, and Y

> On LM Curve: L_a is too low
> $M_s > L$
> So people will buy more bonds,
> driving down the interest rate,
> which will ↓ money supply

> If you overshoot the IS curve, then forces reverse
> and pushes Y up towards equilibrium.

d. What impact will a decrease in the money supply or an increase in the demand for money have on the equilibrium interest rate and income level? [Note that the economy is in the so-called liquidity trap and hence interest rates cannot be lowered by governmental actions.] *people will sell bonds,*

A decrease in the Money Supply so the price for bonds ↓ and i↑ (Y↓)?

e. Assume that because of optimistic expectations, business executives increase investment. Show how this will alter Figure 6–4 and explain the impact on the interest rate and income. Would the effects have been the same if society as a whole had decided to save less?

This will shift the IS curve to the right (I and i), which will make a new ie and Ye, both of which will be higher than before.

f. Now suppose the investment function is completely interest inelastic. Under these circumstances the *IS* curve will be straight up and down.

   (1) If the *IS* curve intersects the *LM* curve in the same place, will a shift to the right of the investment function still increase the interest rate and income level?

   (2) Will a decrease in the money supply still increase the interest rate and decrease the income level?

4. *Inclusion of Government and Foreign Trade in the* IS-LM *Model.* The *IS-LM* model just derived applies to a simple economy with no government purchases, taxation, exports, or imports. It is relatively easy to expand the model to include all of these elements. Keep in mind that when the government sector is added to the model, the equilibrium condition becomes $I + G = S + TX$, and when the foreign sector is also included, the equilibrium condition is $I + G + X = S + TX + M$. Assume here that taxes (TX) are net of transfer payments. [To simplify the labeling, the curve representing these equalities will still generally be labeled *IS.*]

   Figure 6–5 is essentially a reproduction of Figure 6–3. The investment function, saving function, and *LM* curve have been reproduced in parts A, B, and C, respectively. The *LM* curve is included here so that once the curve showing equilibrium in the commodity market (including government and the foreign sector) is derived, the equilibrium level of income can be determined.

FIGURE 6-5

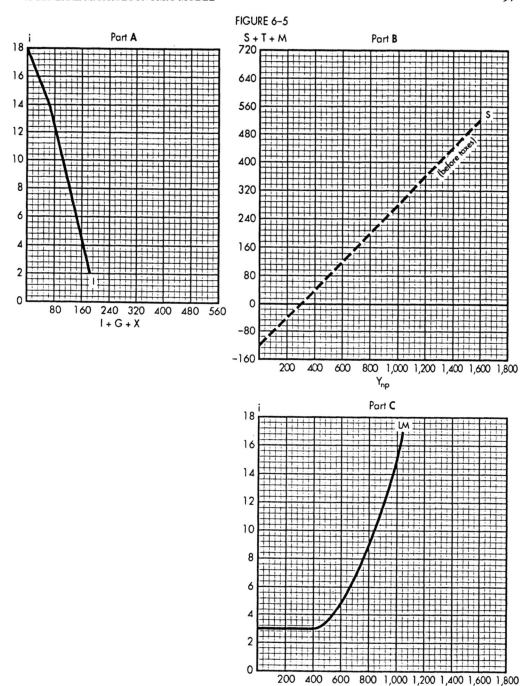

a. Consider, first, part A of Figure 6–5. The interest rate is still measured on the vertical axis but now exports and government purchases, as well as investment, are measured on the horizontal axis.

   (1) Construct a curve in part A representing $I + G$ on the assumption that government purchases of goods and services are $275 billion. Note that the new curve is parallel to the investment curve. Designate it $I + G$.

   (2) Construct a curve for $I + G + X$ assuming that exports equal $100 billion. As exports are autonomous, this curve is parallel to the $I + G$ curve.

b. Now consider part B. The saving function has already been constructed on the graph. Note that income is still measured along the horizontal axis but now S, TX, and M are measured on the vertical axis, where TX stands for net taxes—taxes after deducting transfers.

   (1) What is the equation for the saving function plotted in part B?

   (2) Assume that the tax equation is $TX = \$80$ billion $+ 0.1Y_{np}$, where TX is net taxes. What is the volume of tax revenue at the income levels $0, $200, $400, $600, $800, $1,000, $1,200, $1,400, $1,600, and $1,800 billion?

   (3) The saving curve in part B was constructed on the assumption that taxes were zero. When taxes are levied, part of the taxes come from consumption and part from saving in accordance with the MPC and MPS. Accordingly, the introduction of taxes shifts the saving function to the right as now there is less saving at each income level. The new saving equation with taxes is $S = \${-}120$ billion $+ 0.4[Y_{np} - (\$80 + 0.1Y_{np})]$ which, as taxes at each income level are known, can be rewritten as $S = \${-}120$ billion $+ 0.4(Y_{np} - TX)$. Use this equation and the tax information from b (2) above to find the level of saving when income is $0, $200, $400, $600, $800, $1,000, $1,200, $1,400, $1,600, and $1,800 billion. Plot the new saving curve in part B.

(4) Now add the tax data [from $b(2)$] and the saving data [from $b(3)$] to obtain the $S + TX$ data and plot this information in part B of Figure 6–5.

(5) The remaining step is to include imports (M) in part B. Assume the import equation is $M = \$60$ billion $+ 0.04Y$. What is the value of imports at each income level from 0 to $800 billion?

(6) Add imports to saving and taxes at each income level to obtain the data for $S + TX + M$ and plot this information in part B. What are the values for $S + TX + M$ at various income levels?

c. Construct the curve showing $I + G + X = S + TX + M$ in part C of Figure 6–5. The approach is the same as when deriving the IS curve for saving and investment alone.

(1) What is the equilibrium rate of interest and income level?

(2) What will happen to the equilibrium rate of interest and income level if there is an increase or decrease in I, G, or X?

(3) Explain the effect on the interest rate and income level of an increase or decrease in S, TX, or M.

5. *Modification of the Multiplier.* In previous chapters changes in investment, government purchases, exports, and so forth were assumed to increase or decrease income by the full extent of the multiplier. Hence, if G increased by $10 billion and the multiplier equaled 2.5, the income level was assumed to advance by $25 billion. This analysis ignores conditions in the money market. What happens to the magnitude of the multiplier when the money market is brought into the analysis?

Figure 6–6 contains an *IS* curve and *LM* curve based on hypothetical data for Country A. In addition, an investment function—the same one used in the derivation of the *IS* curve—is plotted in the diagram. Accordingly, both investment and income are measured along the horizontal axis. (Why the investment function has been included in this figure will become apparent very shortly. For simplification assume that the marginal propensities to invest, tax, and import are all zero. Thus the multiplier is the reciprocal of the marginal propensity to save, the numerical value of the MPS used in this problem being 0.4. Assume also that the money supply is completely autonomous.)

FIGURE 6–6

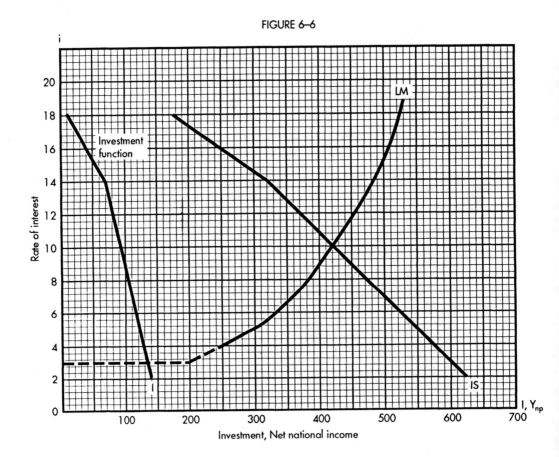

Investment, Net national income

a. What are the equilibrium values of the interest rate, income, and investment?

b. Explain and illustrate in Figure 6–6 the effect of a $25 billion increase in government purchases of goods and services with respect to the following points.

(1) What is the direction and magnitude of shift in the *IS* curve?

(2) What are the equilibrium values of *i*, Y_{np}, and *I* at the new equilibrium?

(3) Explain why the income level advanced by $25 billion instead of by the full $62.5 billion.

(4) Suppose government expenditures are reduced by $25 billion, rather than increased as in the preceding part. Explain how this change affects the *IS* curve and the level of income.

(5) In Figure 6–6 the *IS* curve cuts the *LM* curve in the intermediate range (the intermediate range being where the *LM* curve is neither completely vertical or completely horizontal). Suppose instead that the economy is in the liquidity trap; that is, the *IS* curve cuts the *LM* curve where the latter is infinitely elastic. Now assume *G* increases and decreases by 25, without moving out of the liquidity trap. Is the multiplier modified in this case?

(6) Now assume the *IS* curve intersects the *LM* curve in the classical range; that is, where the *LM* curve is completely vertical. What effect does an increase or decrease of *G* of $25 billion have on the income level in this range? (Construct a completely vertical section of the *LM* curve in Figure 6–6 to aid in answering this question.)

(7) Suppose the economy is in the intermediate or classical range of the *IS-LM* model. If the government finances a $25 billion increase in *G* by increasing the money supply just enough so that the interest rate remains unchanged, what effect will this action have on the value of the multiplier?

(8) Assume the investment function is completely interest inelastic. Using the *IS-LM* analysis, explain the impact of this assumption on the magnitude of the multiplier assuming government purchases increase or decrease by $25 billion.

6. *Alternative Derivation of* IS *and* LM *Curves.* As indicated earlier, there are many graphical techniques for deriving the *IS* and *LM* curves. The purpose of this problem is to present a different graphical approach than that used in problems 1 and 2. Note that this approach does not provide any new information over that obtained in the earlier problems. Its merit lies in presenting another widely used graphical technique. The *IS* curve (which is short for $I + G + X = S + T + M^i$) is derived in part *a* and the *LM* curve is derived in part *b*. [Note: This problem may be skipped with no loss of continuity.]

a. *Alternative derivation of* IS *curve.* Instead of arranging the graphs as in problem 2, we now arrange the parts as in Figure 6–7. Part A (upper left) is the now-familiar quadrant showing the curve for saving (*S*), taxes (*T*), and imports (*M^i*); that is, the leakages. For short, it is referred to as the saving function. Part D (lower right) gives the data for investment (*I*), government purchases (*G*), and exports (*X*); that is, the injections. For short, the sum of *I*, *G*, and *X*, is referred to as investment. Part B (upper right) is an equilibrium quadrant. It has $S + T + M^i$ on the vertical axis and $I + G + X$ on the horizontal axis. The line labelled $S + T + M^i = I + G + X$ is a 45-degree line, any point on which shows the sum of *I*, *G*, and *X* equal to the sum of *S*, *T*, and *M^i*. The *IS* curve will be derived in part C (lower left). [Note carefully that the vertical axes of parts A and B both represent $S + T + M^i$; the vertical axes of parts C and D measure the interest rate; the horizontal axes of parts A and C both measure Y_{np}; and the horizontal axis of parts B and D both represent $I + G + X$.]

FIGURE 6-7

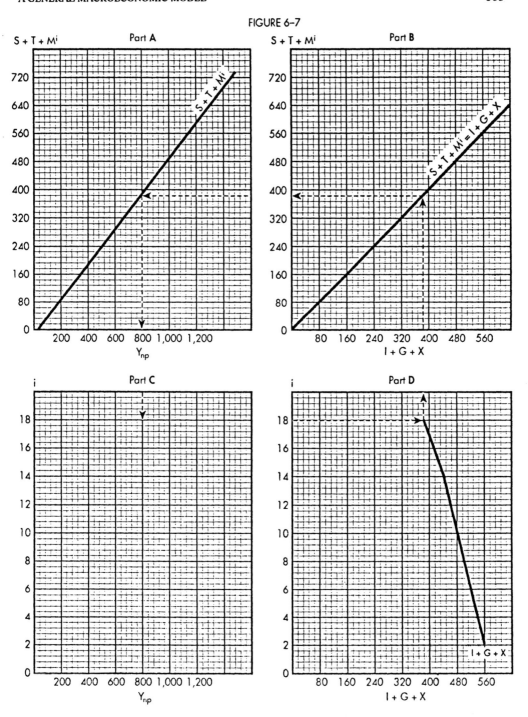

Since plotting data, both from a table and from equations, should now be an easy matter, we dispense with it in this problem. The curve for $I + G + X$ has already been plotted in part D and the curve for $S + T + M^i$ has been plotted in part A. Both curves use the same data contained in problem 4. To derive the IS curve, proceed as indicated below.

(1) First point on IS curve. To derive the IS curve, we start either with the saving function in part A or the investment function in part D. Let us start with the investment function in part D. Follow the arrows.

   (a) If the rate of interest is 18 percent, what is the level of $I + G + X$ given by the investment curve in part D? (Answer is in next question.)

   (b) Having determined that total injections are $385 billion, we must now find the income level that will generate the amount of $S + T + M^i$. To this end, move straight up from the point $i = 18$ percent, $Y_{np} = \$385$ (in part D) to the equilibrium curve in part B. Using this equilibrium curve, we can transpose the $I + G + X$ value of $385 to the vertical axis of part B. Having done this, we move horizontally to the saving function in part A and then down to the horizontal axis to find the income level that will generate $S + T + M^i$ of $385. It is $Y_{np} = \$794$.

   (c) We now know that $I + G + X = S + T + M^i$ at $i = 18$ percent and $Y_{np} = \$794$. Plot this point in part C of Figure 6–7. This is one point on the IS curve.

(2) Second point on IS curve. Repeat the above procedure to find a second point on the IS curve.

   (a) If $i = 14$ percent, what is the level of investment (part D)?

   (b) Having determined that $I + G + X = \$445$, move up to part B, transpose this amount to the vertical axis of part B, and then slide over to the $S + T + M^i$ function in part A to find the level of income that generates leakages of $445 billion. It is $Y_{np} = \$914$ billion. Plot this point in part C.

(3) Third point on IS curve. Now use the same procedure to find the income level that generates an amount of $S + T + M^i$ equal to $I + G + X$ when $i = 10$ percent. It is $485 billion. The coordinates of this third point in the IS quadrant are $i = 10$ percent and $Y_{np} = \$994$ billion. This is a third point on the IS curve.

(4) Fourth point on *IS* curve. What is the point on the *IS* curve when $i = 6$ percent? At 6 percent, $I + G + X$ is $525 billion. The income level that generates this amount of $S + T + M^i$ is $1,074. Thus the point $i = 6$ percent and $Y_{np} = $1,074$ is another point on the *IS* curve.

(5) The *IS* curve. Connect these points with a smooth line to obtain the *IS* curve. The nature and significance of this *IS* curve is identical to that of the one derived in problem 4 using the earlier approach.

(6) Shifts of the *IS* curve. If either the $I + G + X$ curve (part D) or the $S + T + M^i$ curve (part A) shifts, repeat the entire procedure to derive the new *IS* curve. These relationships are all the same as indicated in the earlier problems. Note the mechanical nature of deriving the *IS* curve using this approach—it is merely a matter of choosing a starting point, then drawing rectangles or squares.

b. Alternative derivation of LM *curve.* Instead of deriving the *LM* curve as in problem 1, we can separate the transactions and speculative demands and derive the *LM* in the same manner as we just derived the *IS* curve. This entails using the four quadrants of Figure 6–8. Part A contains the standard transactions demand for money (if we assume $L_t = 0.3Y_{np}$). Part D gives the speculative demand for money, the curve of which is not the same as given in problem 1 ($L_a = 360 - 20i$ for $i \geq 4$ percent). Part B gives a money supply line. Any point on this line shows a specific allocation of the total money supply between the transactions demand (on the vertical axis) and speculative demand (on the horizontal axis). The total money supply is assumed to be completely autonomous and equal to $350 billion. That the money supply is this amount can be seen by noting that if all the money is used for transactions, it amounts to $350 billion. By the same token, if all the money supply is used for speculative purposes, the maximum amount is $350 billion. Note further that if $150 billion is used for transactions purposes, the amount left for speculative purposes is $200 billion—to find this amount slide rightward from $150 billion on the vertical axis to the money supply curve and drop a line to the horizontal axis. Note that both the transactions demand for money (L_t) and money used for transactions purposes (M_t^s) are measured on the vertical axis of part B, whereas the speculative demand (L_a) and money available for speculative purposes (M_a^s) are measured on the horizontal axis. The *LM* curve will be derived in part C.

The approach to deriving the *LM* curve is now the same as that used to derive the *IS* curve. Start with either the transactions or the speculative demand for money. The standard procedure is to treat the speculative demand as "secondary" and the transactions demand as "primary." Hence we will start with the transactions demand for money.

(1) First point on *LM* curve. Assume the income level is $200 billion. This gives a transactions demand for money in part A of $60 billion. Now if the total money supply is $350 billion and we subtract the transactions demand, the amount of money left to satisfy the speculative demand must

FIGURE 6-8

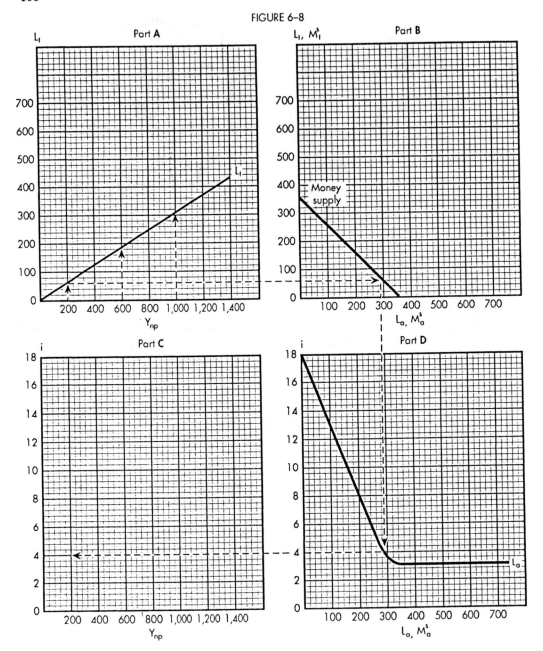

be $290 billion. To see this graphically, slide rightward from the L_t curve to the money supply line in part B. Then drop down to the horizontal axis of part B and read off the speculative supply of money. (Note at this point that $L_t = M_t^s$.) Having this information, drop down to the speculative demand curve in part D and find the interest rate that makes the asset demand for money equal to the asset supply. It is $i = 4$ percent (approximately). Since the total amount of money is now just equal to both demands in total, we have a point on the LM curve at $Y_{np} = \$200$ billion and $i = 4$ percent. Plot this point in part C.

(2) Second point on LM curve. Repeat the above steps to obtain a second point on the LM curve. Let $Y_{np} = \$600$ billion. Move up to the L_t curve to find the amount of money demand for transactions, slide rightward to the money supply curve in part B to find out how much money is left for speculative balances, then drop down to the L_a curve in part D to find the interest rate which makes the speculative demand and speculative money supply equal. It is approximately $i = 9.5$ percent. Thus we have a second point on the LM curve at $Y_{np} = \$600$ billion and $i = 9.5$ percent. Plot this in part C.

(3) Third point on LM curve. Take one more situation. Let $Y_{np} = \$1000$ billion. Then $L_t = \$300$ billion and the money left for speculative balances is thus $60 billion. Taking this amount of asset money to part D, we find that the interest rate must be about 15 percent. Thus a third point on the LM curve is $Y_{np} = \$300$ billion and $i = 15$ percent. Plot this in part C.

(4) Connect these three points and you have the LM curve. Its nature and significance is the same as discussed earlier in this chapter.

(5) Shifts of the LM curve. Shifts of the LM curve may be due to a shift of the transactions demand curve in part A, a shift of the speculative demand curve in part D, or a shift in the money supply line in part B. Once one of these curves shifts, repeat the entire procedure to derive the new LM curve. [Note that increases in the money supply are reflected in an outward shift of the money supply line in part B.]

7. *Inflation, the Keynes Effect, and the Pigou Effect.* The preceding analysis has been almost completely in real terms—the price level being assumed constant throughout. The purpose of this problem is to show how inflation, the Keynes effect, and the Pigou effect affect the equilibrium levels of the interest rate and income in the *IS-LM* model. Subsequently this information is used to derive an aggregate demand curve (for goods and services) related to the price level. Note carefully that the price level *per se* is not explained here; it is brought in as an exogenous variable (for the time being). Assume all the information in Figure 6–9 is given.

a. *Inflation.* Figure 6–9 can be utilized to demonstrate how inflation may alter the level of output and employment. Assume that the appropriate commodity and money equilibrium curves are IS_1 and LM_3.

FIGURE 6–9

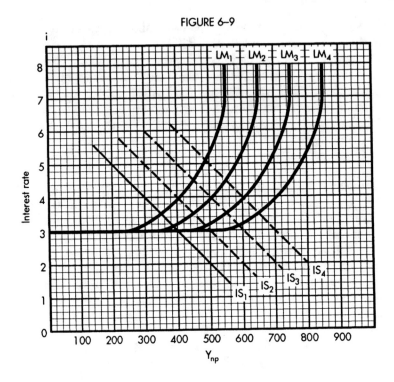

(1) Find the equilibrium interest rate and output level.

(2) Now assume that the economy experiences a mild inflation. Explain how this alters the diagram and the effect on the interest rate, output level, and employment.

(3) Explain in detail why the *LM* curve changes in the manner indicated above.

(4) Does the above imply that the monetary authorities may be able to counteract an increase in unemployment by increasing the money supply as inflation ensues?

b. *Keynes effect.* Assume that equilibrium in the money and goods spheres is initially given by IS_1 and LM_1.

(1) According to Keynes, would a reduction in the price level (that is, deflation) cause any significant shift in the IS curve?

(2) Would a reduction in the price level, according to the Keynes effect, have any impact on the money equilibrium curve? Why or why not?

(3) Does the Keynes effect have any impact on the equilibrium interest rate and output level? Why or why not?

(4) Assume the full-employment income level is $450 billion. Is it possible to reach full employment merely by reducing the price level (or cutting money wage rates)?

(5) Does the above analysis imply that money wage cuts would be an effective measure for reducing unemployment?

c. *Pigou effect.* Assume equilibrium is initially given by the intersection of IS_1 and LM_1.

(1) What effect, if any, will the Pigou effect have on the *IS* curve?

(2) Does the Pigou effect cause shifts in the *LM* curve?

(3) Does the Pigou effect have any impact on the level of output and employment?

(4) Assume, as we did earlier, that the full-employment output level is 450. Is it possible for the price level to fall far enough for the economy to reach full employment?

(5) What does the Pigou effect imply about the efficiency of money wage cuts as a measure for increasing employment?

(6) Evaluate the significance of the Pigou effect.

8. *Derivation of Aggregate Demand from the* IS-LM *Model.* The *IS-LM* model has many uses and for this reason is a popular model. It does not, however, allow us to analyze the price level (inflation) and its relationship to output under a wide range of conditions. One way to get around this difficulty is to develop a model in which aggregate demand and aggregate supply are related to the price level. Once

this is done, we have a model for analyzing inflation. Accordingly, in this problem the aggregate demand curve is derived, in the next problem the aggregate supply curve is derived, and in the following problem aggregate demand and aggregate supply are "combined" and analyzed. [Note: Problems 8 and 9 may be skipped with no loss of continuity.]

Although it may not appear so at first, the aggregate demand for goods and services (related to the price level) can be derived directly from the *IS-LM* model. We already know that changes in the price level cause shifts of the *IS* and *LM* curves. Recognizing this, we should be able to allow the price level to vary and then use the output levels that correspond to the various price levels to find the aggregate demand curve. This will be done using the information conveyed by Figure 6–10.

The Keynes effect and Pigou effect are important explanations of why the aggregate demand curve related to the price level is negatively sloped. Therefore it makes sense to start with an *IS-LM* diagram showing shifts of the *LM* curve and *IS* curve attributable to these two effects. This is shown in part A of Figure 6-10. Note carefully that the various *IS* and *LM* curves are associated with different price levels. For example, the curves *LM* ($p = 2.5$) and *IS* ($p = 2.5$) are the relevant monetary and commodity equilibrium curves when the price level is $p = 2.5$. As the price level decreases, the *IS* and *LM* curves shift to *IS* ($p = 2.0$) and *LM* ($p = 2.0$) and so forth for lower price levels.

Part B of Figure 6–10 has the price level on the vertical axis and income on the horizontal axis. Thus the horizontal axes of the two parts are the same; only the vertical axes differ. The price level data for the vertical axis of part B comes from the price data given in part A for the various *IS* and *LM* curves. To derive the aggregate demand curve (*AD*), proceed as follows:

a. Assume the price level is $p = 2.5$. Given this price level, the relevant *LM* and *IS* curves are *LM* ($p = 2.5$) and *IS* ($p = 2.5$). What is the level of aggregate demand associated with this price level? Plot this price/demand point in part B.

b. Now let prices fall to $p = 2.0$. The relevant *LM* and *IS* curves are thus *LM* ($p = 2.0$) and *IS* ($p = 2.0$). What is the level of aggregate demand for $p = 2.0$? Plot this point in part B of Figure 6–10.

c. Now let the price level fall to $p = 1.5$. Using the relevant *LM* and *IS* curves in part A, plot the level of aggregate demand for $p = 1.5$ in part B.

d. Now find the levels of aggregate demand for $p = 1.0$ and $p = 0.5$ by using the appropriate *IS* and *LM* curves in part A. What is the numerical value of aggregate demand at these two price levels? Plot these two points in part B.

e. Connect all the points in part B of Figure 6–10 to obtain the aggregate demand curve related to the price level. Are there any other reasons besides the Keynes effect and Pigou effect why the quantity demanded expands as the price level falls?

FIGURE 6–10
Part **A**

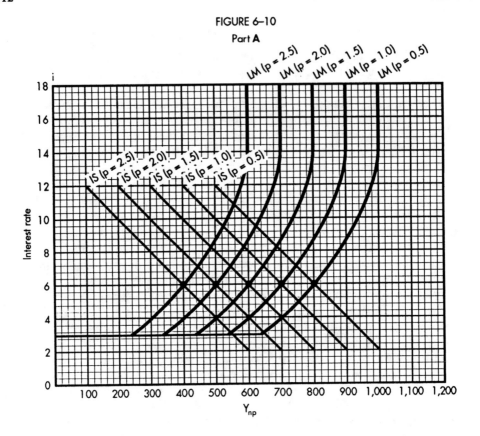

Part **B**

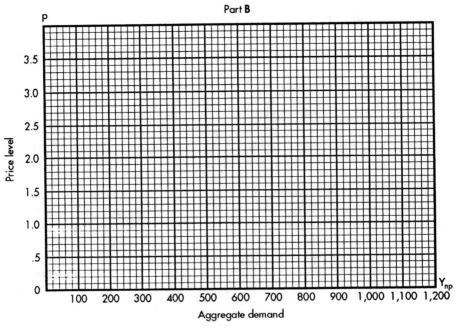

f. What factors will cause the AD curve in part B to shift outward from the origin?

g. As illustrated in part B of Figure 6–10, the aggregate demand curve appears to be significantly affected by changes in the price level; that is, the AD curve appears to be price elastic. Would this be the typical situation?

h. If only the Keynes effect were relevant—that is, all the other effects were zero—what would be the maximum possible level of aggregate demand? Assume the price level is $p = 2.5$.

i. Study part B of Figure 6–10 to see how much aggregate demand increases in quantity for a fall in the price level and vice versa for a rise in the price level. Does the AD curve bear any similarity to the demand curve for a single product?

9. *Derivation of Aggregate Supply Curve.* The above problem derives the aggregate demand curve as a function of the price level. The next step, and the purpose of this problem, is to derive the aggregate supply curve (AS). The procedure in brief is to specify the production function, derive the marginal product of labor (alternatively referred to as the demand for labor) from the production function, incorporate data for the money wage, and then derive the aggregate supply curve from all this information. [Note: The marginal product of labor may be referred to as the demand for labor in the same way as used in the classical model. Keynes accepted the classical demand for labor; it was the classical supply curve that he objected to.]

   The questions below are based on the following hypothetical data and Figure 6–11. Study the data. Note that the money wage is assumed to be $10,000 at all output/employment levels. [Note: Figure 6–11 has four quadrants. Part A is for the production function. Unlike the earlier treatment of Chapter 4, the axes have been reversed so that employment (N) is measured on the vertical axis and output (represented by constant dollar net national product) on the horizontal axis. Part B is for the marginal product of labor (MP_L)—also referred to as the demand for labor—which will be derived from the production function. Again employment is on the vertical axis, while the marginal product of labor and the real wage are measured on the horizontal axis. Part C is for deriving the aggregate supply curve related to the price level, the price level being measured on the vertical axis and output on the horizontal axis. The remaining quadrant, part D, is for the money wage curve; a curve showing the relationship between the price level and marginal product of labor (alternatively, the real wage) for a given money wage. The curve is referred to as the money wage curve.]

FIGURE 6–11

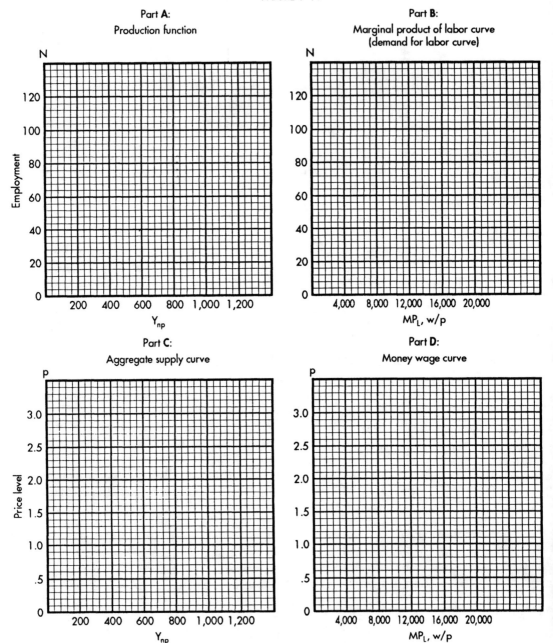

Part A:
Production function

Part B:
Marginal product of labor curve
(demand for labor curve)

Part C:
Aggregate supply curve

Part D:
Money wage curve

(1) Employment N (millions)	(2) Output Y_{np} (billions)	(3) Marginal Product of Labor, MP_L $MP_L = \Delta Y_{np}/\Delta N$	(4) Money Wage w	(5) Price Level p
10	$180	( )	$10,000	( )
20	340	( )	10,000	( )
30	480	( )	10,000	( )
40	600	( )	10,000	( )
50	700	( )	10,000	( )
60	780	( )	10,000	( )
70	840	( )	10,000	( )
80	880	( )	10,000	( )

a. Plot the production function data, columns (1) and (2), in part A of Figure 6–11.

b. Compute the marginal product of labor, column (3), from the production function data given in columns (1) and (2). Plot this data in part B of Figure 6–11. [Note: This entails plotting the data for columns (1) and (3). Recall again that this curve may be referred to as either the marginal product of labor curve or the demand for labor curve.]

c. Now compute the price level, column (5), at all output levels. Plot these data for the price level column (5), and MP_L column (3), in part D of Figure 6–11. This gives the money wage curve showing the relationship between p and MP_L for a given money wage. [Note: Recall that the price level equals the money wage divided by the marginal product of labor, that is, $p = w/MP_L$.]

d. We now have all the data needed to derive the aggregate supply curve in part C. To derive the AS curve graphically, proceed as follows:

(1) Start with part A. Assume N = 10 million. Now slide horizontally over to the MP_L curve in part B, drop a line to the horizontal axis, and find the MP_L associated with this point on the production function. It is $18,000 (which may also be referred to as the real wage). Drop a line down to the money wage curve in part D, slide over to the vertical axis, and find the price level associated with this money wage curve and marginal product of labor. It is 0.556. [Note: You may put this in percentage form by multiplying by 100.] Now we know that when the output level is $180 billion (from part A) and the price level is 0.556 (from part D), we are on the aggregate supply curve. Plot this point in part C.

(2) To find other points on the aggregate supply curve, so we can construct the entire AS curve in part C, do the same thing over again for other levels of employment. This time assume the employment level is 40 million. What is the output level given in part A, the marginal product of labor given in part B, and the price level given in part D? Plot this point in part C.

(3) Find at least one more point on the *AS* curve. Assume $N = 80$ million. What is the output level, the MP_L, and p? Plot this third point in part C.

(4) Connect these three points with a smooth curve to obtain the aggregate supply curve. Study its shape and position.

e. The graphical approach to deriving the aggregate supply curve is as just indicated. We could in this case, however, have obtained the aggregate supply curve merely by plotting the data for column (2) and column (5) in part C. Do this and verify that you get the same *AS* curve either way.

f. Consider the shape of the aggregate supply curve.

(1) Under what circumstances might the *AS* curve have a portion at low income levels that is parallel to the horizontal axis at a "low" price level?

(2) Might the *AS* curve ultimately attain some "high" output level at which it became straight up and down—that is, perpendicular to the horizontal axis?

g. Shifts of the aggregate supply curve. From Figure 6–11 it is apparent that shifts of the *AS* curve can come from basically two sources only. One is a shift in the production function in part A, which will shift the MP_L curve in part B. The other is a shift of the money wage curve in part D, that is, a change in the money wage. [Note: Recall that shifts of the production function are due to changes in technology, real capital, and natural resources.]

(1) Explain how a shift of the production function which increases the MP_L at each employment level (i.e., shifts MP_L curve to the right) will affect the *AS* curve in part C. Show this change graphically in part C.

(2) Explain how an increase in the money wage from $10,000 to $12,000 will affect the *AS* curve.

10. *Aggregate Demand and Aggregate Supply Equilibrium.* This problem combines aggregate demand and aggregate supply (both related to the price level) in a single model. The model is then analyzed using static and comparative statics analysis. [Note: Some instructors may not require that you derive aggregate demand and aggregate supply using the formal framework of problems 8 and 9. Nonetheless you will still be required to understand the *AD/AS* model since it is very useful for analyzing inflation. Recognizing that this may be the case, this problem is developed so that it can be completed even if the prior problems are skipped. For clarity and completeness, this necessitates some redundancy and review.]

The data for aggregate demand and aggregate supply are summarized below.

Aggregate Supply	
Price Level (p)	Y_{np}
0.556	$180
0.625	340
0.714	480
0.833	600
1.00	700
1.25	780
1.67	840
2.5	

Aggregate Demand	
Price Level (p)	Y_{np}
2.50	$400
2.00	515
1.5	625
1.0	725
0.5	820

FIGURE 6–12

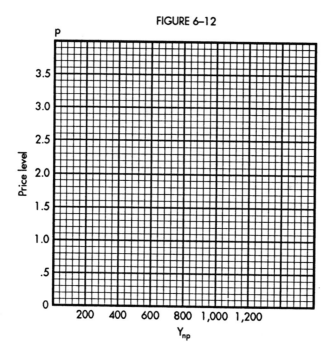

a. Using the above data, construct the aggregate supply curve in Figure 6–12. Label it AS_1. For review purposes answer the questions below.

(1) Explain fully the meaning of the aggregate supply curve and why it is shaped as represented in Figure 6–12.

(2) What factors may cause shifts of the aggregate supply curve?

b. Now plot the data for aggregate demand in Figure 6–12, connect the points with a smooth curve, and label it AD_1. For review purposes answer the following questions.

(1) What is the meaning of the aggregate demand curve given in Figure 6–12?

(2) Why is the aggregate demand curve negatively sloped; that is, why does the quantity of aggregate demand increase as the price level falls? [Hint: Your explanation should be in terms of the Keynes effect, Pigou effect, and so forth.]

(3) What factors cause the aggregate demand curve to shift in and out parallel to itself?

c. What is the equilibrium price level p and output level Y_{np}; that is, the price level and output level at which AD intersects AS and thus insures that everything produced can be sold?

(1) Why can the equilibrium price level not be at, say, $p = 1.5$? Assume prices are flexible upward and downward.

(2) Why can the equilibrium price level not be at, say, $p = 0.75$? Again assume prices are fully flexible both upward and downward.

(3) Is equilibrium at the full-employment level of output?

(4) Must equilibrium necessarily be at full employment?

d. Suppose there is an increase in government purchases of goods and services. Show this change in Figure 6–12 and explain how it will affect prices, output, and employment.

e. Now suppose there is an increase in money wages. Show this change graphically in Figure 6–12 and explain how it will affect prices and output.

f. Explain how an increase in the money supply will affect Figure 6–12 and thereby the price level and output level.

11. According to the neoclassical synthesis, continual equilibrium with substantial unemployment is not possible except in certain special circumstances.

    a. Explain fully and illustrate graphically why this is the case.

    b. Contrast your answer in part *a* of this question with the argument of those economists who dissent from the neoclassical synthesis position.

    c. What is the role of monetary policy and fiscal policy in the neoclassical synthesis position? Explain.

A Self-Test

Completion Questions

1. If the monetary authorities reduce the money supply, the *LM* curve will shift to the (*right, left*), whereas if the money supply is increased, it will shift to the (*right, left*). An overall increase in the demand for money by consumers and business firms would have the same impact on the *LM* curve as (*reducing, increasing*) the money supply. Thus the *LM* curve will shift leftward either from (*an increase, a decrease*) in the money supply or from (*an increase, a decrease*) in the demand for money curve.

2. The *IS* curve shows the various combinations of the _____ and _____ ____ at which _____ and _____ are equal.

3. An increase in saving at all levels of income will shift the *IS* curve to the (*left, right*); a reduction will shift it to the (*left, right*). Thus an increase in saving will have the same effect on the *IS* curve as (*an increase, a decrease*) in investment at all interest rates.

4. If the *LM* curve is horizontal, the usual multiplier (*will, will not*) accurately describe how the income level changes as a result of an autonomous change in government expenditures or investment. If the *LM* curve is not horizontal, the increase in income due to an increase in investment will be (*less, more*) than otherwise. This is because the increase in income sets into motion forces which

cause the rate of interest to (*increase, decrease*), thereby (*reducing, expanding*) investment which causes income to increase (*more, less*) than it otherwise would.

5. The IS curve, excluding government and the foreign sector, shows various combinations of the interest rate and income at which _____ equals _____. If the government is included in the model, the IS curve represents an equality of _____ and _____. When the foreign sector is also included, the IS curve gives an equality of _____, _____, and _____ with _____, _____, and _____.

6. The IS-LM model shows that, *ceteris paribus*, an increase in government purchases of goods and services will have a full multiplier effect when the economy is in the (*liquidity trap, intermediate range, classical range*), because the interest rate (*does, does not*) (*decline, increase*). For higher income levels it is (*likely, not likely*) that some investment will be choked off by (*lower, higher*) interest rates. Thus fiscal policy will have its greatest effectiveness when the economy is in the (*liquidity trap, intermediate range, classical range*).

7. A reduction in the price level will have a similar impact on the LM curve as (*a decrease, an increase*) in the money supply. As the price level falls, the "real" money supply (*decreases, increases*). Some money will be (*required for, freed from*) transactions purposes and will (*increase, decrease*) the amount available for speculative purposes, causing the rate of interest to (*rise, fall*) and investment to (*decline, advance*), thereby (*reducing, increasing*) income—if we assume that the IS curve is unchanged and the economy is at less than full employment. In short, a fall in the price level by one-half has an effect on the LM curve similar to when the money supply is (*cut in half, doubled*).

8. Let the simple saving and investment equations be as follows:

$$S = -210 + 0.2Y_{np}$$
$$I = 190 - 10i.$$

Set the saving equation equal to the investment equation to find the equation of the IS curve. Expressed in terms of income, the IS equation is

$Y_{np} = $ _____. Alternatively, expressing the IS curve in terms of the interest rate, the IS equation is $i = $ _____.

9. Let the demand for money equations and the money supply (M^s) be as follows:

$$L_t = 0.2Y_{np}$$
$$L_a = 200 - 20i$$
$$M^s = 300$$

The equation of the total demand (L) for money is $L =$ _____. The equation for the LM curve, expressed in terms of income, is $Y_{np} =$ _____. Alternatively, expressed in terms of the interest rate, the LM equation is $I =$ _____.

10. For IS-LM equilibrium, the IS and LM curves must intersect at the same income level and interest rate. Solving the relevant equations in the above two completion questions, we find that the equilibrium income level is $Y_{np} =$ _____, whereas the equilibrium interest rate is $i =$ _____. It is a simple matter to expand the above equations to include government and foreign trade.

11. If the money supply is a function of the interest rate, an increase in the interest rate will (*increase, decrease*) the money supply. This is because commercial banks will follow policies that (*reduce, expand*) deposits as interest rates (*rise, fall*).

True and False

_____ 1. A reduction or increase in the price level will have no effect on the LM curve.

_____ 2. The monetary sphere is related to the demand for and supply of money and indicates that monetary equilibrium exists only when the total demand for money equals the money supply.

_____ 3. For an open system *with* government, the IS curve would be similar to the IS curve for a closed economy without government, but would then represent an equality between I, T, X, and S, G, M at various income and interest rate levels.

_____ 4. The IS curve is negatively sloped because lower interest rates increase investment which requires lower income levels to make saving equal investment.

_____ 5. The slope of the IS curve is determined solely by the slope of the investment function.

_____ 6. A change in the marginal propensity to consume will alter the slope of the IS curve.

_____ 7. The LM curve will lie closer to the origin if the money supply is a function of the interest rate than it will if the money supply is not a function of the interest rate.

_____ 8. There will always be some high interest rate beyond which the money supply will become completely interest inelastic.

_____ 9. Introducing an interest elastic money supply function into the *IS-LM* model eliminates the liquidity trap.

_____ 10. An increase in the price level will cause the *LM* curve to rotate upward.

_____ 11. *Ceteris paribus*, an increase in the price level, will reduce the amount of money held in idle balances.

_____ 12. Keynes favored price cuts as a means of reducing unemployment since he did not believe increases in the money supply would have the same result nor be any more acceptable.

_____ 13. According to the Pigou effect, a fall in the price level will increase consumption by increasing the real value of liquid assets and thereby reducing the need to save.

_____ 14. An increase in money wages will shift upward the aggregate supply curve related to the price level.

_____ 15. Modern monetarists argue that monetary policy affects economic activity via the impact of changes in the money supply on money balances.

_____ 16. In evaluating the strength of the Pigou effect, one must recognize not only that a falling price level increases the purchasing power of liquid assets denominated in money terms, but also increases the real burden of debts.

_____ 17. Debtors always gain from a falling price level and lose from a rising price level.

Multiple Choice

1. If there is an increase in government expenditures,
   a. there will be no effect on the *IS* curve.
   b. the *IS* curve will shift to the left.
   c. the *IS* curve will shift to the right.
   d. the *IS* curve will move in the same direction as it would if taxes were increased.
   e. none of the above

2. An increase in government taxes will
   a. cause the *IS* curve to shift to the left.
   b. shift the *IS* curve to the right.
   c. have no impact on the *IS* curve.
   d. have the same impact on the *IS* curve as an increase in investment.
   e. none of the above

3. The *LM* curve will ultimately become completely vertical because
   a. investment is inadequate to further increase income.
   b. the level of consumption is falling as income advances.
   c. the demand for money is very elastic at all interest rates.

d. all the money supply is being used for transactions purposes and thus no further increase in income is possible.

e. the entire supply of money is required for speculative purposes and none is available for further increases in income.

4. If investment is completely interest inelastic, a shift in the *LM* curve due to an increase in the money supply
   a. will not increase income but will reduce the interest rate.
   b. will increase the level of income and reduce the interest rate.
   c. will decrease the income level and interest rate.
   d. will increase investment and therefore income.
   e. none of the above

5. In the Hicksian equilibrium model, the rate of interest is determined by
   a. saving and investment.
   b. the demand for money and the money supply.
   c. the relationship between the money and commodity markets.
   d. saving and investment relative to the money supply.
   e. none of the above

6. The Hicksian *IS-LM* model emphasizes
   a. the difference between the monetary and goods sphere of economic activity.
   b. that the monetary and goods sphere must be related for equilibrium.
   c. that money is not neutral in the Keynesian system.
   d. that the interest rate is determined by both the money and goods markets combined.
   e. all the above

7. Given the *IS* curve, equilibrium can be attained in the goods market as the income level rises only by
   a. increasing the interest rate.
   b. reducing the interest rate.
   c. reducing the money supply.
   d. increasing the demand for money.
   e. none of the above

8. General equilibrium for an economic system requires that
   a. investment equal saving but the demand for money may exceed or be less than the money supply.
   b. the demand for money equal the money supply but saving may be more or less than investment.
   c. investment equal saving and the demand for money equal the supply of money.
   d. the interest rate be determined in the money market and the income level be determined in the goods market with no necessary connection between the two markets.

9. Which of the following is *not* true for those economists adhering to the neoclassical synthesis position?
   a. Unemployment can occur but only for short periods of time.
   b. Unemployment may occur if wages and prices are inflexible downward.

c. Even though the economy tends to adjust to full employment, the lag may be so long that monetary and fiscal policy may be needed.

d. The Keynesian unemployment equilibrium is a special, and not general, case.

e. Given wage and price flexibility, the economy tends to adjust to full employment.

10. Which of the following ideas is *not* true for those economists (such as Clower, Leijonhufud, Minsky, Robinson, Davidson, Weintraub, Harrod, Shackle, and Kaldor) who dissent with the neoclassical synthesis?

a. Because of the crucial role of uncertainty, the economic system cannot be viewed as a self-contained equilibrium system. Moreover, expectations rest on a flimsy foundation.

b. In addition to there being no tendency toward equilibrium, the idea of equilibrium is meaningless because cyclical instability is the normal economic state.

c. Money is not neutral with respect to employment and output and may be a source of fundamental instability, causing excessive unemployment.

d. Like money, the complex financial system of modern industrialized countries is a source of instability.

e. The neoclassical synthesis errs in not paying much attention to the price level theory put forth by Keynes in the *General Theory*.

f. all of the above

11. Assume the economy is in the liquidity trap, the multiplier is 4, and investment increases by $8 billion. From the Hicksian model one can conclude that

a. income will rise by more than $32 billion.

b. income will increase by $32 billion.

c. income will rise by less than $32 billion, because the multiplier is modified.

d. there will be no change in income.

12. Given the ratio of transactions demand for money to income, L_t/Y, is 0.25, an increase in the money supply of $6 billion will shift the *LM* curve to the right by

a. $1.5 billion.

b. $6 billion.

c. $12 billion.

d. $24 billion.

e. $0.25 billion.

13. If the *LM* curve shifts by $10 billion due to an increase in the money supply, and the transactions demand for money is one-half of income, the money supply increased by

a. $10 billion.

b. $5 billion.

c. $20 billion.

d. $7 billion.

e. $4 billion.

14. If an increase in government purchases of goods and services of $10 billion causes the *IS* curve to shift by $40 billion, one can conclude that the regular multiplier is

a. 40.

    b. 4.

    c. 10.

    d. 0.25.

    e. 6.

15. The shift in the *IS* curve is equal to
    a. the change in *I, G,* or *X* divided by the multiplier.
    b. the change in *I, G,* or *X.*
    c. one-half the change in *I, G,* or *X.*
    d. the change in *I, G,* or *X* times the multiplier.
    e. none of the above

16. An increase in autonomous imports will
    a. shift the *LM* curve to the right.
    b. shift the *IS* curve to the right.
    c. shift the *IS* curve to the left.
    d. will have no effect on the *IS* curve.
    e. none of the above

17. According to the neoclassical synthesis, if the level of aggregate demand exceeds the full-employment output level,
    a. the price level will remain constant, while the interest rate increases and chokes off some investment.
    b. the price level, along with money wages, will rise until the *LM* intersects the *IS* at the full-employment output level.
    c. a cycle of deflation with increasing unemployment will be set into motion.
    d. the price level will fall and thereby reduce aggregate demand.

18. According to the neoclassical synthesis, the price level is determined essentially by the
    a. excessive wage demands of big labor unions.
    b. level of U.S. interest rates.
    c. money supply.
    d. monopoly power of big business.

19. The aggregate demand curve (related to the price level) is negatively sloped because of the
    a. Keynes effect.
    b. Pigou effect.
    c. improvement in the trade balance as prices decline.
    d. none of the above
    e. all of the above

20. According to the Keynes effect, aggregate demand may increase with a fall in the price level because of the increase in
    a. investment induced by falling interest rates.
    b. imports and decline in exports.
    c. consumption because the net worth of individuals has increased.
    d. government expenditures.
    e. none of the above

21. According to the Pigou effect, aggregate demand will expand as the price level falls because
    a. investment is a function of the interest rate, and the interest rate will decline.
    b. those people owning land, stocks, and consumers' durables will experience an increase in their net worth, causing them to increase consumption.
    c. the net worth of those individuals holding currency and government bonds will increase and cause them to increase consumer expenditures.
    d. government expenditures will automatically increase.
    e. none of the above

22. The Pigou effect
    a. is theoretically impossible.
    b. may be theoretically valid with many qualifications.
    c. was developed by Marshall to refute the quantity theory of money.
    d. depends on the existence of the liquidity trap.
    e. refutes the effectiveness of wage cuts as a means for increasing employment.

23. The Keynes effect will be zero if
    a. the economy is not in the liquidity trap.
    b. the investment function is interest elastic.
    c. there is any validity to the Pigou effect.
    d. the investment function is completely interest inelastic.
    e. none of the above

24. Assume the IS curve intersects the LM curve in the intermediate range. A fall in the price level will
    a. cause the LM curve to rotate upward, reduce income, and increase the interest rate.
    b. cause both the IS curve and LM curve to shift outward and thereby increase income.
    c. shift the IS and LM curves inward and thereby reduce the income level.
    d. not affect either the IS curve or the LM curve since the model is in real terms.

25. In the IS-LM model the position of the IS curve and the LM curve
    a. is indeterminate until the price level is known.
    b. is determined solely by the monetary and fiscal authorities.
    c. can be located even if the price level is not known since the model is in real terms.
    d. is always such that the economy attains equilibrium at full employment.

26. Even if a reduction in wages and price should promote full employment, it would be unwise to rely on this measure for policy purposes because
    a. prices and wages would not stop falling once they start downward.
    b. prices and wages are inflexible downward.
    c. prices do not respond rapidly enough to increases in aggregate demand.
    d. the Federal Reserve would not allow prices and wages to fall enough to restore full employment.

27. Modern "monetarists" argue that
    a. Federal Reserve policy is highly effective and should be heavily relied on to promote full employment and reasonable price stability.

    b. the rate of growth of the money supply should be expanded and contracted by larger amounts than in the past.

    c. the money supply should be increased at a constant rate.

    d. demand deposits should not be included in the definition of money.

28. Given a rising price level, the Pigou effect will shift the
    a. *LM* curve outward.
    b. *LM* curve inward.
    c. *IS* curve inward.
    d. *IS* curve outward.

29. In general we would expect technological advances to
    a. shift upward the aggregate supply curve related to the price level.
    b. have no effect on the aggregate supply curve related to the price level.
    c. shift downward the aggregate supply curve related to the price level.
    d. reduce the marginal product of labor and hence prices.

30. The aggregate supply curve related to the price level will shift if there is a shift of either the
    a. consumption function or investment function.
    b. production function or the money wage curve.
    c. production function or the money supply.
    d. money wage or the demand for money.

31. Irving Fisher, one of America's leading economists in the 1920s and 1930s, doubted that the Pigou effect would restore full employment during a recession or depression because he doubted that
    a. the positive impact on aggregate demand of a falling price level increasing the real value of assets denominated in money terms would offset the negative impact of a falling price level increasing the real burden of debt (which is fixed in money terms).
    b. changes in the price level had any effect whatsoever on consumer buying and saving decisions.
    c. a falling price level would have a positive effect on the real value of assets but would have a negative effect on debts.
    d. changes in the price level would affect either the real value of assets denominated in money terms or the real burden of debts.

Consumption, Saving, and the Multiplier

DETERMINANTS OF CONSUMPTION—KEYNESIAN MODEL

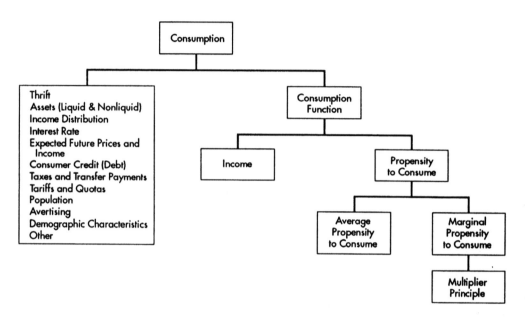

Key Concepts

Consumption function

Keynes's fundamental psychological law

Average propensity to consume (APC)

Marginal propensity to consume (MPC)

Induced consumption

Ex ante saving, consumption, or
   investment

Ex post saving, consumption, or
   investment

Multiplier (*k*)

Parameters

Pigou effect

National Bureau of Economic
   Research (NBER)

Autonomous consumption (C_0)

Saving function

Autonomous saving (S_0)

Induced saving

Average propensity to save (APS)

Marginal propensity to save (MPS)

Disinvestment

Short-run (cyclical) consumption function

Long-run (secular) consumption function

Absolute income hypothesis

Relative income hypothesis

Permanent income hypothesis

Life-cycle income hypothesis

Individual Retirement Account (IRA)

Consumer Credit Controls of 1980 (under
   President Carter)

Problems and Essays

1. Explain the meaning of the consumption function and the basic ideas underlying
   its formulation. How realistic is such a relationship?

2. The equation for the consumption function is usually given in linear form as
   $C = C_0 + aY_d$.

   a. Explain precisely the meaning of this equation. Identify each of the following:
      the dependent variable, the independent variable, the slope, and the autonomous
      consumption. Is the marginal propensity to consume (MPC) represented in this
      expression? Why or why not?

b. By letting the parameters C_0 and a (in the above linear consumption equation) take on different values, we can specify different consumption functions—and this is true even though we limit ourselves to *linear* functions. Changing C_0 causes the function to shift parallel to itself, while changing the value of a alters the slope of the consumption function. Plot the following hypothetical consumption functions in Figure 7–1 (label each) and then compare them. For the time being, you need not be concerned about whether or not they are realistic.

$$C = Y_d$$
$$C = 0.75Y_d$$
$$C = 1.5Y_d$$
$$C = 50 + 0.75Y_d$$

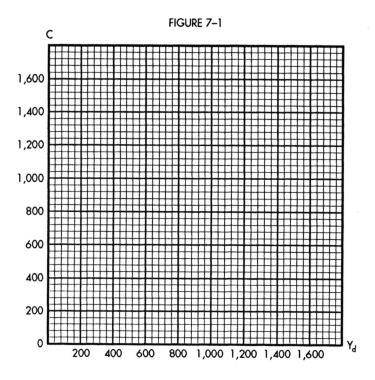

FIGURE 7–1

    c. What is the value of C when $Y_d = 400$ for each of the above equations (in
       part *b*)?

3. There is a definite relationship between the consumption function and the saving
   function. If you are uncertain about the nature of this relationship, work through
   this problem.

    a. Complete the following equations to derive the saving equation from the
       consumption equation $C_0 + aY_d$. [Recall that disposable income Y_d equals the
       sum of consumption C and saving S. Therefore, saving S equals disposable
       income minus consumption C.]
       (1) $Y_d = C + S$ (The basic identity)
       (2) $C = C_0 + aY_d$ (The consumption equation)
       Substitute (2) into (1):
       (3) $Y_d = $ _____
       Collect all terms containing Y_d on the left side:
       (4) _____ = _____
       Factor out Y_d:
       (5) _____ = _____
       Subtract C_0 from both sides:
       (6) _____ = S
       Rearrange the terms as follows:
       (7) $S = -C_0 + (1 - a)Y_d$ (The saving equation)
       Since $(1 - a)$ equals the MPS denoted by s, the saving equation can be
       rewritten as:
       (8) $S = -C_0 + sY_d$ (The saving equation)

    b. We have specified the consumption function in linear form to be $C = C_0 + aY_d$
       To find the MPC, which is defined to equal $\Delta C/\Delta Y_d$, proceed as follows. Let Y_d
       increase so the new higher disposable income level is $Y_d + \Delta Y_d$. The increase in
       income generates a new consumption level equal to $C + \Delta C$. Substituting these
       expressions into equation (1) gives
       (2) $C + \Delta C = C_0 + a(Y_d + \Delta Y_d)$
       or
       (3) $C + \Delta C = C_0 + aY_d + a\Delta Y_d$
       Now subtract equation (1) from equation (3). This gives
       (4) $C + \Delta C - C = C_0 + aY_d + a\Delta Y_d - (C_0 + aY_d)$
       which simplifies to
       (5) $\Delta C = a\Delta Y_d$

The change in consumption due to changes in disposable income is equal to a times the change in disposable income. Dividing both sides of equation (5) by ΔY_d gives

(6) $\Delta C/\Delta Y_d = a$

The MPC thus equals the parameter a; that is, MPC $= \Delta C/\Delta Y_d = a$. Note that whenever the consumption equation is linear, the MPC is the same regardless of the income levels being considered.

The student should now repeat this procedure to obtain the MPS for the saving function derived in part $3a$ above.

c. Give the saving equations associated with the following consumption equations:

$C = 0.75 Y_d$

$C = 50 + 0.90 Y_d$

4. Part A of Figure 7–2 contains a hypothetical consumption function. Construct the saving curve which corresponds to this consumption function in part B. Study the relationship between the two functions.

a. Is the marginal propensity to save (MPS) constant, or does it change as income increases or decreases?

FIGURE 7–2

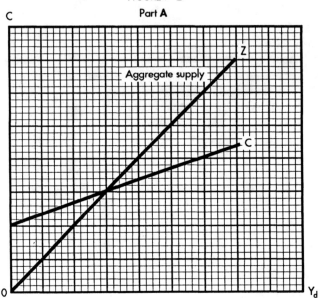

Part **A**

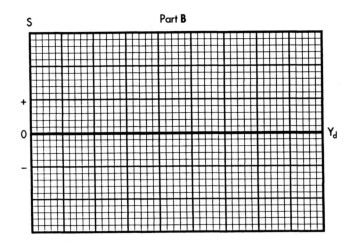

Part **B**

b. What is the relationship between the MPS and the slope of the saving function?

c. What happens to the average propensity to save (APS) as the level of income increases?

d. Suppose autonomous consumption decreases. What effect will this have on the saving function?

e. If the consumption function becomes steeper, what effect will this have on the MPS?

f. Study Figure 7–2. What is the numerical value of the sum of the slopes of the consumption function and the saving function? Must this always be the case? Show algebraically.

g. What is the numerical value of the sum of the APC and APS? Must this always be the case? Show algebraically.

5. Using the hypothetical *ex ante* information in the following table, complete the questions below (billions of constant dollars).

Disposable Income Y_d	Consumption C	Saving S	Investment I	Aggregate Demand (C + I)
$ 0	($)	$ -75	$200	($)
200	( )	-25	200	( )
400	( )	25	200	( )
600	( )	75	200	( )
800	( )	125	200	( )
1,000	( )	175	200	( )
1,200	( )	225	200	( )
1,400	( )	275	200	( )
1,600	( )	325	200	( )
1,800	( )	375	200	( )

a. Complete the columns representing personal consumption and aggregate
   demand $(C + I)$.

b. Plot the consumption and investment data in part A of Figure 7–3. What are the
   equilibrium values of Y_d, I, S, and C? [Careful! First plot the data for C, then
   for $C + I$.]

c. Now plot the saving and investment data in part B of Figure 7–3. Are the
   equilibrium values of income, saving, and investment the same as those
   determined in part A of Figure 7–3? [Careful! First plot the data for saving,
   then plot the data for investment.]

FIGURE 7–3

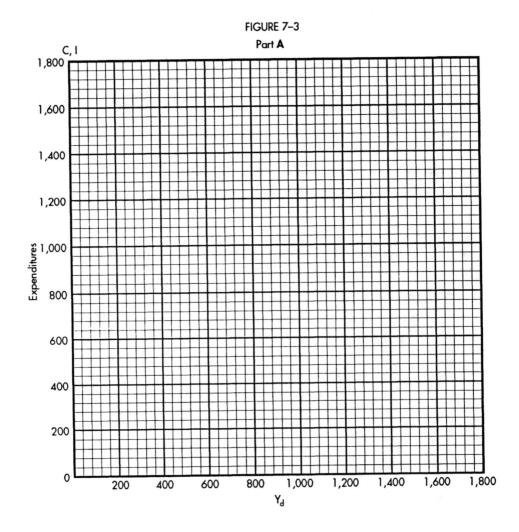

Part A

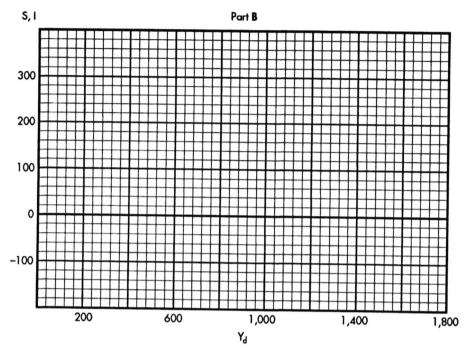

d. Assume that autonomous consumption, C_0, in the equation $C = C_0 + aY_d$ increases by $25 billion.

(1) Illustrate this change in the aggregate demand-aggregate supply part of Figure 7–3. What are the new equilibrium values of income, consumption, and investment?

(2) Now illustrate the change using the saving-investment part of Figure 7–3. Does the new equilibrium value of income correspond with that given by the aggregate-supply-aggregate-demand approach.

(3) Would the equilibrium results have been any different if investment (instead of C_0) had increased $25 billion?

(4) Suppose that instead of increasing, autonomous consumption had decreased by $25 billion. Work through both approaches (AD = AS and S = I) on this assumption. Are the results just the opposite? Do both approaches give the same equilibrium values?

e. Consider the consumption function by itself; the equation being $C = C_0 + aY_d$. Note from Figure 7–3 that whenever the value of C_0 changes, the consumption curve shifts up or down parallel to itself. When the value of a changes, the slope of the consumption function alters. Now consider the saving function equation. Does the same relationship exist?

6. The following parts are designed to aid you in deriving algebraically the simple multiplier and to illustrate how the multiplier can be utilized to calculate income level changes. Continue to assume that disposable income and net national product are equal.

a. Complete the following equations to derive the multiplier associated with autonomous changes in investment (k).
(1) $k = \Delta Y_d / \Delta I$ (The investment multiplier by definition)
(2) $Y_d = C + I$ (The basic identity for a simple system)
A change in Y_d must be due to a change in C and/or a change in I:
(3) $\Delta Y_d = \Delta C + \Delta I$
The change in C is given by:
(4) $\Delta C = a\Delta Y_d$
Substitute (4) into (3):
(5) $\Delta Y_d = $ _____.
Collect all terms containing ΔY_d on the left side:
(6) _____ $=$ _____.
Factor out ΔY_d:
(7) _____ $=$ _____.
Divide through by $(1 - a)$:
(8) _____ $=$ _____.
Now divide through by ΔI:
(9) $\dfrac{\Delta Y_d}{\Delta I} = $ _____.   (The investment multiplier)

b. Assume investment expands by $8 billion and the MPS = 0.2. What is the numerical value of a multiplier, the total change in income, the direction in which income moved, and the total change in consumption?

7. The equilibrium disposable income level can be determined algebraically. Part *a* below is designed to aid the student in finding the algebraic expression of the equilibrium income level, and part *b* is intended to show how this information can be utilized.

a. Complete the following equations to derive the algebraic expression of the equilibrium disposable income level.

(1) $Y_d = C + I$ (The basic identity)

(2) $C = C_0 + aY_d$ (The consumption function)

(3) $I = I_0$ (Investment is exogenously determined)

Substitute (2) and (3) into (1):

(4) $Y_d = $ _____ .

Transfer all terms involving Y_d to the left side:

(5) _____ = _____ .

Factor out Y_d:

(6) _____ = _____ .

Now divide through by $(1 - a)$:

(7) $Y_d = $ _____ .   (Equilibrium disposable income level)

b. Assume $I_0 = \$180$ billion and $C = \$40$ billion $+ 0.8Y_d$. What are the values of the multiplier, the equilibrium level of disposable income, and equilibrium consumption?

[Note: With problem 7a as a background it may be useful to derive the investment multiplier directly from equation (7)—this is an alternative approach to that given in problem 6 above. Equation (7) above is:

(1) $Y_d = \dfrac{1}{1 - a}(C_0 + I_0)$

Now let there be an increase in I such that the new level of investment is $I + \Delta I$. The corresponding higher income level is $Y_d + \Delta Y_d$. Substituting these expressions into (1) gives:

(2) $Y_d + \Delta Y_d = \dfrac{1}{1-a}(C_0 + I_0 + \Delta I_0)$

which can be rewritten as:

(3) $Y_d + \Delta Y_d = \dfrac{1}{1-a}(C_0 + I_0) + \dfrac{1}{1-a}\Delta I_0$

Subtracting equation (1) from equation (3) gives:

(4) $Y_d = \dfrac{1}{1-a}\Delta I_0$

Dividing through by ΔI_0, we obtain the expression for the investment multiplier:

(5) $\dfrac{\Delta Y_d}{\Delta I_0} = \dfrac{1}{1-a} = k$

Note that this expression is identical to that derived by the alternative approach of problem 6 above. At this point it would be well to note that the equilibrium income level and the multiplier can also be derived using the saving—instead of consumption—function. The final equations are the same regardless of which approach is used.]

8. Complete the questions below using the following hypothetical data on disposable income (Y_d) and consumption (in billions of dollars).

Disposable Income	Consumption	MPC (percent)	APC (percent)
$ 0	$ 70	( )	( )
100	155	( )	( )
200	240	( )	( )
300	325	( )	( )
400	410	( )	( )
500	495	( )	( )
600	580	( )	( )
700	665	( )	( )
800	750	( )	( )

a. Compute the MPC and APC for the various levels of disposable income.
b. Study the two columns. Under what conditions would values for the APC and MPC always be equal?

c. What are the MPS and APS for the different income levels?

d. Explain the relationship between the MPC and the APC. [Hint: Recall that the consumption function has been specified (1) $C = C_0 + aY_d$. Dividing both sides of equation (1) by Y_d, we have (2) $C/Y_d = C_0/Y_d + aY_d/Y_d$. This simplifies to (3) $C/Y_d = C_0/Y_d + a$. Thus the APC, which equals C/Y_d, equals the MPC plus the ratio of autonomous consumption to income; that is, (4) $APC = C_0/Y_d + MPC$.]

9. Draw the following consumption functions in Figure 7–4.

FIGURE 7–4

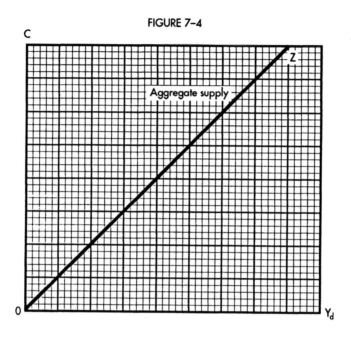

a. A consumption function with a positive *y*-intercept and a constant MPC at all levels of income (designate the function C_1). What happens to the APC as income increases?

b. A consumption function with some autonomous consumption and such that the MPC and APC are declining as output increases (designate the function C_2).

c. A consumption function with the MPC and APC both constant and equal to each other at all income levels (designate the function C_3).

d. Which consumption function is the most realistic one? Does the time period involved have any bearing on your answer?

10. Construct the following functions in Figure 7–5.

FIGURE 7–5

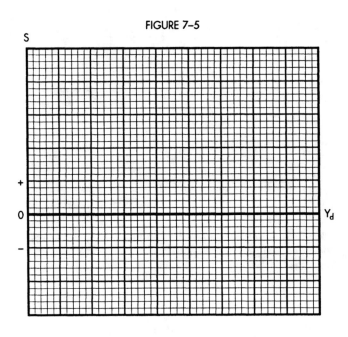

a. A saving function with a positive x-intercept and with the APS increasing while the MPS remains constant as income advances (designate the function S_1).
b. A saving function with a positive x-intercept and such that both the APS and MPS are increasing as income expands (designate the function S_2).
c. A saving function such that the APS and MPS are constant and equal at all income levels (designate the function S_3).
d. Which saving function is the most reasonable one? Does your answer depend on the time period being considered?

11. Construct the aggregate demand function in Figure 7–6 from the following consumption and investment information, and then answer the questions below (billions of dollars).
$$C = 50 + 0.75Y_d$$
$$I = 150$$

FIGURE 7–6

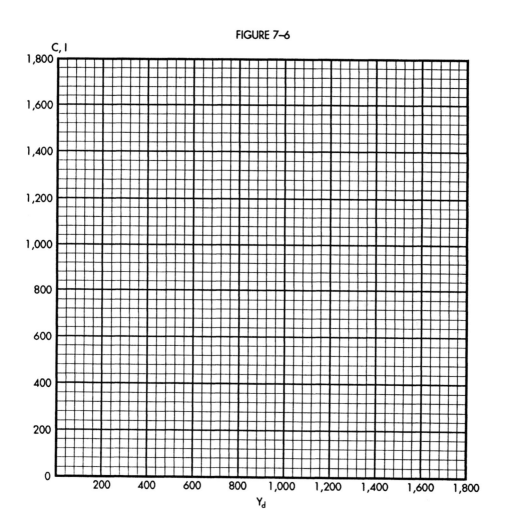

a. What are the equilibrium levels of income, consumption, saving, and investment?

b. Assume the income level is temporarily at $900 billion and explain the process whereby equilibrium is restored.

c. Assume the level of income is at $600 billion and explain the process whereby the economy will adjust to the equilibrium level of income.

d. If there is a permanent increase in investment of $25 billion, what will be the new equilibrium levels of income, consumption, and saving? What will eventually happen to the equilibrium income level if the increase in investment is only temporary?

e. What is the value of the multiplier (*k*), and how can it be determined from the graph?

f. Explain what will happen to the value of the multiplier if the slope of the consumption function increases or decreases.

g. Will a change in autonomous consumption have any effect on the value of the multiplier?

12. Discuss the meaning and significance of the long-run consumption function. How do the following types of hypotheses reconcile the long-run consumption function and short-run (cyclical) consumption function? Be thorough.

   a. Absolute income hypothesis (see, e.g., Arthur Smithies and James Tobin).

   b. Relative income hypothesis (see, e.g., James Duesenberry and Franco Modigliani).

   c. Permanent income hypothesis (see Milton Friedman).

   d. Life-cycle income hypothesis (see Albert Ando and Franco Modigliani).

13. Whenever autonomous investment or consumption (and, as we shall see later, government expenditures) increases or decreases, the income level increases or decreases by a greater amount. This phenomenon is explained by the multiplier process. In Figure 7–7, $C + I$ is the initial aggregate demand function and $C + I'$ is the aggregate demand function after an increase in investment. What is the value of the multiplier in terms of the letters provided?

FIGURE 7–7

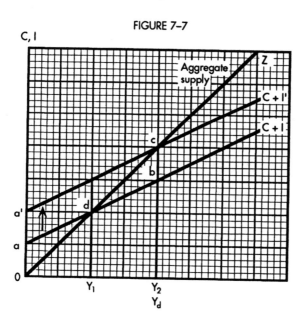

14. Multiplier problems. The long-run impact of a change in investment on the level of income depends on whether the increase or decrease in investment is permanent or temporary.

   a. Assuming a *permanent* increase in investment of $25 billion and a MPC of 0.8, complete the income and consumption columns in the table below.

Period	Y	C	I
1	$400	$350	$50
2	400	350	75
3	( )	( )	75
4	( )	( )	75
5	( )	( )	75
6	( )	( )	75
7	( )	( )	75
8	( )	( )	75
. . .	. . .	. . .	. . .
Final Period	( )	( )	(75)

   b. Now assume investment increases by $25 billion in one income period, then falls back to its initial level in subsequent periods. Continue to assume the MPC = 0.8 and complete the following table.

Period	Y	C	I
1	$400	$350	$50
2	400	350	75
3	( )	( )	50
4	( )	( )	50
5	( )	( )	50
6	( )	( )	50
7	( )	( )	50
8	( )	( )	50
. . .	. . .	. . .	. . .
Final Period	( )	( )	(55)

   c. Compare the results of the two problems. What is the lesson being illustrated?

d. Would the results be any different in either problem if autonomous consumption (or government expenditures), rather than investment, had increased by $25 billion?

A Self-Test

Completion Questions

1. Income is only one, although the most important one, of the many determinants of consumption spending. List below other important determinants given by your author. (Be sure you understand the manner in which they affect consumption.)

   a. _____ .

   b. _____ .

   c. _____ .

   d. _____ .

   e. _____ .

   f. _____ .

   g. _____ .

   h. _____ .

   i. _____ .

   j. _____ .

   k. _____ .

2. The two basic ideas put forth by Keynes concerning the relationship between consumption and income are:

   a. _____

   b. _____

3. The consumption function can be defined as _____

Answer questions 4–7 on the basis of Figure 7–8.

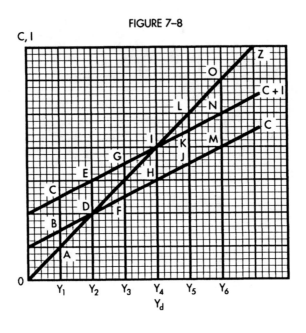

FIGURE 7–8

4. The equilibrium income level is _____.

5. At equilibrium, consumption is _____, saving is _____, and investment is _____.

6. At the income level Y_5, inventories are (*increasing, constant, decreasing*) and at the income level Y_2 inventories are (*increasing, constant, decreasing*).

7. At Y_2 the APC is _____. At lower income levels the APC is (*greater, less*) than at Y_2 and at higher levels the APC is (*greater, less*) than at Y_2.

Answer questions 8–16 from Figure 7–9 below. (Billions of dollars.)

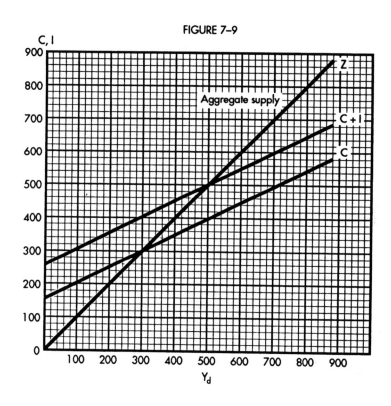

FIGURE 7–9

8. At equilibrium, income is _____, saving is _____, and consumption is _____.

9. The marginal propensity to consume is _____, the marginal propensity to save is _____, and the multiplier equals

_____.

10. The APC equals unity at the income level of _____.

11. Given the consumption function as constructed, the MPC (*increases, remains constant, decreases*) and the APC (*increases, remains constant, decreases*) as income rises.

12. The APS equals zero at the income level of _____.

13. At the income level of $150 billion, people are (*saving, dissaving*), while at the income level of $450 billion they are (*saving, dissaving*).

14. From the diagram it can be concluded that the APS (*decreases, increases, remains unchanged*) and the MPS (*decreases, increases, remains unchanged*) as the level of income advances.

15. At all income levels above _____, the APS is positive.

16. If autonomous consumption increases by $10 billion, the income level will rise by

    _____, consumption by

    _____, and saving by _____.

17. In referring to either the MPC or the MPS, one is speaking of the (*induced, autonomous*) consumption or saving that results from the change in income. The multiplier is based on (*induced, autonomous*) consumption.

18. The minimum and maximum values of the multiplier are _____ and

    _____, respectively.

True and False

_____ 1. The MPC is given by the slope of the consumption function.

_____ 2. The attributes of the consumption function given by Keynes necessarily denote a function which has a positive *y*-intercept value.

_____ 3. Keynes assumed that the consumption function was relatively stable in his short-run analysis.

_____ 4. Keynes made no distinction between the propensity to consume and his fundamental psychological law.

_____ 5. In general it can be said that empirical evidence tends to verify the Keynesian consumption-income relationship.

_____ 6. If the MPC has a positive slope, then the MPS must have a negative slope.

_____ 7. If aggregate demand and aggregate supply are in equilibrium, then investment must be equal to saving.

_____ 8. The crucial relationship, from the point of view of equilibrium and disequilibrium, is between *ex ante* saving and investment.

_____ 9. The difference between *ex ante* and *ex post* investment is equal to the increase or decrease in business inventories.

_____ 10. The multiplier effect is applicable only to changes in investment and does not apply if there is an autonomous change in consumption.

_____ 11. If the MPC equals unity, the multiplier equals infinity.

_____ 12. The multiplier is the reciprocal of all net leakages from the current income stream.

_____ 13. When a parameter changes, it causes a movement along, as opposed to a shift of, the function.

_____ 14. According to the Pigou effect, a fall in the general price level will shift the consumption function upward and thus raise the equilibrium income level.

_____ 15. The Pigou effect implies that as the price level increases, an individual will have to save more to keep the real value of his financial assets intact.

_____ 16. If consumer preferences are interdependent, as indicated by Duesenberry's hypothesis, a redistribution of income may shift the consumption function downward.

_____ 17. Friedman's concept of permanent income refers basically to the "average expected return on the sum of all wealth at the disposition of the individual . . ."

_____ 18. According to Friedman's permanent income hypothesis, an increase in transitory income will cause an increase in saving.

_____ 19. Friedman's definition of consumption relates to the flow of services realized from owning durable goods.

_____ 20. In the Keynesian model, the equality of saving and investment is brought about by changes in income, whereas in the classical model it is brought about by changes in the rate of interest.

_____ 21. The life-cycle income hypothesis says people consume more than their income in early years, consume less than their income in the following years until retirement, and dissave after retirement.

_____ 22. Whereas the life-cycle hypothesis makes consumption depend on the present value of wealth, the permanent-income hypothesis makes consumption depend on wealth times the rate of interest.

Multiple Choice

1. Keynes's "fundamental psychological law" states, in effect, that
   a. consumption will always increase by the same amount as income.
   b. people will save part of their income if they are in the higher income brackets but will not save anything if in the lower income brackets.
   c. people will save some part of any increase in income.
   d. as consumption increases, so will income.
   e. none of the above

2. The slope of the consumption function is determined by
   a. the average propensity to consume.
   b. the amount of autonomous consumption.
   c. the marginal propensity to consume.

    d. the amount of investment that is induced by changes in income.
    e. none of the above

3. If the MPC is a constant, then the consumption function will be
    a. a straight line.
    b. a curve convex to the horizontal axis.
    c. a curve concave to the horizontal axis.
    d. none of the above

4. If the APS is negative,
    a. the APC must be equal to 1.
    b. the APC exceeds 1.
    c. the sum of APC and APS is less than 1.
    d. the APC must be less than 1.
    e. the MPS must also be negative.

5. If autonomous consumption is $30 billion, investment $40 billion, and the MPS is
    0.1, then, if we assume that there is no government or foreign trade, the
    equilibrium level of income is
    a. about $77 billion.
    b. $430 billion.
    c. $700 billion.
    d. $400 billion.
    e. $340 billion.

6. The multiplier is equal to
    a. the change in income divided by the change in investment.
    b. the change in investment divided by the change in income.
    c. the reciprocal of the marginal propensity to consume.
    d. the reciprocal of 1 minus the MPS.
    e. none of the above

7. If there is a temporary increase in investment of $15 billion, and the MPC is 0.8,
    the income level will
    a. increase by about $19 billion and remain at the new higher level indefinitely.
    b. increase by $75 billion and remain at the new higher level indefinitely.
    c. increase by $75 billion but, as time passes, return to the initial equilibrium.
    d. increase by $15 billion but ultimately return to the old equilibrium.
    e. none of the above

8. If there is a sustained decrease in investment—investment decreases and remains
    at the lower amount—by $10 billion, and the MPC is 0.75, the income level will
    a. decline by $40 billion and remain at the lower equilibrium level indefinitely.
    b. decline by $40 billion but gradually move back to the higher initial equilibrium.
    c. decline by about $13 billion and remain at the lower level indefinitely.
    d. decline by $10 billion but ultimately return to the initial equilibrium.
    e. none of the above

9. The greater the leakages from the income stream, the
    a. greater will be the multiplier.
    b. more taxes the government will realize.

    c. larger the marginal propensity to consume.

    d. smaller the multiplier effect.

    e. smaller the average propensity to save.

10. The argument that a redistribution of income will cause the consumption function to shift upward is based on the

    a. past-income hypothesis.

    b. relative income hypothesis.

    c. absolute income hypothesis.

    d. permanent income hypothesis.

    e. life-cycle income hypothesis.

11. Empirical evidence implies that the long-run consumption function is a straight line running through the origin. Therefore, the

    a. MPC is less than the APC.

    b. MPC equals the APC and both are constant.

    c. MPC is greater than the APC.

    d. APS is equal to unity.

    e. APS is declining as the income level rises.

12. The relative income hypothesis reconciles the short-run and the long-run consumption functions by indicating that

    a. there has been a long-run upward drift in the short-run consumption function.

    b. permanent consumption is a function of permanent income.

    c. consumption of an individual depends only on his past income.

    d. people have become wealthier over time, altering the function.

    e. consumption depends partly on an individual's past peak income and partly that consumer wants are interdependent.

13. Which of the following is *not* emphasized by Modigliani as a factor causing consumption to move along the short-run function?

    a. consumer resistance to a reduction in consumption

    b. consumer expectations of a fall in future prices

    c. the increase in unemployment as income declines

    d. a redistribution of income occurs as income declines

    e. none of the above

14. The permanent-income hypothesis is associated with

    a. Duesenberry.

    b. Hicks.

    c. Modigliani.

    d. Friedman.

    e. Kuznets.

15. In the 1960's the U.S. Council of Economic Advisers found the numerical value of the U.S. multiplier to be about

    a. 10.0.

    b. 7.0.

    c. 4.5.

    d. 2.0.

    e. zero.

16. The relative income hypothesis is attributable mainly to
    a. Milton Friedman.
    b. James Duesenberry.
    c. James Tobin.
    d. Arthur Smithies.
    e. John Kenneth Galbraith.

17. In terms of the relative income hypothesis, in order for urbanization to cause the short-run consumption function to shift upward over time,
    a. farmers must have a higher MPC than city-dwellers.
    b. farmers must have a lower MPC than city-dwellers.
    c. the MPC of farmers and city-dwellers must be the same.
    d. none of the above

18. It is customary to distinguish between the absolute income hypothesis, relative income hypothesis, and permanent income hypothesis. In terms of the absolute income hypothesis, which of the following may account for the secular upward drift of the consumption function over time?
    a. an increase in assets owned by households
    b. a redistribution of income toward greater equality
    c. the movement of people from farms to the city—i.e., urbanization
    d. change in the age composition of the population
    e. the introduction of new consumer goods
    f. all of the above

19. According to Friedman's permanent income hypothesis, the permanent income of an individual is
    a. the same as the income the individual actually received in a certain year.
    b. the income he receives and which cannot be taken away from him.
    c. based on real wealth, financial wealth, and the value of human capital.
    d. highly erratic and hence cannot be used as an explanation of consumer expenditures.

20. According to Friedman's permanent income hypothesis,
    a. permanent consumption is proportional to permanent income over the long run.
    b. transitory consumption is dependent on permanent income.
    c. transitory consumption is a function of transitory income.
    d. saving will increase when there is an increase in transitory consumption.
    e. all of the above

21. In terms of the permanent income hypothesis, the short-run (or cyclical) consumption function
    a. is explained by the idea that all transitory increases in one's income are spent.
    b. can be explained by the attempt by people to maintain their living standard as their income falls.
    c. is explained by the view that transitory increases in income are saved and not spent.
    d. represents durable goods purchases from which people will receive services over time.

22. During 1980–90 the average propensity to consume, C relative to NNP, was about
    a. 75 percent.
    b. 80 percent.
    c. 85 percent.
    d. 90 percent.
    e. 95 percent.

23. The life-cycle hypothesis says that
    a. people always borrow and hence never save any of their current income.
    b. consumers plan their consumption expenditures over their lifetime instead of just on the basis of current income.
    c. today's consumption is determined by how much you expect to make over the next three years.
    d. consumer spending is determined by the relationship between their current income and their past peak income.

24. A simple interpretation of the life-cycle hypothesis is that over a lifetime the average person consumes the present value of his or her
    a. wealth.
    b. current income.
    c. present savings.
    d. wealth times the rate of interest.

25. Assume the economy is in less than full equilibrium with $IS = LM$. If the MPC is increased the IS curve will
    a. not be affected.
    b. rotate inward and thereby reduce equilibrium income.
    c. rotate outward and thereby increase equilibrium income.
    d. rotate outward and thereby reduce equilibrium income.
    e. rotate inward and thereby increase equilibrium income.

26. Unlike the period from 1947 to 1970, during the 1980s
    a. the inequality of the distribution increased.
    b. the personal saving rate increased.
    c. there was no change in the distribution of income.
    d. median family income in constant dollars increased significantly.

27. The permanent income and life-cycle income-consumption hypotheses agree that most families
    a. hold their spending relatively constant in the face of fluctuations in current disposable income.
    b. increase their consumption the more their current disposable income fluctuates.
    c. take a short view of their income prospects in planning their consumption.
    d. will put the bulk of any increase in their long-run income into saving.

28. The APC increased from an average annual figure of about (_____) during the 1970s to about (_____) during the years 1980–93.
    a. 60 percent; 62 percent
    b. 70 percent; 72 percent
    c. 80 percent; 82 percent

d. 90 percent; 92 percent

e. 96 percent; 98 percent

29. Which of the following is not correct?

   a. The change in the APC from the 1970s to the 1980–93 period accords well with Duesenberry's relative income hypothesis.

   b. Changes in tax programs during the 1960s, 1970s, and 1980s, generally had the effect on consumption that would be predicted by Friedman's permanent income hypothesis.

   c. Current income is the most important determinant of consumer expenditures.

   d. The life-cycle hypothesis has been totally rejected as an explanation of consumer spending.

CHAPTER 8

Investment and Finance

KEYNESIAN THEORY OF INVESTMENT

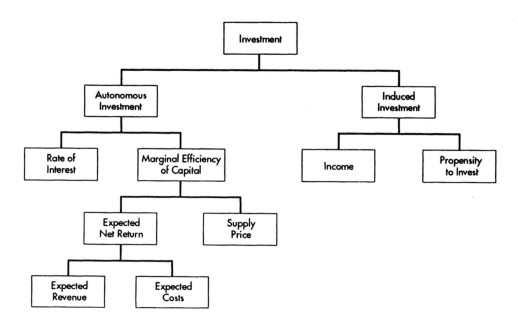

Key Concepts

Productive instruments
Gross investment (I)
Net investment (I_n)
Replacement investment
Autonomous investment
Demand for capital
Supply (curve) of capital goods
Induced investment
Supply price of capital
Financial cost
Opportunity cost
Expected yield
Rate of return over cost
Marginal efficiency of capital (MEC)
Marginal efficiency of capital schedule
Marginal efficiency of investment
Discounting
Present value
Capitalization
Optimum capital stock

Investment demand schedule
Innovation
Accelerated depreciation
Investment tax credit
Internal financing of investment
Equity financing of investment
Debt financing of investment
Marginal (physical) product of capital
Technology
Interest elasticity of investment function
Shift parameters
Expectations (relevance to investment)
Marginal propensity to invest (MPI)
Marginal propensity to spend
Multiplier associated with investment
Acceleration principle
Marginal capital-output ratio ($\Delta/\Delta Y$)
Average capital-output ratio (K/Y)
Simple accelerator
Flexible accelerator hypothesis

Problems and Essays

1. There are two basic approaches for deciding whether or not an investment project
   will be profitable. One approach is to compare the present value of the proposed
   investment with its present cost (that is, its supply price). Investment will be
   profitable whenever the present value exceeds the supply price. The other
   approach is to compare the marginal efficiency of capital with the rate of interest.
   An investment will be profitable if its marginal efficiency of capital exceeds the
   interest rate. The following problems are designed to illustrate these two
   approaches. (For simplification, assume that all returns occur at the end of the
   year. When the yield is continuous, whether daily, weekly, or monthly, the
   mathematics is more complicated but the principle is the same.)

   a. Comparison of present value (V_p) and supply price (K_s).

   (1) Assume a machine costs $5,000 and will last only one year. The proposed
       investment is expected to yield $5,450. Would this be a profitable
       investment if the current interest rate is 7 percent? What is the net profit or
       loss?

$$1.07 (5000) = 5350$$
$$5450 - 5350 \quad \$100$$

There is a $100 net profit, so it would
be a profitable investment.

(2) Assume that instead of lasting one year, the machine yields its return over a four-year period at the rate of $1,600 per year. (Continue to assume that the interest rate is 7 percent.)

(a) Is the proposed project profitable? What is the net profit or loss?

$1,600 \times 4 = 6400$

cost of investment is still $5350

so the investment is still profitable, but with a higher return.

(b) Suppose operating expenses are expected to be $50 in the first year, $100 in the second, $150 in the third, and $200 in the fourth year. How does this alter your answer?

It lowers the profit rate by $500

to $550 profit over the first 4 years.

b. Comparison of marginal efficiency of capital (MEC = r) and rate of interest (i).

(1) Work through the problem in part a(1) above using the MEC and interest rate approach. Is the proposed investment profitable according to this approach? What is the net profit, or loss, *rate*?

(2) Now work out the problem in part a(2a) above using the MEC and interest rate approach. Is the investment profitable? What is the net profit, or loss, *rate*?

c. Compare and contrast the two approaches. Will they always give the same results? Is there any reason why one approach should be utilized and the other not? [Note: In some works a distinction is made between the marginal efficiency of *capital* and the marginal efficiency of *investment*, the essential difference being that the latter is equal to or less than the former since it incorporates the possibility of a rising supply price due to rising costs and falling excess capacity in the capital goods producing industries. For our purposes no harm is done by assuming both are the same and thus using the terms interchangeably. This corresponds to the approach of most intermediate macro texts.]

2. Suppose that Firm XYZ is considering six investment projects for the coming year. The cost of each project and its marginal efficiency is indicated in the following table:

Project	Cost ($)	MEC (%)
A	10,000	10
B	4,000	14
C	21,000	7
D	25,000	5
E	16,500	8
F	6,000	12

a. Construct a MEC schedule for this firm in Figure 8–1.

FIGURE 8-1

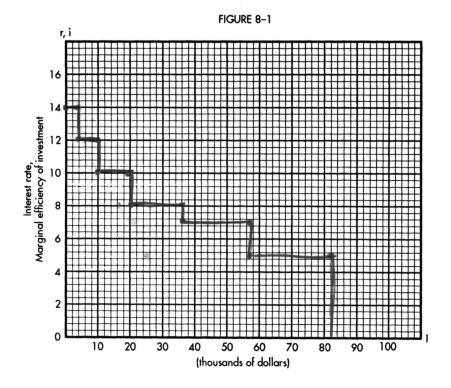

(thousands of dollars)

b. How much investment (*I*) will be profitable if the interest rate is 9 percent?

$20,000

c. How much investment will be profitable if the rate of interest is 6 percent?

$57,500

3. The simple multiplier including induced investment. Induced investment (I_i) can be incorporated into the multiplier, along with autonomous investment (I_0), by expanding the analysis of the preceding chapter. In completing the following parts, continue to assume an economic system with no government or foreign trade and that $Y_d = Y_{np}$.

a. Derive the simple multiplier including induced investment (k_i) by completing the following equations.

(1) $k_i = \dfrac{\Delta Y_{np}}{\Delta I_0}$ (The multiplier by definition. This assumes that the change in income is due to a change in autonomous investment.)

(2) $Y_{np} = C + I_i + I_0$ (The basic identity including induced investment)

If there is a change in income, it must be equal to:

(3) $\Delta Y_{np} = \Delta C + \Delta I_i + \Delta I_0$

The changes in consumption and induced investment are given by:

(4) $\Delta C = a\Delta Y_{np}$ (Where a = MPC)

(5) $\Delta I_i = b\Delta Y_{np}$ (Where b = marginal propensity to invest, MPI).

Substitute (4) and (5) into (3):

(6) $\Delta Y_{np} = \underline{a\Delta Y_{np} + b\Delta Y_{np} + \Delta I_0}$

Collect all terms with ΔY_{np} on the left side:

(7) $\underline{\Delta Y_{np} - a Y_{np} - b Y_{np} = \Delta I_0}$.

Factor out ΔY_{np}:

(8) $\underline{\Delta Y_{np}(1 - a - b) = \Delta I_0}$.

Divide through by $(1 - a - b)$:

(9) $\Delta Y_{np} = \underline{\Delta I_0 / (1 - a - b)}$

Now divide through by ΔI_0 to obtain the multiplier including induced investment:

(10) $\dfrac{\Delta Y_{np}}{\Delta I_0} = \underline{\dfrac{1}{1 - a - b}}$.

b. Assume the consumption equation is $C = 30 + 0.75Y_{np}$, and the marginal propensity to invest (MPI) is 0.15.

(1) What is the numerical value of the simple multiplier if there is no induced investment? $\dfrac{1}{.25} = 4$

(2) What is the numerical value of the multiplier when induced investment is included in the analysis? $\dfrac{1}{1 - .75 - b} = \dfrac{1}{1 - .75 - .15} = \dfrac{1}{.10} = 10$

(3) If autonomous investment increases by $4 billion, what is the change in income without induced investment and with induced investment?

$16 \text{ billion}, \quad $40 billion

4. Induced investment can be included in the algebraic expression for the equilibrium income level with little difficulty. The approach is similar to that used in the preceding chapter.

a. Derive the algebraic expression for the equilibrium level of income including induced investment by completing the equations below.

(1) $Y_{np} = C + I$ (The basic identity)

(2) $C = C_0 + aY_{np}$ (The consumption function)

(3) $I = I_0 + bY_{np}$ (The investment function with induced investment)

Substitute (2) and (3) into (1):

(4) $Y_{np} = \underline{C_0 + aY_{np} + I_0 + bY_{np}}$

Transfer all terms involving Y_{np} to the left side:

(5) $\underline{Y_{np} - aY_{np} - bY_{np} = 1_0}$.

Factor out Y_{np}:

(6) $\underline{Y_{np}(1 - a - b)} = \underline{1_0}$.

Divide through by $(1 - a - b)$:

(7) $Y_{np} = \underline{1_0 / (1 - a - b)}$

b. Assume the consumption and investment equations are $C = 45 + 0.65Y_{np}$, and $I = 95 + 0.10Y_{np}$, respectively, Find the numerical value of the multiplier and the equilibrium level of income.

$$Y_{np} = C + I = 45 + .65Y_{np} + 95 + .10Y_{np}$$

$$Y_{np} - .65Y_{np} - .10Y_{np} = 45 + 95$$

$$.25Y_{np} = 140$$

$$\boxed{Y_{np} = 560}$$

$$\text{Multiplier} = \frac{1}{.25} = \boxed{4}$$

5. Induced investment, the multiplier, and income.

a. Assume the MPC = 0.6 and *there is no induced investment.*

  (1) What is the value of the multiplier?

$$\frac{1}{1 - .6} = \frac{1}{.4} = 2.5$$

  (2) If investment increases by \$25 billion, what will be the total increase in income?

$$\$62.5 \text{ billion}$$

  (3) If autonomous consumption and investment are \$60 billion and \$90 billion, respectively, what is the equilibrium income level?

$$Y_{np} = 60 + .6Y_{np} + 90$$

$$.4Y_{np} = 150 = \boxed{375 \text{ billion}}$$

b. Continue to assume the MPC = 0.6, but now suppose there is some induced investment and the marginal propensity to invest (MPI) is 0.2.

  (1) What is the value of the multiplier?

$$\frac{1}{1 - .6 - .2} = \frac{1}{.2} = \boxed{5}$$

  (2) If autonomous investment increases by \$25 billion, by how much will income increase?

$$Y_{np} = 60 + .6Y_{np} + 115 + .2Y_{np} \qquad \frac{Y_{np}}{1} \Big/ \frac{1}{(1-a-b)}$$

$$.2Y_{np} = 175 \qquad 70$$

$$Y_{np} = 875 \text{ billion} - 375 \text{ billion}$$

$$= 500 \text{ billion}$$

(3) **If autonomous consumption and investment are \$60 billion and \$90 billion, respectively, what is the equilibrium level of income?**

$$Y_{np} = 60 + .6Y_{np} + 90 + .2Y_{np}$$

$$.2Y_{np} = 150$$

$$\boxed{Y_{np} = \$750 \text{ billion}}$$

c. **Compare the results of parts *a* and *b*. How do they differ?**

b is twice as large as A because the multiplier is twice as large for b as for A

d. **Plot the data utilized above ($C = 60 + 0.6Y_{np}$, $I_0 = 90$, $MPI = 0.20$) in Figure 8–2 and answer the following questions (from the graph).**

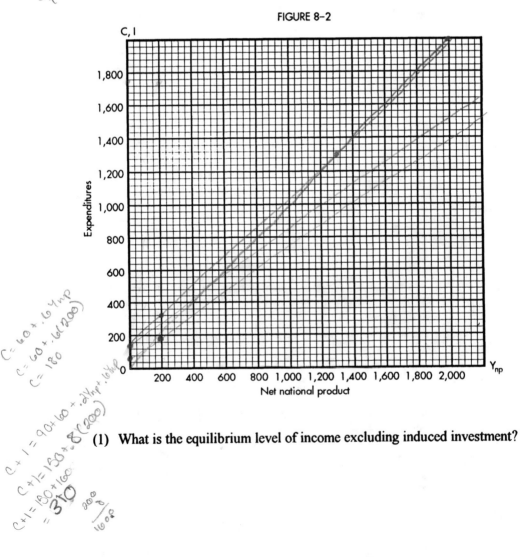

FIGURE 8–2

$C = 60 + .6Y_{np}$

$C = 60 + .6(200)$

$C = 180$

$C + I = 90 + 60 + .2Y_{np} + .6(200)$

$C + I = 150 + .6 \cdot$

$C + I = 150 + 160$

$= 310$

$\dfrac{200}{1600}$

(1) **What is the equilibrium level of income excluding induced investment?**

(2) What is the equilibrium level of income including induced investment?

1,300

(3) Suppose autonomous investment increases by $25 billion. Illustrate this change in Figure 8–2. What is the new equilibrium income level with and without induced investment?

6. The simple accelerator. The following table is designed to show the impact of the simple accelerator on investment during expansions and contractions of the business cycle. Assume the industry capital-output ($K - Y$) ratio is 3 and replacement investment is 10 percent of the capital stock of the preceding period. (Assume the 10 percent replacement investment applies to the new capital as well as to the old, even though this is a gross oversimplification. All figures are in billions of dollars.)

Period	Output Y	Capital Stock K	Replacement Investment I_r	Required New Capital I_n	Total Investment I
Expansion					
1	$200	$600	$60	$0	$60
2	220	( )	( )	( )	( )
3	260	( )	( )	( )	( )
4	300	( )	( )	( )	( )
5	320	( )	( )	( )	( )
Contraction					
6	320	960	$96	0	96
7	300	( )	( )	( )	( )
8	260	( )	( )	( )	( )
9	220	( )	( )	( )	( )
10	200	( )	( )	( )	( )
Expansion					
11	200	( )	( )	( )	( )
12	210	630	$60	30	84

a. Complete the columns for capital stock, replacement investment, required new capital, and total investment.

b. Compare the rate of change of output with the change in net investment for each period. What happens to the magnitude of net investment when:

(1) output increases by increasing amounts? (See periods 1–3.)

(2) output increases by constant amounts? (See periods 2–4.)

(3) output increases by decreasing amounts? (See periods 3–6.)

(4) output decreases by increasing amounts? (See periods 6–8.)

c. What does the accelerator imply with respect to the stability of investment?

d. Are fluctuations in total investment as large as the fluctuations in net investment? What does your answer imply?

e. Does total investment always increase when output is increasing and decrease when output is decreasing?

f. What limitations are inherent in the accelerator concept? (Study periods 6–12 before answering this question.)

g. Is it possible to combine the acceleration principle with the multiplier? If so, what can the interaction between the multiplier and accelerator be used to explain?

7. The flexible accelerator. Explain the flexible accelerator and tell how it differs from the simple accelerator.

8. Discuss the role played by expectations in the investment decision. In your discussion, distinguish between short-term and long-term expectations and indicate the significance of this distinction for investment. What impact do expectations have on the stability of investment?

If you expect the interest rate will increase, you will invest now, while if you expect the interest rate will fall, you will wait to invest.

9. What is the impact of each of the following on the MEC and hence the magnitude of investment? Be thorough and emphasize the difficulties involved in making general statements.

   a. Innovation.

   b. Technological change.

   c. Market structures.

   d. Government (purchases, transfer payments, taxes and tax laws, antitrust laws).

e. Finance (supply of funds).

f. Tariffs and quotas on imports from other nations.

10. Distinguish between internal and external financing of investment. If the bulk of investment funds comes from internal financing, what are the implications for the effectiveness of monetary policy?

11. John Meyer and Edwin Kuh have developed a "residual-funds" theory of investment. Explain the residual funds theory and evaluate its significance. (The student is advised to read Meyer and Kuh, *The Investment Decision*, Chapters 2 and 12.)

A Self-Test

Completion Questions

1. According to the simple accelerator, if output increases by increasing amounts from one period to the next, net investment (*decreases, increases, remains constant*).

2. According to the simple accelerator, if output increases by a constant amount each period, net investment (*decreases, increases, remains constant*).

3. According to the simple accelerator, if output increases by a decreasing amount from one period to the next, net investment (*decreases, increases, remains constant*).

4. Theoretically, there are three major sources of investment funds. They are
   Sale of new equities , _borrowing_ ,
   and _retained earnings_ .

5. Keynes defined the marginal efficiency of capital (MEC) to be the rate of discount
   which makes the _present value of the net expected income stream_ derived from a capital good just
   equal to the _supply price_ of that good.

6. The present value of a capital good depends on the net expected _income stream_
   and the _interest rate_

7. The marginal propensity to invest is defined as the _investment induced from
   changes in income_

8. Investment is defined to include expenditures on
   plant and equipement , _residential construction_ ,
   and _net changes in business inventories._

9. Gross investment is equal to _net investment_ plus
   replacement investments

10. The two basic causes of shifts in the investment demand schedule are changes in
    the _stream of expected returns on capital_ and shifts in the _supply curve of capital goods_

True and False

____T____ 1. Net investment is an inherently dynamic concept because it increases the
economy's productive capacity.

____F____ 2. The theory of investment applies most aptly to expenditures on new plant
and equipment rather than to residential construction and inventory
changes.

____F____ 3. A proposed investment project will be profitable if the present value is
less than the cost of the capital good.

____F____ 4. The MEC does not refer to the rate of return being earned on existing
capital but rather to the expected rate on incremental units of capital.

____T____ 5. The longer the time period over which a capital good is expected to yield
its return, the smaller its present value will be.

____T____ 6. An increase in the operating cost of an asset will, *ceteris paribus*, lower
its MEC.

_____ 7. If the supply price of a proposed investment project increases, the MEC of this possible investment will also increase.

_____ 8. Even if the MEC is less than the interest rate, profit-maximizing business executives will still invest in such projects if there are no investment opportunities available for which the interest rate is less than the MEC.

_____ 9. The MEC should be computed net of risk.

_____ 10. Economists frequently go astray on investment decisions because they think investment is a function of the interest rate only.

_____ 11. If risk is insurable and *uncertainty* is not, then it is the latter which gives the subjective character to investment decisions.

_____ 12. If the marginal propensity to invest has a positive value, the investment function will have a positive slope of its own.

_____ 13. If the average productivity of capital is 1/4, the capital-output ratio is equal to 4.

_____ 14. It is not possible to combine the Keynesian multiplier theory with the accelerator.

_____ 15. The simple accelerator fails to explain why investment expenditures tend to be so volatile.

_____ 16. According to the simple accelerator, the less durable is capital the more will be the fluctuations in total investment.

_____ 17. Most economists believe that technology and innovation are two of the most important factors affecting the volume of investment.

_____ 18. If all business firms have the optimum stock of capital, no investment is taking place.

_____ 19. Most economists agree that the investment demand schedule is relatively interest elastic.

_____ 20. The demand for capital curve is negatively sloped basically because of diminishing returns to capital.

_____ 21. If the current supply price of capital increases, the marginal efficiency of capital will decline.

Multiple Choice

1. The opportunity cost of using funds to purchase a machine is
   a. the cost involved in setting up the machine.
   b. the interest one could receive from loaning out the funds.
   c. the cost associated with operating another machine which was rejected.
   d. the cost of the machine.
   e. none of the above

2. If the rate of interest is 7 percent, the present value of a machine yielding $2,500 and lasting only one year is about
   a. $2,500.
   b. $2,336.
   c. $2,675.
   d. $2,269.
   e. $2,421.

3. If the supply price of an asset, which will last only one year, is $3,000 and the expected yield is $3,500, the marginal efficiency of capital is about
   a. 12 percent.
   b. 9 percent.
   c. 83 percent.
   d. 117 percent.
   e. 17 percent.

4. When the MEC exceeds the rate of interest, the
   a. investment proposal is unprofitable.
   b. supply price of the capital good exceeds its present value.
   c. supply price of the capital good is less than its present value.
   d. rate of interest is too low.
   e. none of the above

5. If the present value of the return on an investment project is greater than the current purchase price of the asset, we can conclude that
   a. the investment outlay should not be made.
   b. the MEC is less than the rate of interest.
   c. the MEC is greater than the interest rate.
   d. the present value has been determined with the wrong interest rate.
   e. the current supply price of the asset will decrease in the future.

6. If the price of the product to be produced with the proposed investment declines, the
   a. MEC will rise.
   b. MEC will fall.
   c. MEC will be unaffected.
   d. interest rate will fall.
   e. none of the above

7. If investment increases from $20 billion to $24 billion when the interest rate declines from 7 percent to 6 percent, the point elasticity of the investment function is
   a. 2.3.
   b. 1.7.
   c. 4.3.
   d. 2.0.
   e. 1.4.

8. Which of the following is *not* a reason why investment may tend to be interest inelastic?
   a. The payoff period for new capital is relatively short.

b. Many firms finance their investment by borrowing in the market.

c. Many firms undertake most of their investment with internal funds.

d. Business executives tend to expect any investment project to have a relatively high return so that a small change in the rate of interest has little effect on investment.

e. none of the above

9. One of the major reasons why investment tends to be so volatile is that

a. it depends so heavily on the expectations of business executives.

b. consumer demand changes so erratically that it affects investment.

c. government expenditures substitute for investment and government expenditures fluctuate rather sharply.

d. the interest rate fluctuates sharply.

e. none of the above

10. If some investment is induced whenever there is a change in income, we can conclude that the multiplier will be

a. smaller than the simple multiplier.

b. unchanged.

c. larger than the simple multiplier.

d. larger for increases in income than for decreases in income.

e. none of the above

11. The multiplier including induced investment is equal to the

a. reciprocal of the marginal propensity to save.

b. reciprocal of the marginal propensity to spend.

c. reciprocal of the marginal propensity to invest.

d. reciprocal of 1 minus the marginal propensity to spend.

e. the marginal propensity to consume and invest.

12. If the MPS is 0.3, the MPI is 0.1, and investment decreases by $5 billion, the level of income will fall by

a. about $17 million.

b. $12.5 billion.

c. about $8 billion.

d. $5 billion.

e. $25 billion.

13. If the MPI is 0.2 and income increases by $10 billion, induced investment will be

a. zero.

b. $50 billion.

c. $2 billion.

d. about $12 billion.

e. none of the above

14. If autonomous consumption is $35 billion, autonomous investment is $35 billion, the MPI is 0.2, and the MPC is 0.7, the equilibrium level of income is

a. $700 billion.

b. $350 billion.

c. $210 billion.

    d. $850 billion.
    e. $650 billion.

15. Which of the following is *not* a limitation of the simple accelerator?
    a. It has no motivational content.
    b. It applies only when capacity is fully utilized.
    c. It does not depend on the interest rate.
    d. It applies only when entrepreneurs think the increase in demand is permanent.
    e. none of the above

16. The "residual-funds" theory of investment implies that
    a. investment is significantly affected by the rate of interest.
    b. investment depends mainly on the volume of funds that firms have left over after they have made conventional dividend payments.
    c. there are always investments that a firm can undertake and make a profit.
    d. firms rely heavily on external financing.
    e. none of the above

17. An increase in the rate of interest will cause the
    a. demand for capital to increase.
    b. demand for capital to decline.
    c. optimum capital stock to increase.
    d. present value to rise.
    e. none of the above

18. If the productivity of capital rises, one would expect the
    a. demand for capital to fall.
    b. output of capital to decline.
    c. present value of the stream of expected net yields to fall.
    d. optimum stock of capital to increase.
    e. disinvestment to take place.

19. A reduction in the interest rate, *ceteris paribus*, will tend to
    a. make production more labor intensive.
    b. reduce investment.
    c. make production more capital intensive.
    d. reduce present value.

20. Which one of the following factors will *not* cause a shift in the supply curve of capital goods?
    a. a reduction in factor costs
    b. technological change
    c. an increase in wages
    d. an increase in the stream of expected net yield from an investment
    e. none of the above

21. The greater the elasticity of the supply curve of capital goods, the
    a. less will be the decrease in the MEI for any given increase in the production of capital assets.
    b. greater will be the increase in the MEI for any given increase in the production of capital goods.

    c. greater the chance that the MEI will increase when net revenue falls.

    d. more the supply price of capital goods will decline.

22. The more inelastic the supply schedule of capital goods, the
    - *a.* more effective a drop in interest rates will be in increasing investment.
    - *b.* less effective a drop in interest rates will be in increasing investment.
    - *c.* less the price of capital will increase for any given increase in the demand for capital goods.
    - *d.* the more effective monetary policy will be when it results in falling interest rates.

23. The majority of economists feel that the investment demand schedule is
    - *a.* nonexistent.
    - *b.* relatively interest inelastic.
    - *c.* highly interest elastic.
    - *d.* totally inelastic with respect to the interest rate.
    - *e.* explained by the same factors as the consumption function.

24. Empirical econometric studies generally support the view that
    - *a.* real output is the most important single determinant of investment.
    - *b.* the interest rate is a statistically significant determinant of investment.
    - *c.* both of the above
    - *d.* neither of the above

25. Which of the following is *not* one of the three basic ways in which firms can get money to undertake investments?
    - *a.* selling machinery that is no longer being used
    - *b.* from retained earnings
    - *c.* equity financing—selling shares in the firm
    - *d.* borrowing, by issuing bonds or other types of debt

26. Accelerated depreciation may increase investment by
    - *a.* in effect giving the firm an interest-free loan for the years in which the taxes are deferred and by increasing the present value of a potential investment.
    - *b.* increasing the amount of money the firm has to pay out in the form of dividends.
    - *c.* forcing the interest rate to increase at a much faster pace than otherwise.
    - *d.* using up capital at a faster pace and therefore necessitating more replacement investment.

27. The investment tax credit, introduced in 1962 and eliminated in 1986, may increase investment because it
    - *a.* means consumers can get a tax credit on food, clothing, and housing purchases.
    - *b.* results in a much higher tax on machinery.
    - *c.* permits a firm to deduct a stated percentage of its investment expenditures from its income taxes and hence gives it more funds for investment.
    - *d.* permits the government to invest the taxes it receives from business.

28. The flexible accelerator relates net investment to the relationship between the
    - *a.* current and past levels of real income.
    - *b.* desired stock of capital and the capital stock of the prior income period.

c. current investment and current consumption.
d. the desired capital stock and the current capital stock.

29. The higher the value of the marginal propensity to invest (MPI), the
    a. less the slope of the IS curve.
    b. greater the slope of the IS curve.
    c. the less the slope of the LM curve.
    d. the greater the slope of the LM curve.
    e. slopes of both the IS and LM curves will not be affected.

30. The more interest inelastic the investment function, the
    a. steeper will be the LM curve.
    b. the smaller will be the slope of the LM curve.
    c. steeper will be the IS curve.
    d. the smaller will be the slope of the IS curve.
    e. none of the above

31. From 1977 to 1987, the amount of capital per employed worker increased from about $40,000 to about
    a. $45,000.
    b. $50,000.
    c. $60,000.
    d. $70,000.
    e. $75,000.

32. Generally speaking, which of the following is most sensitive to changes in nominal interest rates?
    a. acquisitions by business firms of other firms
    b. inventory investment
    c. housing starts
    d. business equipment purchases

33. Housing starts, over the time period 1970 to present,
    a. generally increased when there was a drop in mortgage rates.
    b. were not affected by changes in mortgage rates.
    c. showed no consistent relationship with mortgage rates.
    d. increased during recessions.

34. With respect to GDP and business investment, most studies show that, in general,
    a. there is no relationship between changes in GDP and changes in investment.
    b. whenever there is an increase in GDP there is an increase in investment.
    c. whenever there is a decrease in GDP there is an increase in investment.
    d. none of the above

35. Most studies show that the elasticity of business investment in plant and equipment with respect to output is
    a. less than 1.0.
    b. probably greater than 1.5–2.0.
    c. in the range of 5.0 to 6.0.
    d. is zero.

Public Expenditures, Taxes, and Finance

Key Concepts

Government purchases of goods and services (G)
Leakages
Transfer payments (TR)
Marginal propensity to tax (MPT) *or* marginal rate of taxation (t)
Proportional tax
Progressive tax
Regressive tax
Crowding-out effect
Monetizing the government debt
Misery index
Active versus passive deficit or surplus
Bracket creep
Full-employment budget (or high-employment budget)
Automatic stabilizers

Built-in (fiscal) stabilizers
Balanced budget thesis
Balanced budget multiplier
Effective multiplier
Multiplier associated with taxes (k_{tx})
Multiplier associated with transfer payments (k_{tr})
Multiplier associated with government expenditures on goods and services (k_g)
1964 Kennedy-Johnson tax cut
1968 Johnson 10 percent tax surcharge
Ford's Tax Reduction Act of 1975
Carter's tax reduction of 1977
Reagan's tax cut of 1981
Tax Reform Act of 1986
Gramm-Rudman-Hollings Act
Structural deficit
Cyclical deficit

Problems and Essays

1. Equilibrium for an economic system with no international trade is given by the equation $I + G = S + TX - TR$.

    a. Given equations (1) and (2) below, prove that equilibrium for a closed system requires that the sum of investment (I) and government expenditures on goods and services (G) equals the sum of saving (S) and taxes (TX) minus transfer payments (TR).

    (1) $Y = C + I + G$ (The origin of income)
    (2) $Y = C + S + TX - TR$ (The disposition of income)
    (3) _____
    (4) _____
    Therefore:
    (5) $I + G = S + TX - TR$.

    b. If $TX = \$70$ billion, $TR = \$0$, $S = \$80$ billion, and $G = \$90$ billion, what is the amount of investment at equilibrium? Does the government have a balanced budget?

2. This problem illustrates how government purchases (*G*), taxes (*TX*), and transfer payments (*TR*) alter the aggregate demand-aggregate supply and saving-investment approaches to determining the equilibrium level of income for a closed economy. Assume, for the time being, that the marginal propensity to tax (MPT) is zero, autonomous taxes are $60, and transfer payments are $10; thus net autonomous taxes are $50. (Billions of dollars.)

a. Aggregate demand-aggregate supply approach to determining equilibrium income. The following table contains hypothetical data (in billions of dollars) on income, consumption, investment, and government expenditures on goods and services. (Note: Now that taxes and transfers are included, *C* represents the level of consumption after both these items have been considered.)

Y_{np}	C	I	G
$ 0	$ 75	$ 25	$400
125	125	50	400
250	175	75	400
375	225	100	400
500	275	125	400
625	325	150	400
750	375	175	400
875	425	200	400
1,000	475	225	400
1,125	525	250	400
1,250	575	275	400
1,375	625	300	400
1,500	675	325	400

(1) What are the equations for consumption and investment?

(2) Plot the data for *C*, *I*, and *G* in part *A* of Figure 9–1 below. What are the equilibrium levels of income, consumption, and investment?

FIGURE 9–1

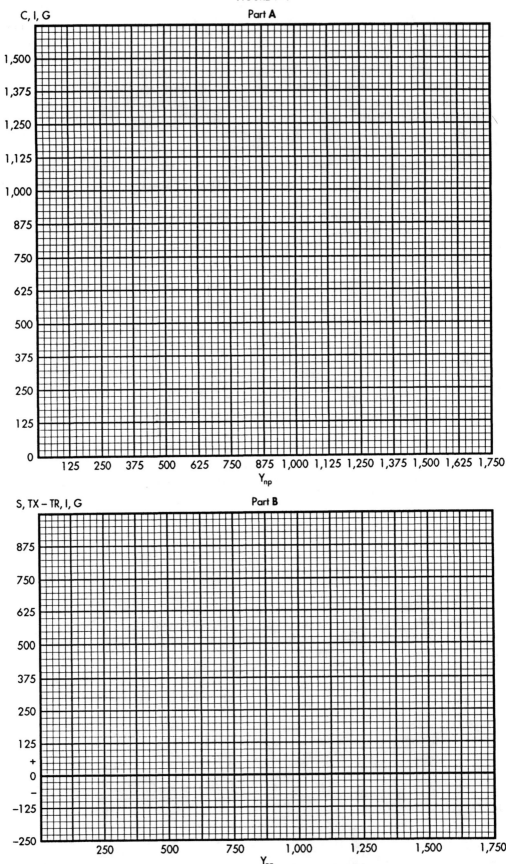

(3) What is the equilibrium income level *excluding* government purchases (but keeping net autonomous taxes in the consumption function)?

(4) What is the numerical value of the multiplier associated with the government expenditures? [Use the results to (2) and (3) to aid in answering this question.] Is it different from the numerical value of the multiplier that would be associated with autonomous investment expenditures?

(5) Assume government expenditures on goods and services rise by $25 billion. Illustrate this change in part A of Figure 9–1 and find the new equilibrium income level. [Assume the initial equilibrium is $Y_{np} = \$1,250$ billion.]

(6) In which direction and by how much would the aggregate demand curve shift if the government should raise taxes by $25 billion without increasing government expenditures? What would be the new equilibrium income? [Assume the initial equilibrium is $Y_{np} = \$1,250$ billion.]

(7) In which direction and by how much would the aggregate demand schedule change if, *ceteris paribus*, government transfer expenditures increase $25 billion? What is the new equilibrium income level? [Assume the initial equilibrium is $Y_{np} = \$1,250$.]

(8) Explain the process whereby taxes and transfer payments alter aggregate demand.

b. Saving-investment approach to determining equilibrium income.

Y_{np}	$S + TX - TR$		$I + G$	
$ 0	(	)	(	)
125	(	)	(	)
250	(	)	(	)
375	(	)	(	)
500	(	)	(	)
625	(	)	(	)
750	(	)	(	)
875	(	)	(	)
1,000	(	)	(	)
1,125	(	)	(	)
1,250	(	)	(	)
1,375	(	)	(	)
1,500	(	)	(	)

(1) Complete the table for $S + TX - TR$ and $I + G$ using the information provided in part a above.

(2) Plot the data in part B of Figure 9–1 and determine the equilibrium level of income, consumption, and investment.

(3) Assume governmental expenditures decline by $25 billion and illustrate the change in part B of Figure 9–1. What is the new income equilibrium?

(4) If people decide to save a greater amount of their income, what impact will this have on equilibrium income level?

(5) Show graphically (in part B) and explain what happens to the equilibrium level of income if, *ceteris paribus*, the federal government raises taxes by $25 billion.

(6) Assume transfer payments increase by $25 billion. Show graphically and explain how this alters the equilibrium income level.

c. Do both the aggregate demand-aggregate supply and saving-investment approaches give the same results? Will this always be the case?

3. There is only one multiplier applicable to an economic system. For purposes of understanding, however, economists frequently speak of multipliers associated with government expenditures, taxes, transfer payments, and so forth, referring to them as the government expenditures multiplier, tax multiplier, transfer multiplier, and so forth. These multipliers may be relatively simple or they may be somewhat complex ones which bring in induced investment, the distinction between the MPC out of disposable income and the MPC out of net national product, and other complications. In either case, whether simple or complex, the relationship between the various multipliers is the same.

This problem is designed to aid you in deriving "simple" multipliers (which do not include induced investment) for government expenditures on goods and services, taxes, and transfer payments. [Should it be desirable, you may skip this problem and proceed to the more sophisticated problems which follow.]

a. Derive the simple government expenditures multiplier (k_g) by completing the equations below.

(1) $k_g = \dfrac{\Delta Y_{np}}{\Delta G}$ (The government expenditures multiplier by definition)

(2) $Y_{np} = C + I + G$ (The basic identity for a closed system)

If we assume all investment is autonomous and given, the change in income is equal to:

(3) $\Delta Y_{np} = $ _____ .

The change in consumption is equal to:

(4) $\Delta C = $ _____ .

Substitute (4) into (3):

(5) $\Delta Y_{np} = $ _____ .

Collect all terms with ΔY_{np} on the left side:

(6) _____ = _____ .

Factor out ΔY_{np}:

(7) _____ = _____ .

Divide through by $(1 - a)$:

(8) $\Delta Y_{np} = $ _____ .

Now divide through by ΔG:

(9) $\dfrac{\Delta Y_{np}}{\Delta G} = $ _____ .   (The government expenditures multiplier)

b. Complete the following equations to derive the government transfer expenditures multiplier (k_{tr}).

(1) $k_{tr} = \dfrac{\Delta Y_{np}}{\Delta TR}$ (The transfer multiplier by definition)

(2) $Y_{np} = C + I + G$ (The basic identity for a closed system)

If we assume no change in I or G, the change in income must be given by:

(3) $\Delta Y_{np} = \Delta C_0 + \Delta C_i$ (Where C_i = induced consumption)

The change in autonomous consumption is given by:

(4) $\Delta C_0 = $ _____ .

The change in induced consumption is equal to:

(5) $\Delta C_i = $ _____ .

Substitute (4) and (5) into (3):

(6) $\Delta Y_{np} = $ _____ .

Collect all terms with ΔY_{np} on the left side:

(7) _____ = _____ .

Factor out ΔY_{np}:

(8) _____ = _____ .

Divide through by $(1 - a)$:

(9) $\Delta Y_{np} = $ _____ .

Now divide through by ΔT_r:

(10) $\dfrac{\Delta Y_{np}}{\Delta T_r} = $ _____ .   (The transfer multiplier)

c. Complete the following equations to derive the government tax multiplier (k_{tx}).

(1) $k_{tx} = \dfrac{\Delta Y_{np}}{\Delta TX}$ (The tax multiplier by definition)

(2) $Y_{np} = C + I + G$ (The basic identity for a closed system)

If we assume no change in I or G, a change in income is given by:

(3) $\Delta Y_{np} = $ _____.

The change in autonomous consumption is equal to:

(4) $\Delta C_0 = $ _____.

The change in induced consumption is given by:

(5) $\Delta C_i = $ _____.

Substitute (4) and (5) into (3):

(6) $\Delta Y_{np} = $ _____.

Collect all terms with ΔY_{np} on the left side:

(7) _____ $= $ _____.

Factor out ΔY_{np}:

(8) _____ $= $ _____.

Divide through by $(1 - a)$:

(9) $\Delta Y_{np} = $ _____.

Divide through by ΔT_x:

(10) $\dfrac{\Delta Y_{np}}{\Delta T_x} = $ _____.   (The tax multiplier)

d. Parts 5b and 5c show that the tax and transfer multipliers have the same value. The difference is that the tax multiplier is negative, whereas the transfer multiplier is positive.

(1) Assume the MPC = 0.8 and the government raises *taxes* by $15 billion. What is the numerical value of the tax multiplier? By how much and in which direction does income change?

(2) Assume the MPC = 0.8 and the government increases *transfer payments* by $15 billion. What is the value of the transfer multiplier? By how much and in which direction does income change?

(3) Explain in your own words why government taxes and transfer payments affect income by the same amount but in opposite directions.

4. In problem 3a the simple multiplier associated with government expenditures on goods and services was derived if we assume no induced investment. The approach is similar when induced investment is included in the analysis.

a. Complete the equations below to derive the multiplier associated with government expenditures on goods and services when induced investment (I_i) is included in the equations.

(1) $k_g = \dfrac{\Delta Y_{np}}{\Delta G}$ (The government expenditures multiplier by definition)

(2) $Y_{np} = C + I + G$ (The basic identity for a closed system)

A change in Y_{np} must be given by:

(3) $\Delta Y_{np} = \underline{\hspace{3cm}}$.

The change in consumption is given by:

(4) $\Delta C = \underline{\hspace{3cm}}$.

The change in investment is given by:

(5) $\Delta I = \underline{\hspace{3cm}}$.

Substitute (4) and (5) into (3):

(6) $\Delta Y_{np} = \underline{\hspace{3cm}}$.

Collect all terms with ΔY_{np} on the left side:

(7) $\underline{\hspace{3cm}} = \underline{\hspace{3cm}}$.

Factor out ΔY_{np}:

(8) $\underline{\hspace{3cm}} = \underline{\hspace{3cm}}$.

Divide through by $(1 - a - b)$:

(9) $\Delta Y_{np} = \underline{\hspace{3cm}}$.

Divide through by ΔG:

ΔY_{np}

(10) $\dfrac{\Delta Y_{np}}{\Delta G} = \underline{\hspace{3cm}}$.   (The multiplier associated with a change in government expenditures including induced investment)

b. Is the multiplier associated with a change in government expenditures (derived in 4a) the same as the multiplier associated with a change in autonomous investment?

5. The inclusion of taxes and transfer payments into the analysis alters the consumption equation.

a. Prove, by completing the following equations, that the consumption function including taxes and transfer payments can be expressed as:

$$C = C_0 - aT_0 + Y_{np}(a - at).$$

[Note: Some taxes are independent of income (T_0) and others are a function of income. The magnitude of the latter depends upon the marginal propensity to tax (t).]

(1) $C = C_0 + aY_{np}$ (Consumption equation without taxes and transfers: $Y_d = Y_{np}$)

(2) $C = C_0 + a(Y_{np} - TX + TR)$ (Consumption equation including taxes and transfers)

The difference between taxes and transfers is net taxes (T):

(3) $T = TX - TR$

Substitute (3) into (2):

(4) $C = $ _____.

Net taxes can also be defined as:

(5) $T = $ _____.

Substitute (5) into (4):

(6) $C = $ _____.

Remove the brackets and/or parentheses:

(7) $C = $ _____.

By factoring out Y_{np}, this can be rewritten as:

(8) $C = $ _____.   (Thus the above expression is correct.)

b. If $C_0 = 25$, $t = 0.2$, $a = 0.8$, $T_0 = 15$, and $Y_{np} = 700$, what is the level of consumption expenditures?

c. Now that endogenous taxes are included in the consumption function, what is the slope of the consumption function?

6. The "effective" multiplier takes into account taxes, transfers, and induced investment but excludes the effect of income changes on imports.

a. Derive the effective multiplier k' by completing the equations below. [Note that the multiplier relates changes in income to changes in autonomous aggregate demand (ΔDD).]

(1) $k' = \dfrac{\Delta Y_{np}}{\Delta DD}$ (The effective multiplier by definition)

(2) $Y_{np} = C + I + G$ (The basic identity)

Assume the ΔDD is due to a ΔG. Thus, a change in income is given by:

(3) $\Delta Y_{np} = \Delta C + \Delta I + \Delta G$.

The change in consumption is given by:

(4) $\Delta C = a\Delta Y_{np} - at\Delta Y_{np}$ (See the preceding problem.)

The change in investment is given by:

(5) $\Delta I = $ _____.

Substitute (4) and (5) into (3):

(6) $\Delta Y_{np} = $ _____.

Collect all terms with ΔY_{np} on the left side:

(7) _____ $=$ _____.

Factor out ΔY_{np}:

(8) _____ $=$ _____.

Divide through by $(1 - a + at - b)$:

(9) $\Delta Y_{np} = $ _____.

Divide both sides by ΔG:

(10) $\dfrac{\Delta Y_{np}}{\Delta G} = $ _____.

But the $\Delta G = \Delta DD$. Substituting this into (10) gives:

(11) $\dfrac{\Delta Y_{np}}{\Delta DD} = $ _____.   (The effective multiplier)

b. Assume the MPC = 0.5, MPI = 0.2, and MPT = 0.2. What is the value of the multiplier?

7. An algebraic equilibrium model for a closed system including the government.

    a. Complete the following equations to derive the algebraic expression for income equilibrium. (Note: The consumption equation including taxes and transfers was derived in problem 5.)

        (1) $Y_{np} = C + I + G$ (The basic identity)
        (2) $C = C_0 - aT_0 + Y_{np}(a - at)$ (The consumption function)
        (3) $I = I_0 + bY_{np}$ (The investment function)
        Substitute (2) and (3) into (1):
        (4) $Y_{np} = $ _____ .
        Remove the parentheses:
        (5) $Y_{np} = $ _____ .
        Gather all terms with Y_{np} on the left side:
        (6) _____ = _____ .
        Factor out Y_{np}:
        (7) _____ = _____ .
        Divide through by $(1 - a + at - b)$:
        (8) $Y_{np} = $ _____ .

    b. Assume the MPC = 0.75, MPT = 0.20, MPI = 0.15, C_0 = $45 billion, T_0 = $40 billion, I_0 = $60 billion, and G = $90 billion. What is the equilibrium level of income?

8. The balanced budget thesis. For this problem, we return to the simple model in which there is no induced investment and all taxes and transfer payments are autonomous with respect to the income level.

    a. Assume the federal government increases taxes by $20 billion to finance an increase in government expenditures of $20 billion. What effect, if any, will this have on the income level? Assume the MPC is 0.75.

    b. If the numerical value of the government expenditures multiplier is 5, what is the value of the government tax multiplier? Why?

    c. Using all the knowledge you have gained so far, explain under what circumstances the balanced budget multiplier might not equal unity (1).

9. *Crowding-Out Effect.* Use Figure 9–2 to assist in answering the various parts to this question.

FIGURE 9–2

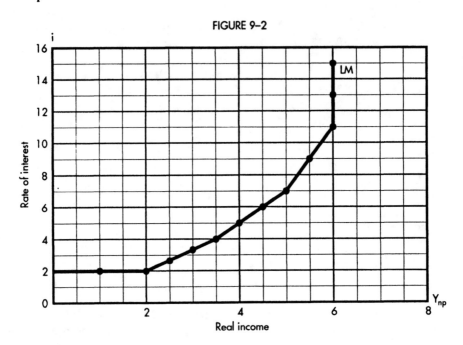

a. Explain what is meant by the "crowding-out effect."

b. Assume the *IS* and *LM* curves intersect in the intermediate range of the *LM* curve illustrated in Figure 9–2. Explain and illustrate graphically the crowding-out effect of an increase in government purchases of goods and services (*G*).

c. Compare the magnitude of the crowding-out effect from an increase in government purchases (*G*) when the *IS* curve intersects the *LM* curve in the (1) Keynesian range, (2) intermediate range, and (3) classical range. Is it the same in all three cases? Why or why not?

d. Assume *IS-LM* equilibrium is in the intermediate range and that the economy is producing at less than full employment. Explain and illustrate graphically how fiscal policy and monetary policy could be used jointly to promote full employment without crowding out investment (and consumption).

e. Explain what is meant by "monetizing" the debt.

10. Distinguish between the full-employment budget and the official administrative budget. What is the usefulness of the full-employment budget?

11. Distinguish between the "structural" deficit and the "cyclical" deficit. What is the usefulness of this distinction?

A Self-Test

Completion Questions

1. A change in taxes will alter consumption through its effect on _____.

2. The simple transfer expenditures multiplier is given by the algebraic expression

_____.

3. If the MPC is 0.75 and government transfer payments decline by $15 billion, the income level will (*fall, rise*) by _____.

4. If the MPC is 0.8 and government taxes are reduced by $11 billion, the income level will (*fall, rise*) by _____.

5. If the marginal rate of taxation is zero and the government increases taxes by $12 billion to finance a $12 billion increase in transfer payments, the income level will (*rise, fall, remain unchanged*). If the $12 billion increase in taxes were used instead to finance an increase in government expenditures, the income level would (*rise, fall, remain unchanged*), in the simple case, by

_____.

6. Generally the (*investment, government, tax*) multiplier will be less than all the others.

7. If the government tax multiplier is numerically equal to 3, the government expenditures multiplier is equal to _____.

8. The marginal propensity to tax refers to the _____.

9. If the tax rate structure is proportional, the tax curve depicted on a taxes-income diagram will be _____, but if the rate structure is progressive, the tax function will be _____. A regressive rate structure would be represented by a tax curve that is _____.

10. The following information is given: $G = \$70$ billion, $I = \$65$ billion, MPS $= 0.25$, $C_0 = \$25$ billion, $TX = \$40$ billion, and $TR = \$10$ billion. The equilibrium income level is _____. If the government desires to raise income to $650 billion, it could increase G by _____, increase transfer payments by _____, or reduce taxes by _____. (Assume that both the MPT and MPI are zero.)

True and False

_____ 1. If autonomous I and G are added to C, and there is no foreign trade or induced investment, the slope of the aggregate demand function is given by the MPC.

_____ 2. Given identical information, the saving-investment approach will not give the same results as the aggregate-demand-aggregate-supply approach because the former also considers saving.

_____ 3. In the $S + TX = I + G$ approach to equilibrium, saving must equal investment and taxes must equal government expenditures.

_____ 4. Both taxes and transfer payments of the government affect consumption via their impact on disposable income.

_____ 5. The marginal propensity to tax is given by the slope of the tax function.

_____ 6. If a nation has an income tax, then taxes will be a function of income.

_____ 7. A positive value of the MPT will reduce the multiplier effect associated with a shift in the aggregate demand function.

_____ 8. A proportional tax rate structure has a greater dampening effect on income than a progressive tax rate structure.

_____ 9. The income tax and unemployment compensation are built-in stabilizers tending to mitigate fluctuations in income.

_____ 10. The balanced budget thesis indicates that an equal increase in government expenditures and taxes will have no impact on income.

_____ 11. One reason why government economic policy designed to stabilize the business cycle can be more effective today than in preceding decades is that now the public sector is much larger and thus its potential impact considerably greater.

_____ 12. Inflation pushes families into higher tax brackets and thereby tends to lower consumption.

_____ 13. The crowding-out effect implies that expansionary fiscal policy will stimulate economy even more than would be expected.

Multiple Choice

1. One approach to equilibrium is:
   a. $S - TX = I - G$ ex ante.
   b. $S + TX = I + G$ ex post.
   c. $S + I = TX + G$ ex ante.
   d. $S + I = G - TX$ ex post.
   e. $S + TX = I + G$ ex ante.

2. The government expenditures multiplier is
   a. equal to the investment multiplier.
   b. the reciprocal of the investment multiplier.
   c. one less than the investment multiplier.
   d. equal to the transfer expenditures multiplier.
   e. none of the above

3. When there is a change in government taxes or transfer payments, consumption will
   a. change by the same amount.
   b. remain unaltered as disposable income will not change.
   c. change by a smaller extent.
   d. change by more than the change in taxes or transfers.
   e. none of the above

4. The only difference between the tax and transfer multiplier is that
   a. the tax multiplier is always one less than the transfer multiplier.
   b. the tax multiplier is negative whereas the transfer multiplier is positive.
   c. one is always the reciprocal of the other.
   d. the transfer multiplier is negative whereas the tax multiplier is positive.
   e. none of the above

5. If the MPS is 0.2, the tax multiplier has a value of
   a. 5.
   b. 0.25.
   c. 4.

d. 2.
e. 1.

6. If transfer payments increase by $8 billion and the MPS is 0.3,
   a. the consumption function will shift upward by $5.6 billion.
   b. the consumption function will shift downward by $5.6 billion.
   c. the aggregate demand function will shift upward by $8 billion.
   d. the aggregate demand function will shift downward by $8 billion.
   e. aggregate demand will remain unchanged.

7. If the government expenditures multiplier is equal to 8, the tax multiplier (in the simple case) is equal to
   a. 6.
   b. 8.
   c. 7.
   d. 5.
   e. cannot determine without the MPC.

8. Assume the MPT and MPI are both zero. If taxes and government expenditures are both increased by $8 billion, income will
   a. remain unchanged.
   b. decline by $8 billion.
   c. increase by $8 billion.
   d. decrease by $2 billion if the MPC is 0.8.
   e. increase by $2 billion if the MPC is 0.8.

9. A government budget containing automatic stabilizers
   a. causes fluctuations in economic activity to be greater than otherwise.
   b. tends to reduce fluctuations in economic activity.
   c. has no effect on the magnitude of economic fluctuations.
   d. cannot be developed because society will not accept automatic stabilizers.

10. A progressive income tax
    a. is not reflected in the multiplier.
    b. increases the numerical value of the multiplier.
    c. decreases the numerical value of the multiplier.
    d. none of the above

11. According to the balanced budget thesis, an increase in government purchases that is fully paid for by an increase in taxes will
    a. be neither inflationary nor deflationary since one effect exactly offsets the other.
    b. cause a recession since the increase in taxes will have a greater contractionary effect than the expansionary effect of the increase in government purchases.
    c. cause the economy to expand since the positive effect of the increase in government purchases will exceed the contractionary effect of the increase in taxes.
    d. be difficult to realize since the positive effect of the increase in government purchases will be set into motion a chain of events that reduces investment and thus corporate profits.

12. Which of the following government policies will cause the income level to increase by the largest amount?
    a. a $5 billion increase in government purchases of goods and services
    b. a $5 billion increase in government purchases that is financed by an increase in taxes
    c. a $5 billion reduction in taxes
    d. an increase in government purchases of $5 billion which is partially financed by a $3 billion increase in taxes

13. Should the economy be experiencing an inflationary gap, it can be partly or wholly eliminated by
    a. increasing government purchases.
    b. reducing personal income taxes.
    c. reducing both government purchases and taxes by the same amount.
    d. increasing both government purchases and taxes by the same amount.

14. Fiscal policy attempts to stabilize economic activity at the full-employment level by
    a. ensuring that the money supply does not expand too fast or too slowly.
    b. changing the level of government purchases and taxes.
    c. altering the composition of the federal debt.
    d. undertaking policies that keep the federal budget in a balanced state over the business cycle.

15. A reduction in the personal income taxes will
    a. reduce the income level because the government cannot spend without having tax money.
    b. increase the income level because business firms will be able to borrow more funds at a lower interest rate.
    c. have no effect on the income level because experience shows that people pay all their taxes out of their savings.
    d. increase disposable income and thereby tend to increase GDP.

16. Monetizing the government debt, which is one way—but not necessarily the best one—to get around the crowding-out effect, refers to
    a. the Federal Reserve printing Federal Reserve notes.
    b. financing a government deficit by the Federal Reserve buying Treasury bills and bonds directly from the Treasury or on the open market.
    c. the Treasury financing the deficit by printing more money.
    d. financing a government deficit by the Fed selling U.S. Treasury bonds on the open market.

17. During the severe recession of 1981–82, the official unemployment rate reached a high of almost
    a. 8 percent.
    b. 9 percent.
    c. 10 percent.
    d. 11 percent.
    e. 14 percent.

18. Many economists believe that one of the major causes of the 1973–75 recession was the
    a. devaluation of the U.S. dollar in December 1971 and again in February 1973.
    b. inflation caused a drop in real income of consumers.
    c. increase in investment.
    d. inflation caused increase in real income of consumers.

19. During part of the first half of the 1970s, rapid inflation combined with a progressive tax structure resulted in a
    a. decrease in U.S. federal government tax revenues and expenditures.
    b. decrease in U.S. real consumer income.
    c. increase in U.S. real consumer income.
    d. sharp drop in interest rates.

20. The crowding-out effect argues that the level of aggregate demand will remain basically unchanged because
    a. the stimulus from expansionary fiscal policy will be offset by the negative effect of higher interest rates on private spending.
    b. expansionary fiscal policy will force up interest rates and thereby cause an expansion of the money supply.
    c. an increase in government purchases will result in an increase in taxes that discourages consumption.
    d. none of the above

21. The major cause of the 1981–82 recession, according to most economists, was the
    a. curtailment of defense expenditures.
    b. Reagan 5–10–10 tax cut.
    c. deregulation of the major sectors of the economy.
    d. high and rising interest rates.
    e. the sharp increase in inflation.

22. The full-employment budget
    a. measures the surplus or deficit that would exist if the economy were operating at full employment.
    b. assumes total federal taxes equal total federal expenditures.
    c. is a measure of the actual federal deficit or surplus.
    d. has no relevance since the economy seldom operates at full employment.

23. Compared to the official administrative budget, the full-employment budget deficit or surplus will vary depending on the
    a. rate of inflation.
    b. rate of economic growth.
    c. unemployment rate chosen as representing full employment.
    d. level of government expenditures.

24. With respect to taxes, bracket creep refers to
    a. increasing the size of each income tax bracket.
    b. inflation shifting taxpayers into higher income tax brackets.
    c. expanding the different types of income to which the tax applies.
    d. people having to pay higher marginal tax rates because of an increase in their real income.

25. During the recession of 1990–91, the official unemployment rate (which is not adjusted for discouraged workers or part-time workers wanting full-time jobs) reached
    a. 6.9 percent but did not peak until reaching 7.7 percent in June 1992.
    b. 7.3 percent but did not peak until reaching 7.7 percent in June 1992.
    c. 7.7 percent but did not peak until reaching 8.0 percent in June 1992.
    d. 8.1 percent but did not peak until reaching 8.7 percent in June 1992.
    e. 8.7 percent and was down to 7.7 percent by June 1992.

26. In general, the Full- (or High-) Employment Budget was
    a. more restrictive during the Reagan administration than during the Carter administration.
    b. generally expansionary during the Reagan administration and relatively contractionary during the Carter administration.
    c. about the same degree of restrictiveness under both administrations.
    d. highly expansionary under both administrations.

27. The Gramm-Rudman-Hollings Act was designed to
    a. achieve a balanced federal budget by 1991.
    b. promote exports and thus improve the balance of trade.
    c. slow down the rate of inflation.
    d. create more jobs by increasing productivity.

28. If the *IS* curve intersects the *LM* curve in the classical range, an increase in government purchases will
    a. crowd out some private investment if investment is interest elastic.
    b. crowd out some investment if the investment function has zero interest elasticity.
    c. not have any effect on investment.
    d. will generate enough tax revenue to pay for the increase in *G*.

29. If the *IS-LM* intersection is in the intermediate range and the government wants to promote full employment without changing private investment and consumption, it could do so by
    a. implementing an easier monetary policy.
    b. implementing a more expansionary fiscal policy.
    c. increasing the money supply at the same time that it follows expansionary fiscal policy.
    d. reducing *G* and increasing taxes while simultaneously increasing the money supply.

30. Throughout the 1980s the structural proportion of the U.S. federal deficit
    a. fell consistently to about 20 percent.
    b. increased to well over 80 percent.
    c. increased to about 40 percent.
    d. decreased to about 40 percent.
    e. was zero since all the deficits were due to recessions.

31. During the Great Depression, the federal surplus or deficit as a percent of GDP was about -3.4 percent. In the 1980s it was about
    a. −0.42

    b. −0.83

    c. −2.51

    d. −4.13

    e. −9.99

32. Professor Robert Eisner argues that the federal government deficit is

    a. grossly understated.

    b. grossly overstated.

    c. unimportant since it has no effect on the economy.

    d. not a problem since the inflation-adjusted high-employment budget has always been in surplus.

The International Economy

THE FOREIGN SECTOR—KEYNESIAN MODEL

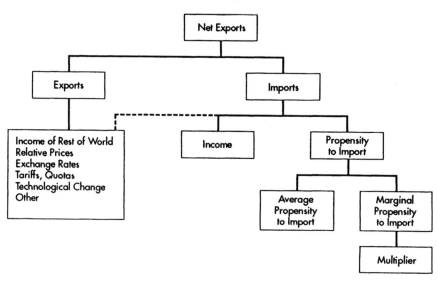

Key Concepts

Balance-of-payments statement
Balance of merchandise trade (BOT)
Credit entries in balance-of-payments
   statement
Debit entries in balance-of-payments
   statement
Current account
Capital account
Open economy
Monetary gold
Unilateral transfers
Capital export (outflow)
Capital import (inflow)
Active current-account balance

Official reserves account
Basic balance
Balance on current account
Balance-of-payments equilibrium
Induced movements
Autonomous movements
Import function
Invisible items
Visible items
International reserves
Freely fluctuating (floating or flexible)
   exchange rate (system)
Pegged exchange rate system
   (Bretton Woods system)

Passive current-account balance
Net exports
Average propensity to import (APM)
Marginal propensity to import (MPM)
Foreign trade multiplier (k_f)
Foreign repercussion effect
Net foreign investment
Foreign exchange
Foreign exchange market
Rate of exchange (or, exchange rate)
Devaluation (depreciation)
Revaluation (appreciation)
Supply of foreign exchange (dollars, sterling, DM, pesos, etc.)
Demand for foreign exchange (dollars, sterling, DM, pesos, etc.)

Crawling peg exchange rate (system)
Internal balance
External balance
Special Drawing Rights (SDRs)
International Monetary Fund (IMF)
Managed floating exchange rates
World Bank
Balance on official reserve transactions
Official reserve assets
Group of Five (G-5)
Group of Seven (G-7)
Real rate of interest
Purchasing power parity
Arbitrage
Real rate of interest

Problems and Essays

1. The balance-of-payments statement is frequently broken down into three major accounts: current account, capital account, and official reserves account. Discuss the nature and significance of *each account* with emphasis on the following points:

   a. Meaning.

   b. Relationship to other accounts.

   c. Induced vs. autonomous movements.

d. Relative importance of each account for national income considerations.

e. Meaning of debits and credits.

f. Deficits and surpluses in each account and for the overall balance of payments.

2. Income equilibrium for a closed economy can be expressed by the equality of investment plus government purchases of goods and services with saving plus taxes minus transfer payments. Equilibrium including the foreign sector requires that exports be added to the former and imports to the latter.

a. Given equations (1) and (2) below prove that income equilibrium for an open economy requires that the sum of I, G, and X equals the sum of S, $TX - TR$, and M by completing the following equations.
(1) $Y_{np} = C + I + G + X - M$ (The origin of income)
(2) $Y_{np} = C + S + TX - TR$ (The disposition of income)
Subtract C from both sides of (1) and (2):
(3) _____ = _____.
(4) _____ = _____.
As the right sides of both (3) and (4) equal $Y_{np} - C$, they must equal each other.
   Therefore:
(5) _____ = _____.
Now add imports to both sides:
(6) _____ = _____.

b. Does saving have to equal domestic investment? Why?

3. This problem is designed to integrate the foreign sector into the aggregate-demand–aggregate-supply and saving-investment approaches to income equilibrium. Assume the marginal rate of taxation equals zero and net autonomous taxes equal $50 billion. [Keep in mind that the consumption function now includes

taxes and transfers, even though we are assuming for simplicity that the marginal rate of taxation is zero. Thus the consumption equation is $C = C_0 + a(Y_{np} - T_0)$; where T_0 equals autonomous taxes minus transfer payments.] (Billions of dollars.)

a. *Aggregate-demand--aggregate-supply approach.* The following data on income, consumption, and investment are based on that in problem 2 of Chapter 9. The additional information on exports (X), imports (M), and government purchases (G) is assumed.

Y_{np}	C	I	G	X	M
$ 0	$75	$25	$400	$120	($)
125	125	50	400	120	( )
250	175	75	400	120	( )
375	225	100	400	120	( )
500	275	125	400	120	( )
625	325	150	400	120	( )
750	375	175	400	120	( )
875	425	200	400	120	( )
1,000	475	225	400	120	( )
1,125	525	250	400	120	( )
1,250	575	275	400	120	( )
1,375	625	300	400	120	( )
1,500	675	325	400	120	( )
1,625	725	350	400	120	( )
1,750	775	375	400	120	( )
1,875	825	400	400	120	( )
2,000	875	425	400	120	( )

(1) Given that the import equation is $M = 60 + 0.04Y_{np}$, complete the column representing imports of goods and services.

(2) What is the numerical value of the multiplier?

(3) Plot the above information for C, I, G, X, and M in part A of Figure 10–1 below. What are the equilibrium levels of income, consumption, investment, and imports?

FIGURE 10–1

Part **A**

C, I, G, X, M

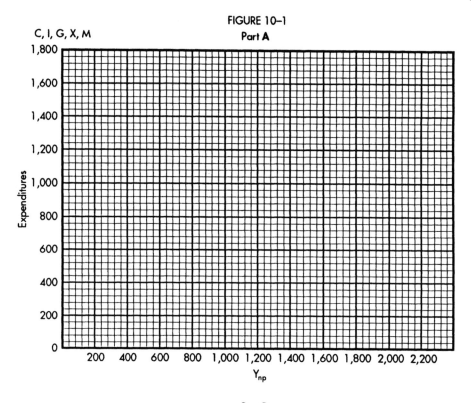

Part **B**

S, TX – TR, M, I, G, X

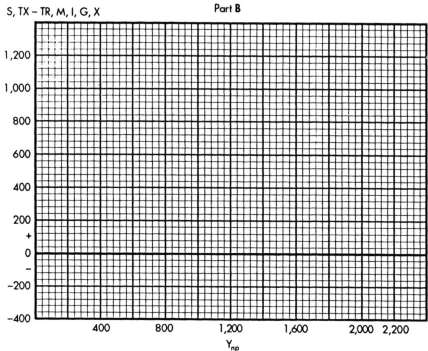

(4) What impact will an increase or decrease in the marginal propensity to import (MPM) have on the aggregate demand curve and equilibrium level of income? Illustrate in Figure 10–1.

(5) What effect will an increase or decrease in autonomous imports have on the aggregate demand function and the income level? Compare your answer given here to that given for the immediately preceding question.

(6) How will an increase or decrease in exports alter the aggregate demand function and the equilibrium income level?

b. *Saving-investment approach.* This part of the problem incorporates the foreign sector into the saving-investment approach to equilibrium. The results must be the same as in part *a* of this problem.

Y_{np}	S + TX - TR + M	I + G + X
$ 0	($)	($)
125	( )	( )
250	( )	( )
375	( )	( )
500	( )	( )
625	( )	( )
750	( )	( )
875	( )	( )
1,000	( )	( )
1,125	( )	( )
1,250	( )	( )
1,375	( )	( )
1,500	( )	( )
1,625	( )	( )
1,750	( )	( )
1,875	( )	( )
2,000	( )	( )

(1) Complete the columns for $S + TX - TR + M$ and $I + G + X$ using the information in part a of this problem (above).

(2) Plot the $S + TX - TR + M$ and $I + G + X$ schedules in part B of Figure 10–1 above and find the equilibrium level of income. Is equilibrium income at the same level as in part A above?

(3) How will a change in the MPM alter the $S + TX - TR + M$ function and the income level?

(4) If autonomous imports increase, what will happen to the equilibrium income level? Compare the answer to this question with the answer to the preceding question.

(5) Assume autonomous imports and exports both increase by 10. How will this affect the equilibrium value of income? Illustrate the change in part B of the graph.

4. Figure 10–2 illustrates how exports and imports relate to net national income. Answer the questions below using the information provided in this diagram. Assume exports and imports are given by the solid lines (X and M) until otherwise indicated.

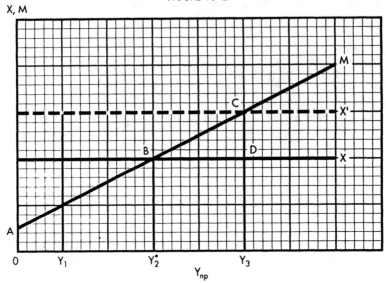

FIGURE 10–2

a. What is the MPM? Write it in terms of the letter provided in the graph.

b. What is the import equation (in terms of the letters provided)?

c. Is the trade balance in deficit or surplus at the income level Y_3?

d. Is there a surplus or deficit in the balance of trade at the Y_1 income level?

e. Assume exports increase to X'—represented by the dashed line. What is the algebraic value of the foreign-trade multiplier (in terms of the letters provided)?

f. Will a change in autonomous imports have the same effect on income as a change in exports?

g. If we assume exports remain constant, what changes could occur in the import function that would increase the level of income?

5. The multiplier associated with foreign trade may be relatively simple or relatively complex. In this problem a simple foreign-trade multiplier will be derived. Assume induced investment and the marginal rate of taxation are both zero. (A complex foreign-trade multiplier will be derived in problem 6.)

a. Complete the following equations to derive a simple foreign-trade multiplier (k_f); that is, a simple multiplier associated with exports and imports.

(1) $k_f = \dfrac{\Delta Y_{np}}{\Delta X}$ (A simple foreign-trade multiplier by definition)

(2) $Y_{np} = C + I + G + X - M$ (The basic identity for an open economy)

If we assume no change in G or I, the change in income is given by:

(3) $\Delta Y_{np} =$ _____.

The change in consumption is equal to:

(4) $\Delta C =$ _____.

The change in imports is equal to:

(5) $\Delta M =$ _____.

Substitute (4) and 5 into (3):

(6) $\Delta Y_{np} =$ _____.

Gather all terms with ΔY_{np} on the left side:

(7) _____ $=$ _____.

Factor out ΔY_{np}:

(8) _____ $=$ _____.

Divide through by $(1 - a + m)$:

(9) $\Delta Y_{np} =$ _____.

Divide through by ΔX:

(10) $\dfrac{\Delta Y_{np}}{\Delta X}$ = _____.   (A simple foreign-trade multiplier)

b. Suppose it had been assumed that saving equaled zero. What would be the expression for the foreign-trade multiplier in this case?

c. Does the introduction of imports reduce or increase the multiplier?

d. In deriving this simple multiplier, it was assumed that all investment is autonomous. Work through the steps above, assuming everything is the same except that now there is induced investment as well as autonomous investment. What is the algebraic expression for the new multiplier?

e. Assume exports fall by $8 billion, MPM = 0.2, and MPS = 0.2. What is the numerical value of the multiplier, and how much will domestic income decline?

6. This problem integrates exports and imports into the multiplier and points out some of the implications of such a change.

a. Complete the equations below to derive the effective multiplier (k') for an open economy.

(1) $k' = \dfrac{\Delta Y_{np}}{\Delta DD}$ (The effective multiplier for an open economy by definition)

(2) $Y_{np} = C + I + G + X - M$ (The basic identity for an open economy)

If we assume no change in government purchases, a change in income is given by:

(3) $\Delta Y_{np} =$ _____.

The change in consumption is equal to:

(4) $\Delta C =$ _____.

The change in investment is equal to:

(5) $\Delta I =$ _____.

The change in imports is equal to:

(6) $\Delta M =$ _____.

Substitute (4), (5), and (6) into (3):

(7) $\Delta Y_{np} =$ _____.

Collect all terms with ΔY_{np} on the left side:

(8) _____ $=$ _____.

Factor out ΔY_{np}:

(9) _____ $=$ _____.

Divide through by $(1 - a + at - b + m)$:

(10) $\Delta Y_{np} =$ _____.

Divide through by ΔX:

(11) _____ $=$ _____.

But $\Delta X = \Delta DD$. Substitute ΔDD into (11):

(12) _____ $=$ _____.   (The effective multiplier for an open economy)

b. Assume $a = 0.85$, $m = 0.05$, $b = 0.12$, and $t = 0.2$. What is the numerical value of the effective multiplier?

c. Is the effective multiplier for an open economy larger or smaller than the effective multiplier for a closed economy? Why?

d. Compare the effect of imports and the marginal rate of taxation on the effective multiplier. Is the impact of imports similar to that of induced taxes?

e. What is the algebraic expression of the effective multiplier if:

(1) The marginal rate of taxation and induced investment are zero?

(2) The marginal rate of taxation is zero?

f. What happens to the numerical value of the effective multiplier if the MPT declines?

7. In the preceding chapter the algebraic expression for income equilibrium was derived for a closed economy. It is a relatively simple matter to include exports and imports in the algebraic model.

a. Derive the algebraic expression for income equilibrium by completing the following equations.

(1) $Y_{np} = C + I + G + X - M$ (The basic identity for an open economy)
(2) $C = C_0 + aY_{np} - aT_0 - atY_{np}$ (The consumption function)
(3) $I = I_0 + bY_{np}$ (The investment function)
(4) $M = M_0 + mY_{np}$ (The import function)

Substitute (2), (3), and (4) into (1):

(5) $Y_{np} = $ _____.

Remove the parentheses:

(6) $Y_{np} = $ _____.

Collect all terms containing Y_{np} on the left side:

(7) _____ = _____.

Factor out Y_{np}:

(8) _____ = _____.

Divide through by $(1 - a + at - b + m)$:

(9) $Y_{np} = $ _____.

b. What is the equilibrium level of income, consumption, investment, imports, and balance of trade, if $a = 0.85$, $m = 0.05$, $b = 0.12$, $t = 0.2$, $C_0 = 30$, $T_0 = 40$, $I_0 = 84$, $G = 200$, $X = 100$, and $M_0 = 60$? (C_0, T_0, I_0, G, X, and M_0 are in billions of dollars.)

8. Discuss fully the foreign repercussion effect and illustrate how it works. Give particular emphasis to the following points:

a. Meaning.

b. What it implies about the relationship between exports and imports of a particular country.

c. What it implies about the relationship between domestic and foreign incomes.

d. Cases in which the effect would be relatively large.

e. Cases in which the effect would be relatively insignificant.

f. The factors which determine the magnitude of the foreign-repercussion effect.

9. In problem 2 of this chapter it was proven that income equilibrium requires that $I + G + X = S + TX - TR + M$. Assume for simplicity that $G = TX - TR$ and cancel these two items out of the equation. The equilibrium condition can now be written as $I + X = S + M$. By manipulating the variables algebraically, the equilibrium condition becomes $S - I = X - M$; the difference between saving and domestic investment must equal the balance of trade. We shall now use this equilibrium condition to illustrate the relationship between domestic income changes and the balance of trade. The following data are hypothetical. (Billion of constant dollars.)

Y	S	I	S – I	X	M	X – M
$ 0	$–25	$ 25	($)	$50	$10	($)
100	–5	35	( )	50	18	( )
200	15	45	( )	50	26	( )
300	35	55	( )	50	34	( )
400	55	65	( )	50	42	( )
500	75	75	( )	50	50	( )
600	95	85	( )	50	58	( )
700	115	95	( )	50	66	( )
800	135	105	( )	50	74	( )
900	155	115	( )	50	82	( )
1,000	175	125	( )	50	90	( )

a. Complete the columns for $S – I$ and $X – M$.

b. Plot the $S – I$ and $X – M$ data in Figure 10–3. What is the equilibrium level of income?

FIGURE 10–3

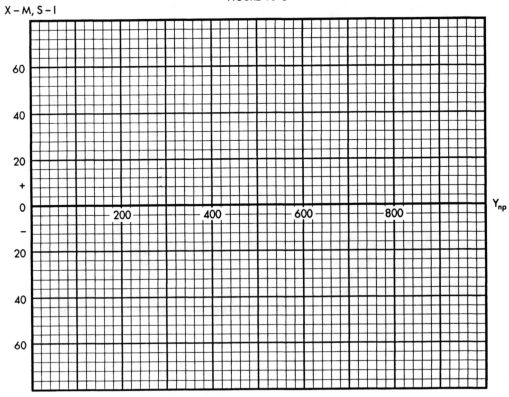

c. Consider the mechanics of Figure 10–3.

   (1) What is the slope of the $X - M$ curve, and why does it slope downward to the right?

   (2) What happens to the slope of the $X - M$ curve if the MPM increases or decreases?

   (3) What is the slope of the $S - I$ curve, and why does it slope upward to the degree indicated in the diagram?

   (4) What would be the slope of the $S - I$ curve if there were no induced investment?

   (5) Would the slope of the $S - I$ curve be altered if the MPS and MPI increased or decreased by the same amount?

   (6) Explain what happens to the balance of trade as the income level moves upward from zero.

(7) Which is greater, saving or investment, at all income levels up to $500 billion? Which is greater at income levels beyond $500 billion?

(8) If the data are as given in Figure 10–3, would it be correct to say that a deficit in the balance of trade is associated with a condition in which investment exceeds saving?

d. This diagram vividly illustrates how changes in the domestic economy $(S - I)$ affect a nation's balance of trade $(X - M)$.

(1) How will an increase in autonomous investment alter the $S - I$ curve, income level, and balance of trade?

(2) Suppose society decides to save a greater portion of its income. What impact will this have on the $S - I$ curve, income, and the trade balance?

e. Now consider the impact of changes in exports and imports on the domestic economy.

(1) Explain how an increase in exports will alter the $X - M$ curve, income, the trade balance, and the net difference between saving and investment.

(2) Explain how the $X - M$ curve, income, the trade balance, and saving would be affected by an increase in autonomous imports (such as might occur if a domestic crop failure necessitates a sharp rise in the volume of imports).

f. According to the foreign repercussion effect, an increase in domestic income may have some effect on the volume of exports. Explain and illustrate the foreign repercussion effect in terms of Figure 10–3.

g. Does it appear that there is any systematic relationship between changes in domestic income and the export-income balance? Explain.

10. *Exchange Rates, Exports, and Imports.* Within a country goods and services are bought and sold on the basis of one price—the local currency price of the merchandise or service. This is not true of international trade. In this case buyers and/or sellers have to deal in terms of two prices, the domestic price of the good or service and the price of foreign exchange (foreign money). The price of foreign money, the amount of domestic currency that must be paid to obtain a unit of foreign currency, is the rate of exchange.

The purpose of this problem is to illustrate how exchange rate changes affect exports and imports of goods and services. Generally speaking, depreciation (or devaluation) of a country's currency relative to other currencies will increase that country's exports and reduce its imports. Appreciation (or revaluation) has the opposite effect. To develop an understanding of why this is the normal situation, consider how changes in the exchange rate between the U.S. dollar and German Deutsche Mark (DM) affect the dollar price of a German car and the Deutsche Mark price of an American car. Once we establish how changes in exchange rates affect these items, we can generalize to other goods and services. Obviously, in the real world there may be exceptions but these need not detain us here. [Note: The analysis of this problem makes the widely used assumption that all relevant demand and supply curves are elastic with respect to price, an assumption that is necessary to ensure that the *value* of exports moves in the same direction as the physical volume of exports and that the *value* of imports moves in the same direction as the physical volume of imports.]

a. *U.S. demand for imports from Germany.* To comprehend what happens to the U.S. demand for products produced in Germany as the exchange rate fluctuates, we must determine how such fluctuations alter the price of German products expressed in U.S. dollars ($P_\$$). Suppose you are considering purchasing a Volkswagen from a German wholesaler and that the German DM price is DM20,000; this DM price remains unchanged regardless of what happens to the exchange rate between the U.S. dollar and German DM. This assumption is incorporated in the following table. Note that column 1 gives various rates of exchange expressed as so many American cents per DM; column 2 gives the DM price of the VW, which is the same at all exchange rates; and column 3 is for showing the dollar price ($P_\$$) of the German VW.

(1) Rate of Exchange (DM1 = \$.xx)	(2) Price of VW in Deutsche Marks (P_{DM})	(3) Price of VW in Dollars ($P_\$ = $ col. 1 × 2)
$0.70	DM20,000	$14,000
0.65	20,000	( )
0.60	20,000	( )
0.55	20,000	( )
0.50	20,000	( )
0.45	20,000	( )

(1) When the dollar price of the Deutsche Mark is DM1 – $.70 (column 1), the dollar price of the VW is $14,000 (column 3). Complete column 3 to ascertain the DM price of the VW at all the other exchange rates. This merely involves multiplying column 1 by column 2.

(2) What happens to the dollar price an American would have to pay for the VW as the exchange rate falls; that is, as the dollar appreciates relative to the DM? How would this affect the U.S. demand for imports from Germany?

(3) What happens to the dollar price of a VW when the exchange rate increases; that is, when the dollar depreciates relative to the DM? Would Americans want to buy more or less VWs from Germany if all other things are held constant?

b. *U.S. exports to Germany.* Assume a German resident is considering the purchase of a new American Ford Escort II (with no optional equipment) that costs $11,000 in the United States. This assumption is incorporated in the following table.

(1) Rate of Exchange (DM1 = $.xx)	(2) Price of Escort in Dollars (P_s)	(3) Price of Escort in Deutsche Marks (P_{DM} = col. 2 ÷ 1)
$0.70	$11,000	DM15,714
0.65	11,000	( )
0.60	11,000	( )
0.55	11,000	( )
0.50	11,000	( )
0.45	11,000	( )

(1) When the exchange rate is DM1 = \$.70, the DM price of the Ford Escort is DM15,714. Complete column 3 to find the price of the Escort in DMs at the other rates of exchange; divide column 2 by column 1.

(2) Study column 3. What happens to the DM price of the Ford Escort when the rate of exchange falls; that is, when the dollar appreciates relative to the the German DM? Will this tend to increase or decrease the amount of goods and services that German residents purchase from the United States?

(3) How does an increase in the rate of exchange affect the DM price of the Ford Escort? Note that an increase in the rate of exchange is a depreciation of the dollar relative to the DM, or, what is the same, an appreciation of the DM relative to the dollar. Would this tend to expand or curtail the German demand for American exports?

11. The above problem illustrates what happens to U.S. exports and imports when the dollar is devalued or revalued, that is, when the exchange rate is increased or decreased. It should thus be helpful to those trying to understand the domestic economic effects of currency realignments. That problem, however, says nothing about what determines the rate of exchange or what the forces are that cause the exchange rate to fluctuate. We must now turn to this consideration.

   a. Explain (and illustrate) how the exchange rate is determined in a free market setting. Be thorough. Assume for the time being that there are no government controls over trade or capital movements and further that the government does not intervene in the foreign exchange market.

b. Explain and illustrate graphically how each of the following will affect the equilibrium exchange rate:

(1) An increase in U.S. GDP.

(2) An increase in GDP of other industrialized nations.

(3) An increase in both U.S. and foreign incomes but with the foreign incomes expanding faster than that of the U.S.

(4) An increase in U.S. prices relative to those of other countries.

(5) A technological breakthrough abroad that reduces their need for U.S. agricultural products.

(6) The imposition by the United States of tariffs and quotas on a wide range of imports.

(7) An increase in U.S. real interest rates relative to those of other nations.

(8) An energy crisis that necessitates the United States rely heavily on foreign sources of gas and oil.

c. Explain and illustrate graphically how the U.S. government (or any government) can peg the exchange rate at some particular level by intervening in the foreign exchange market.

12. *The BP Curve.* The *IS-LM* model can be expanded to include a curve showing all those interest rates and income combinations at which the balance of payments (*BP*) is in equilibrium. *BP* equilibrium exists when the current account balance is offset by an equal net capital account balance (K_n); a current account surplus should be offset by a net capital outflow and a current account deficit offset by a net capital inflow. For this problem assume net unilateral transfers = 0 so the current account balance is roughly equal to net exports ($X - M$). Assume further that foreign income, interest rates, and prices are constant unless otherwise indicated. Recall that the domestic price level is also constant for this model. Based on earlier analysis, U.S. exports are a function of the (real) exchange rate (*er*), imports are a function of domestic income and the exchange rate. Net capital flows are assumed to be a function of the spread between domestic and foreign interest rates, a reasonable assumption for the bulk of short-term and portfolio capital flows, but not for international direct investments. Since the foreign interest rates are assumed constant, we can represent K simply as a function of domestic interest rates (*i*). Hence, we can represent the *BP* function as:

$$BP = X(er) - M(Y_{np}, er) + K_n(i) = 0.$$

The exchange rate is expressed as the amount of domestic currency you have to give for one unit of foreign currency, e.g., DM1 = $.60, £1 = $1.65, or SF1 = $.65; hence, a decrease in the price of foreign exchange (currency) is the same as an appreciation of the U.S. dollar, and vice versa. This point is important to note because, had we expressed the exchange rate as so much foreign currency per U.S. dollar, the sign (whether positive "+" or negative "−") would have been the opposite. Accordingly, the X is positively (+) related and the M negatively (−) related to the exchange rate. A decrease in the exchange rate (appreciation of the U.S. dollar)—e.g., a drop in the $/DM rate from DM1 = $.60 to DM1 = $.50— will reduce the U.S. price of foreign goods and thus increase imports while making U.S. exports more expensive and thus reducing them. Imports are also positively related to Y_{np}. Moreover, the higher U.S. interest rates, the less the net capital outflow (or greater the net capital inflow).

a. *Plot data.* Plot the data below for $X - M$ (which assumes $X = 70$ and $M = 10 + 0.08Y$) in Part C of figure 10–4 and the net capital flow data in Part A. Note that positive numbers for the net capital flow data indicate the capital outflow exceeds the capital inflow while negative numbers signify there is a net capital inflow. [The capital flow signs are the opposite of what they would be in the balance-of-payments statements, but this notation may simplify understanding.] Note that the 45° line in Part B is the equilibrium condition for net exports $(X - M)$ to equal the net capital flow (K_n); it is a graphical technique for equating the $X -- M$ data in Part C and the capital flow data in Part A so as to derive the BP curve in Part D.

Net Capital Flow Data		*Net Exports Data (X – M)*			
i	K_n	Y_{np}	X	M	X – M
2	80	0	70	10	60
4	60	200	70	26	44
6	40	400	70	42	28
8	20	600	70	58	12
10	0	800	70	74	−4
12	−20	1,000	70	90	−20
14	−40	1,200	70	106	−36
16	−60	1,400	70	122	−52
18	−80	1,600	70	138	−68

b. *Derive BP curve.* Let us start with Part C. Note that when $Y_{np} = 200$, $X = 44$. Move left to the 45° line in Part B and then project the net export surplus down to the K_n curve in Part A. Note that the interest rate needed to make the net capital outflow equal to 44 is about 5.6 percent. Thus when $Y_{np} = 200$ and $i = 5.6$ percent, net exports equals the net capital outflow. Plot this point in Part D.

(1) Repeat this procedure for $Y_{np} = 600$ and $Y_{np} = 1,000$. What are the corresponding interest rates that yield a net capital flow equal to net exports? [Note that, at $Y_{np} = 1,000$, net exports is a deficit and the interest rate in Part A must be high enough to cause a net capital inflow.]

(2) Connect the three points in Part D and you have the *BP* curve.

c. *Meaning.* What is the meaning of the *BP* curve?

d. *Slope.*

(1) Why is the *BP* curve positively sloped?

(2) How will an increase in the marginal propensity to import affect the slope of the *BP* curve?

(3) How would an increase in the interest elasticity of capital flows affect the *BP* curve?

e. *Shifts.* Explain and illustrate graphically how the *BP* curve will shift in the following cases:

(1) There is an autonomous increase in exports.

(2) Due to political instability abroad, there is a "flight to safety" that results in an increase in foreign investment in the United States.

(3) Suppose the United States is on a pegged exchange rate system and the U.S. dollar is devalued. How will this affect the *BP* curve?

(4) There is an increase in foreign interest rates.

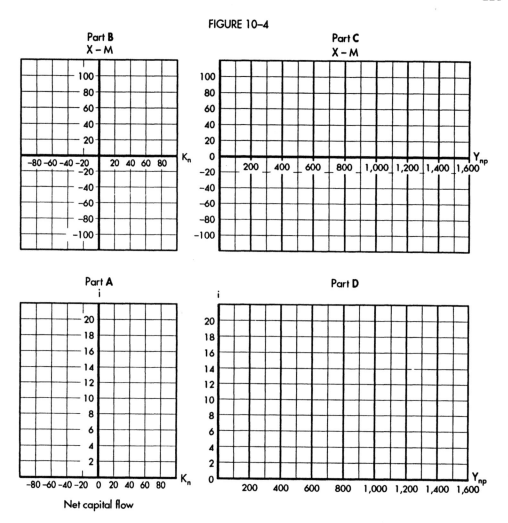

FIGURE 10-4

(5) The U.S. inflation rate increases faster than that of its trading partners. Assume the exchange rate is pegged.

13. *The Open Economy IS-LM-BP Model.* Figure 10–5 includes the *BP* curve in the
    IS-LM model developed earlier. With freely-fluctuating exchange rates, general
    equilibrium exists at the intersection of all three curves, the equilibrium interest
    rate and income being i_e and Y_{npe}. In this case the domestic economy is in
    equilibrium and the *BP* equals zero. With an adjustable peg exchange rate system,
    the *IS* and *LM* curves jointly determine the equilibrium domestic income level and
    interest rate, and the *BP* curve could lie to the left (signifying a *BP* deficit at the
    equilibrium Y_{np}) or right (signifying a *BP* surplus at the equilibrium Y_{np}) of the *BP*
    curve illustrated in Figure 10–5. Note that the model does not tell how adjustment
    is brought about—it may be automatically via market forces or via government
    policy. [Recall that equilibrium need not be one of full-employment income.
    Unless otherwise indicated, assume that the economy is at less than full
    employment in what follows.]

FIGURE 10–5

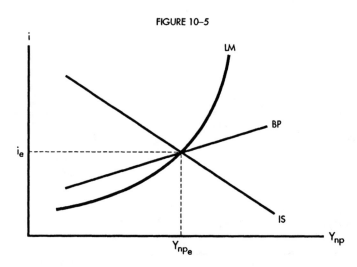

a. By now you should be able to derive all three functions and combine them on a
   single graph to analyze economic conditions and formulate government policy.

(1) Explain fully why the economy and *BP* are in equilibrium at the income
    level Y_{npe}.

   (2) Explain how *BP* surpluses and deficits, if not sterilized by the Fed, affect the *LM* curve in an adjustable peg exchange rate system.

   (3) Continue to assume an adjustable peg exchange rate system is in effect, and explain how a *BP* surplus might be inflationary and, if so, what the effect is on the *LM* and *IS* curves.

   (4) Explain why, under a freely fluctuating exchange rate system, the *BP* curve will, in theory, always pass through the intersection of the *IS* and *LM* curves.

b. Assume an adjustable peg exchange rate system is in operation.

   (1) Explain fully and illustrate graphically how an easier monetary policy will affect interest rates, income, and the *BP*.

   (2) Explain fully and illustrate graphically how an expansionary fiscal policy will affect interest rates, income, and the *BP*.

   (3) Explain fully and illustrate graphically how each of the following "*BP* measures" will affect interest rates, income, and the *BP*.

      (a) A devaluation of the U.S. dollar.

(b) An across-the-board increase in tariffs and quotas on imported products.

(c) Direct measures to restrict the net capital outflow from the United States.

c. Assume a freely fluctuating (flexible) exchange rate system is in operation.

(1) Explain fully and illustrate graphically how an easier monetary policy will affect interest rates, income, and the *BP*.

(2) Explain fully and illustrate graphically how an expansionary fiscal policy will affect interest rates, income, and the *BP*.

(3) Explain fully and illustrate graphically how a depreciation (devaluation) of the U.S. dollar will affect interest rates, income, and the *BP*.

d. *A non-dilemma situation.* Assume exchange rates are pegged and the United States is running a *BP* surplus combined with a recession. Using the *IS-LM-BP* model, explain what policies (the policy mix) the United States might be able to implement to simultaneously achieve both full employment and equilibrium in its balance of payments without changing the exchange rate. Would it make any difference if the United States had a deficit *BP* position combined with inflation? Explain.

e. *Dilemma situation #1.* Assume exchange rates are pegged and the United States is running a *BP* deficit and recession at the same time. Using the *IS-LM-BP* model, explain what policies (the policy mix) the United States might be able to implement to simultaneously achieve both full employment and equilibrium in its balance of payments without changing the exchange rate.

f. *A dilemma situation #2.* Assume exchange rates are pegged and the United States has a *BP* surplus combined with full employment and inflation. Using the *IS-LM-BP* model, explain what policies (the policy mix) the United States might be able to implement to simultaneously contain inflation and promote equilibrium in its balance of payments without changing the exchange rate.

A Self-Test

Completion Questions

1. If autonomous imports equal 10 and the marginal propensity to import is 0.2, the import equation is _____.

2. If the income level is $1,300 billion, autonomous imports are $30 billion, and the marginal propensity to import is 0.05, the total volume of imports is

_____.

3. In an open economy with government, the factors that generate income are

_____, _____,

_____, and _____.

The total income derived from these sources can be disposed of in the form of

_____, _____,

_____, and _____.

4. (*Exports, Imports*) create income, while (*exports, imports*) use up income.

5. Keynesian theory implies that an increase in domestic income will tend to (*deteriorate, improve*) the trade balance, whereas a reduction in domestic income will (*deteriorate, improve*) the balance of trade.

6. The foreign-trade multiplier which includes both saving and government will cause a (*larger, smaller*) change in income than the foreign-trade multiplier that excludes government.

7. The larger the MPS, MPT, and MPM, the (*larger, smaller*) the change in income from an autonomous change in exports.

8. The account in the balance of payments most closely related to domestic income and employment is the (*current, capital*) account.

9. The simple foreign-trade multiplier excluding saving, government, and induced investment is equal to _____. When saving is included, the multiplier becomes _____ and if the government is also included, it is _____. If included investment is taken into consideration, along with the other factors, the multiplier is _____.

10. Assume the MPC is 0.7, MPT is 0.1, MPI is 0.1, and MPM is 0.2. The multiplier excluding saving, induced investment, and government is _____. The multiplier including saving but excluding government and induced investment is _____. The multiplier including all factors except induced investment is about _____. The multiplier including all factors is about _____.

11. The magnitude of the foreign repercussion effect is determined mainly by the size of the _____, _____, _____, and the _____. Excluding investment, the smaller these items, the (*smaller, larger*) will be the repercussion effect.

True and False

_____ 1. The marginal propensity to import is given by the slope of the import function.

_____ 2. In the net expenditures approach (that is, $X - M$ and $S - I$), if the slope of the import function is 0.2, the slope of the $X - M$ function is a negative 0.2.

_____ 3. The smaller the MPM, the smaller will be the slope of the $X - M$ curve.

_____ 4. If we assume no induced investment, the slope of the $S - I$ curve is equal to the reciprocal of the MPS.

_____ 5. Debit transactions in the balance of payments provide foreigners with the means to make payments to residents of the domestic economy.

_____ 6. In the balance of payments, merchandise is classified as an invisible item and services as visible items.

_____ 7. The official reserves account records only international transactions involving monetary gold.

_____ 8. Like exports and imports of goods and services, an export of gold is a debit, and an import a credit in the balance of payments.

_____ 9. The capital account of the balance of payments deals with financial claims and liabilities.

_____ 10. An induced change in the current account is one that is unrelated to the gold or capital account.

_____ 11. Keynesian analysis assumes that exports fluctuate directly with domestic income, whereas imports are autonomously determined.

_____ 12. Imports are an injection into the income stream and analogous to investment in their effect on economic activity.

_____ 13. For equilibrium in an open economy, it is not necessary that exports equal imports if the surplus or deficit is offset by appropriate and sustainable capital transactions.

_____ 14. An increase in exports tends to increase domestic income, whereas an increase in imports tends to reduce income.

_____ 15. The foreign-trade multiplier is equal to the ratio of the change in exports to the change in domestic income.

_____ 16. The foreign repercussion effect refers to the impact that changes in domestic exports and imports may have on foreign income and to the subsequent effect that changes in foreign income may have on domestic exports.

_____ 17. In most cases, the foreign repercussion effect will be relatively small if nations trading with each other are relatively small, but the effect may be significant if one nation is large compared to others.

_____ 18. There has been increasing concern over the past two and a half decades that the floating exchange rate system is serving the desires of speculators at the expense of more important needs of international trade.

Multiple Choice

1. Assume the MPS = 0.4, MPT = 0, MPM = 0.1, and the MPI = 0. If exports increase by $3 billion, domestic income will increase by
   a. $7.5 billion.
   b. $4.5 billion.
   c. $15 billion.

    d. $6 billion.
    e. none of the above

2. The X - M curve is negatively sloped because
    a. imports decline as income advances.
    b. exports fall as domestic income rises.
    c. exports remain constant, while imports decline as income increases.
    d. exports remain constant, while imports increase as income advances.
    e. none of the above

3. The S - I curve including induced investment is positively sloped because
    a. saving advances at a faster rate than investment.
    b. saving and investment tend to move in the same direction as income fluctuates.
    c. saving increases at a slower rate than the increase in investment.
    d. increasing income is only possible with less imports and more investment.
    e. none of the above

4. In general, an increase in domestic investment will tend to
    a. reduce domestic exports to other countries.
    b. increase exports, while imports remain unchanged.
    c. improve the trade balance.
    d. deteriorate the balance of trade.
    e. increase imports but by a smaller amount than the increase in exports.

5. Starting from a position of equilibrium, an increase in exports will
    a. reduce the trade balance.
    b. cause saving to exceed domestic investment.
    c. cause investment to exceed saving.
    d. reduce the equilibrium level of income.
    e. none of the above

6. Assume the MPT = 0, MPI = 0, MPC = 0.6, MPM = 0.1, C_0 = $35 billion,
    I = $105 billion, T_0 = 0, G = $140 billion, X = $40 billion, and M = $35 billion.
    The equilibrium level of income is
    a. $570 billion.
    b. $900 billion plus.
    c. $710 billion.
    d. $360 billion (approximately).
    e. $480 billion (approximately).

7. If the current account balance is "active," then
    a. imports exceed exports.
    b. exports exceed imports.
    c. exports and imports are changing.
    d. exports equal imports and both are changing at the same rate.
    e. none of the above

8. If the current account balance is "passive," then
    a. exports and imports are declining.
    b. exports and imports are equal.
    c. exports and imports are equal and declining.

d. exports are less than imports.

e. none of the above

9. The import equation can be represented as
   a. $M = Y$.
   b. $M = M_0 - mY$.
   c. $M = M_0 + mY$.
   d. $M = -M_0 - mY$.
   e. $M = -M_0 + mY$.

10. If autonomous imports are \$60 billion, MPM = 0.1, MPS = 0.2, MPT = 0.1, and the income level is \$450 billion, total imports are
    a. \$45 billion.
    b. \$105 billion.
    c. \$135 billion.
    d. \$150 billion.
    e. none of the above

11. In an open system with government, the equilibrium condition is
    a. $I + TX + TR + G = S + I + M$.
    b. $S - TX = I + G + X - M$.
    c. $M - X = I - G - S - TX - TR$.
    d. $S + TX - TR + M = I + G + X$.
    e. $S = I + G + X + TX + TR$.

12. If autonomous imports = 15, the MPM = 0.03, and income is \$500 billion, the value of imports is
    a. \$15 billion.
    b. \$20 billion.
    c. \$25 billion.
    d. \$30 billion.
    e. \$35 billion.

13. Assume the MPC = 0.55, MPI = 0.14, MPT= 0.2, and MPM = 0.08. The numerical value of the effective multiplier for an open economy is
    a. 1.5.
    b. 2.0.
    c. 2.5.
    d. 3.0.
    e. 3.5.

14. Assume the MPC = 0.55, MPT= 0.2, MPI = 0.14, MPM = 0.08, C_0 = \$138 billion, T_0 = \$20 billion, I_0 = \$100 billion, G = \$220 billion, X = \$100 billion, and M_0 = \$47 billion. The equilibrium level of income is about
    a. \$800 billion.
    b. \$900 billion.
    c. \$1,000 billion.
    d. \$1,100 billion.
    e. \$1,200 billion.

15. In the question immediately above, the equilibrium level of consumption is (about)
    a. $440 billion.
    b. $550 billion.
    c. $567 billion.
    d. $743 billion.
    e. $765 billion.

16. If we use the data in question 14 above, the equilibrium level of investment is (about)
    a. $100 billion.
    b. $240 billion.
    c. $265 billion.
    d. $285 billion.

17. If we use the data in question 14 above, the level of imports at equilibrium is (about)
    a. $47 billion.
    b. $80 billion.
    c. $90 billion.
    d. $112 billion.
    e. $127 billion.

18. If we use the data in question 14 above, the balance of trade at equilibrium is (about)
    a. -$27 billion.
    b. -$12 billion.
    c. $17 billion.
    d. $35 billion.
    e. none of the above

19. A devaluation of the American dollar will tend to
    a. expand U.S. exports and reduce its imports.
    b. reduce U.S. exports and imports.
    c. increase U.S. exports and imports.
    d. reduce U.S. exports and increase its imports.
    e. have no effect on American foreign trade.

20. A revaluation of the Japanese yen will tend to
    a. increase U.S. exports to Japan.
    b. reduce inflationary pressures in Japan.
    c. increase inflationary pressures in the United States.
    d. improve the U.S. balance of payments.
    e. all of the above

21. If prices in the rest of the world increase faster than prices in the United States,
    a. the U.S. dollar will strengthen in international markets.
    b. foreign currencies will increase in value relative to the U.S. dollar.
    c. the U.S. balance of payments will get worse.
    d. the United States could offset the effect of this on the balance of trade by using restrictive fiscal and monetary policies.

22. The net international investment position of the United States in 1987 was
    a. positive at about $140 billion.
    b. positive at about $90 billion.
    c. negative at about $110 billion.
    d. negative at well over $250 billion.

23. The country with the largest international debt is
    a. Brazil.
    b. Mexico.
    c. United States.
    d. Argentina.
    e. Poland.

24. The huge U.S. balance-of-trade deficit is due to, among other things,
    a. the large surplus in the U.S. federal budget.
    b. lower interest rates in the United States than in other nations.
    c. slower growth of the United States compared to Japan and West Germany.
    d. massive "unfair import competition" by Japan, Hong Kong, and South Korea.
    e. a major deterioration in the international competitive position of the United States.

25. Some people argue that a fixed exchange rate system
    a. is conducive to stability in the international economy because everyone knows the price they must pay for foreign exchange.
    b. would remove the need for the International Monetary Fund.
    c. would eliminate the international debt problem.
    d. solve the U.S. balance-of-trade problem.

26. At the G-5 meeting in September 1985 and the G-7 meeting in February 1987, the participants agreed to
    a. an eighth round of GATT multilateral trade negotiations.
    b. intervene in the foreign exchange market to strengthen the yen and weaken the U.S. dollar.
    c. ultimately implement a system of fixed exchange rates.
    d. form a free-trade area so as to promote a more rapid growth of trade.

27. One reason for the U.S. balance-of-trade deficit is the combination of U.S. fiscal and monetary policies that
    a. lowered interest rates in the United States compared to other nations.
    b. caused the United States to slow down and stagnate compared to other nations.
    c. resulted in U.S. real interest rates exceeding those of other nations.
    d. caused serious inflation in the United States.

28. Suppose the Japanese yen appreciates relative to the U.S. dollar. This means that
    a. official intervention would be undertaken to return the exchange rate to its former pegged position.
    b. each dollar could now buy more yen than before.
    c. each dollar could now buy fewer yen than before.
    d. an immediate adjustment back to the original exchange rate should be expected as a result of third-currency arbitrage.

29. Assume exchange rates are freely fluctuating. In this case we know that
    a. the economy must be in equilibrium at full employment.
    b. at the income level that gives *IS-LM* equilibrium, the *BP* will be in equilibrium.
    c. there is no relationship between *BP* equilibrium and domestic economic conditions.
    d. an expansionary monetary policy will throw the *BP* into a deficit position.
    e. none of the above

30. Which of the following will not shift the *BP* curve?
    a. a change in domestic interest rates
    b. a devaluation of the U.S. dollar
    c. a change in foreign interest rates
    d. an increase in U.S. inflation relative to foreign inflation
    e. none of the above

31. The *BP* curve is positively sloped because the interest rate
    a. must decline to raise the net capital outflow enough to offset the deterioration of net exports as the income level rises.
    b. must rise to reduce investment and thereby the income level.
    c. will not change unless the U.S. dollar is devaluated.
    d. must rise to reduce the net capital outflow or increase the net capital inflow enough to offset the deterioration of net exports as the income level rises.
    e. none of the above

32. In a fixed exchange-rate system
    a. the *BP* curve must run through the *IS-LM* intersection point.
    b. a balance-of-payments surplus tends to shift the *LM* curve outward.
    c. a balance-of-payments deficit tends to shift the *LM* curve outward.
    d. there is no relationship between the balance of payments and the *LM* curve.
    e. none of the above

33. In the *IS-LM-BP* model, the *BP* curve shows all of those combinations of the interest rate and income where
    a. exports of goods and services equal imports of goods and services.
    b. the balance on current account equals the change in international reserves.
    c. the balance on capital transactions equals the change in international reserves.
    d. the balance of current account equals the net capital outflow.
    e. none of the above

DETERMINANTS OF THE INTEREST RATE (KEYNESIAN MODEL)

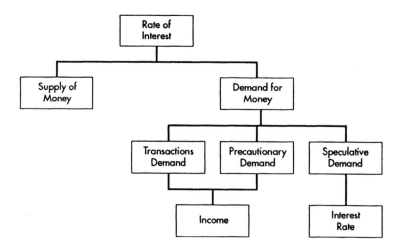

Key Concepts

Fisherian version of quantity theory
Cambridge (Marshallian) version of
    quantity theory
Demand for money (L)
Transactions demand for money (L_t)
Precautionary demand for money (L_p)
Speculative demand for money (L_a)
Monetary equilibrium
Liquidity trap
Keynesians vs. monetarists
"Monetarist counter-revolution"
Friedman's modern quantity theory
Chicago school of thought
Demand for money function (of
    monetarists

Liquidity-preference theory of interest
Keynes's "normal" interest rate
Tobin's explanation of demand for
    money
Baumol's inventory approach to the
    demand for money
Interest elasticity of demand for
    money
Income elasticity of demand for money
Ratio of nonhuman to human wealth
Opportunity cost of holding money
Friedman-Meiselman study
Money illusion
Stagflation

Problems and Essays

1. Explain and illustrate the role of money in classical theory. Be sure to distinguish between the Fisherian and Cambridge versions of the quantity theory of money.

2. *Transactions Demand for Money* (L_t). It is now apparent that there are three motives (or demands) for holding money—the transactions, precautionary, and speculative demands. Since the precautionary demand is least important and further since it is largely determined by the same variables as the transactions demand, we shall adopt the commonly used approach of lumping the precautionary demand with the transactions demand and referring to them as the transactions demand for money. Hence subsequent analysis refers only to transactions and speculative demands for money.

   This problem and the two that follow are designed to assist you in understanding and analyzing the transactions demand (problem 2), speculative demand (problem 3), and total demand (problem 4) for money. A later problem (problem 6) shows how the demand for money can be combined with the money supply (problem 5) to find the equilibrium rate of interest.

   The data below give the transactions demand for money at different income levels. Plot this hypothetical data in Figure 11-1 and connect all the points to obtain the transactions demand for money curve. All data are in billions of dollars. [Note that $L_t = f(Y)$. If we use linear relationships, this may be specified as $L_t = jY$, where j tells us the average (and marginal) amount of income that society wants to hold in cash balances. That is, $j = L_t/Y = \Delta L_t/\Delta Y$.]

Income	L_t
$ 0	$ 0
200	60
400	120
600	180
800	240
1,000	300
1,200	360
1,400	420
1,600	480
1,800	540
2,000	600

FIGURE 11–1

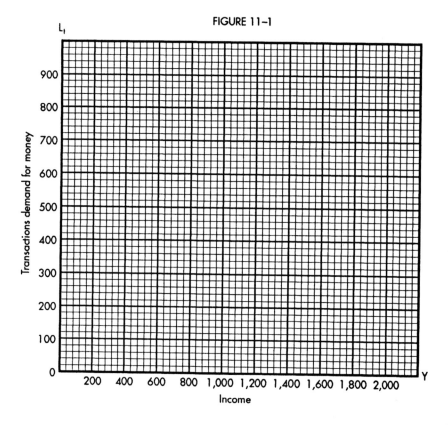

a. Why is the transactions demand for money curve positively sloped?

b. To which function of money does the transactions demand for money relate?

c. What is the ratio of the transactions demand for money to income, L_t/Y? Is this also the slope of the transaction curve?

d. What does the demand for money curve in Figure 11–1 imply with respect to the transactions velocity of money? Would this normally be true? What is the transactions velocity assumed above?

e. What are the major determinants of the transactions demand curve; that is, what factors determine its slope?

f. For later analysis it is necessary that the transactions demand for money be related to the interest rate, even though the interest rate is not listed as a major determinant of the transactions demand. Assume the transactions demand is completely interest inelastic—that is, the transactions demand for money is completely independent of the interest rate—and plot the data given above in Figure 11–2 below. Note that in this figure the transactions demand for money is on the horizontal axis

FIGURE 11–2

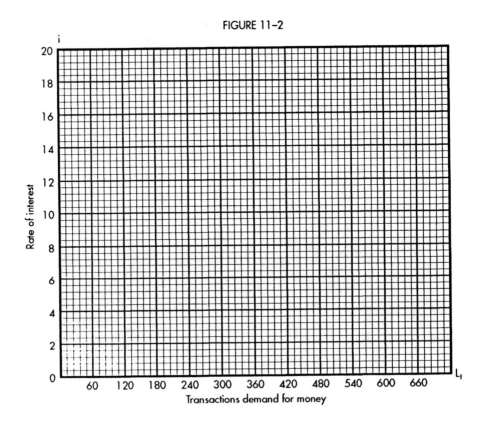

and the rate of interest on the vertical axis. [Hint: For each L_t given above, there is one and only one income level. Thus, when you know L_t, you also know Y and vice versa. Recognizing this, take different income levels, find L_t, and then plot this amount of transactions demand at every interest rate—since it is here assumed that L_t is not responsive to the interest rate. For example, at $Y = 200$ we know $L_t = 60$. When $Y = 200$ and $i = 2$, L_t is 60; when $Y = 200$ and $i = 4$, $L_t = 60$; when $Y = 200$ and $i = 6$, $L_t = 60$, and so forth. This gives a vertical straight line at $L_t = 60$. Now plot the transactions demand at the various interest rates when $Y = 400$, $Y = 600$, $Y = 800$, and so forth.]

(1) Is it possible that the curves just constructed might bend toward the vertical axis at very high interest rates?

3. *The Speculative Demand for Money* (L$_a$). The following hypothetical data pertain to the speculative demand for money or, what is the same thing, the demand for money to hold as an asset. Plot the information in Figure 11–3 to obtain the speculative demand for money curve.

FIGURE 11–3

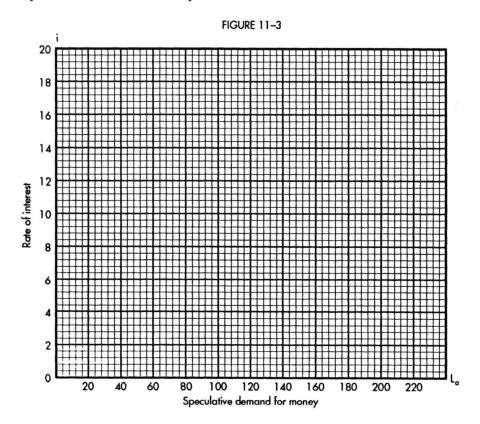

Speculative demand for money

Interest Rate (%) i	Speculative Demand for Money L_a
18%	$ 0
13	20
9	40
6	60
4	80
3	100 or more

Data for the demand for money are in billions of dollars. [Note: If we assume linearity in the mathematical relationships as we have done throughout and will continue to do—even though many of the graphical relationships are portrayed in nonlinear form—the speculative demand for money function [which has $L_a = F(i)$] can be specified as $L_a = L_0 - li$. In this equation L_0 is the speculative demand for money when the interest rate is zero and l is the marginal responsiveness of the asset demand to the interest rate, that is, $l = \Delta l_a / \Delta i$.]

a. If the interest rate declines from 9 to 6 percent, the demand for money to hold as an asset increases. What happens to the price of bonds when this occurs?

b. *Why the speculative demand curve is negatively sloped.* There are many reasons why the speculative demand curve is negatively sloped; that is, why the amount of money desired as an asset increases as the rate of interest falls. Consider three of them. One explanation is based on the opportunity cost of holding money, a second is the one given by Keynes, and a third is the one presented by James Tobin.

   (1) Explain how the opportunity cost of holding money causes the speculative demand curve to be negatively sloped.

   (2) How did Keynes explain the inverse relationship between the interest rate and the demand for money to hold as an asset? [See J. M. Keynes, *The*

General Theory of Employment, Interest and Money (New York: Harcourt, Brace & World, 1936), Ch. 15, pp. 199–204.]

(3) How realistic is Keynes' explanation of the inverse relationship between the interest rate and the asset money demand? What criticism(s) can be levied against his explanation?

(4) James Tobin explains the negative slope of the speculative demand for money curve in a manner different from Keynes' explanation. What is Tobin's explanation? (For Tobin's view see J. M. Tobin, "Liquidity Preference as Behavior Toward Risk," Review of Economic Studies, February 1958, pp. 65–86.)

c. Identify the liquidity trap. What does the liquidity trap imply about the effectiveness of monetary policy?

d. What factors may cause the speculative demand for money curve to shift up or down?

4. The Total Demand for Money (L). Using the information on the transactions demand for money given in problem 2 and the speculative demand for money given in problem 3, as well as the data in the following table, complete the questions below relative to the total demand for money. Data for income and the demand for money are in billions of dollars. [Note: Since $L_t = jY$ and $L_a = L_0 - li$,

it follows that the total demand for money L, which equals $L_t + L_a$, is given by the equation $L = jY + L_0 - li$. The general functional form of the total demand for money is $L = f(Y, i)$.]

i	L_a	L when Y=$200	L when Y=$400	L when Y=$600	L when Y=$800	L when Y=$1,000	L when Y=$1,200	L when Y=$1,400	L when Y=$1,600
18%	$ 0	($)	($)	($)	($)	($)	($)	($)	($)
13	20	($)	($)	($)	($)	($)	($)	($)	($)
9	40	($)	($)	($)	($)	($)	($)	($)	($)
6	60	($)	($)	($)	($)	($)	($)	($)	($)
4	80	($)	($)	($)	($)	($)	($)	($)	($)
3	100+	($)	($)	($)	($)	($)	($)	($)	($)

a. Complete the above columns for the total demand for money, L, when income is $200, $400, $600, $800, $1,000, $1,200, $1,400, and $1,600.

b. Plot the data for the total demand for money when the income level is $200 billion in Figure 11–4. Note where the curve commences. What explains the curvature of the total demand for money?

c. Now use the additional data to construct the curves for the total demand for money when the income level is $400, $800, $1,000, $1,200, and $1,400 billion, respectively, in Figure 11–4. Explain in your own words what happens to the total demand for money curve as the income level rises. Note that the curve keeps shifting, or rotating, to the right by the amount of the increase in transactions demand for money (in this case by $60 billion each time).

FIGURE 11–4

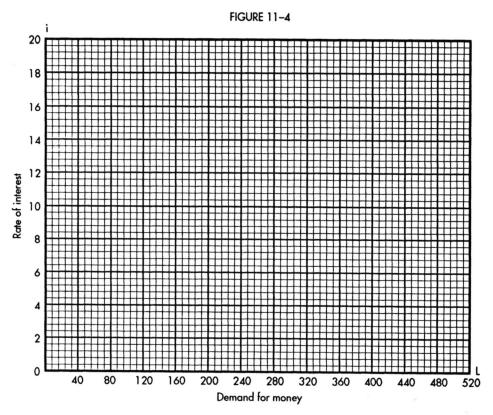

Demand for money

5. *Supply of Money*. In much of the subsequent analysis the money supply will be assumed to be completely determined by the monetary authorities—that is, by the Federal Reserve. As such, the money supply will not be functionally related to any variable, the equation for the money supply being

$$M^s = M^o$$

where M^s is the money supply and M^o signifies that the money supply is autonomously determined—M^o is a specific number which is assumed to be determined by the Fed.

That this assumption about the money supply might not be totally realistic under all circumstances can be seen by considering the nature of the components of the money supply. Certainly the coins and paper money are determined by the Federal Reserve (and Treasury to some extent) and therefore can "safely" be assumed to be autonomous. Demand deposits, however, are created by banks and other financial institutions, not the Federal Reserve. True, the Federal Reserve controls the maximum potential amount of demand deposits via its open market operations and reserve requirement regulations. The point to note, however, is that the money supply is dependent (at least partly) on the actions of banks and other financial institutions whenever the existing supply of money is less than the maximum potential supply that can be created based on the level of free reserves.

In recent years several hypotheses have been put forth to the effect that the money supply is functionally related to the rate of interest; that is,

$$M^s = f(i)$$

although this is a simplified statement of the relationship. The standard argument is that as the interest rate increases, the money supply increases.

Explain fully why the money supply may be positively related to the rate of interest. To get started, recall that banks are business organizations and, like any private business firm, are profit-oriented. [Note: Even if the money supply is positively related to the interest rate, it does not alter the analysis and conclusions based on the assumption that the money supply is completely autonomous. It is recommended that the student consult, Ronald L. Teigen, "The Demand for and Supply of Money," in *Readings in Money, National Income, and Stabilization Policy,* ed. Warren L. Smith and Ronald L. Teigen, rev. ed. (Homewood, Ill.: Richard D. Irwin, 1970), pp. 91ff.]

6. *Keynes' Liquidity Preference Theory of Interest.* There are at least four major theories of interest rate determination; that is, four theories explaining the forces that determine the level of the interest rate. They are the classical theory of interest, the Keynesian liquidity preference theory of interest, the loanable funds theory of interest, and the *IS-LM* theory of interest rate determination. It might be noted that the *IS-LM* theory of interest, which is far more inclusive than any of the others, is not always referred to as a theory of interest since it covers income determination as well. Nonetheless, it is a major theory explaining the interest rate level and must be recognized as such.

This particular problem deals with the liquidity preference theory of interest as put forth by Keynes. Stated simply and concisely, the theory argues that the rate of interest is determined by the demand for money as an asset and the supply of money available for asset purposes, the equilibrium interest rate being that given by the intersection of these two functions. Figure 11–5 contains a quadrant showing the speculative demand for money curve (used in the prior problems). The interest rate is measured on the vertical axis, while both the asset demand for money L_a and asset supply of money M_a^0 are measured on the horizontal axis. Use this diagram as a basis for answering the questions below.

Interest Rate i	Speculative Demand for Money L_a
18%	$ 0
13	20
9	40
6	60
4	80
3	100 or more

FIGURE 11-5

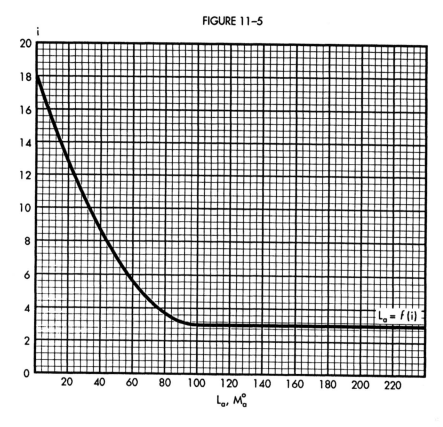

a. Assume that the amount of money available to hold as an asset is $60 billion. Construct a curve in the above figure showing the asset supply of money at $60 billion and assuming that the money supply for asset purposes is *completely* interest inelastic.

(1) What is the equilibrium rate of interest?

(2) How is equilibrium restored if the interest rate is temporarily at 9 percent?

(3) How is equilibrium restored if the interest rate is temporarily at 4 percent?

(4) Is it "realistic" to portray the money supply as being completely autonomous; that is, completely interest inelastic? Why or why not?

b. The equilibrium rate of interest will change if there is an alteration in the asset supply of money or if the speculative demand for money curve shifts up or down.

(1) Assume the interest rate is at equilibrium with the asset money supply (M_a^0) equal to $60 billion. Now let the asset supply of money increase to $80 billion. What is the process whereby equilibrium is restored, and what is the new equilibrium rate of interest?

(2) Start over with the initial M_a^0 being $60 billion and the L_a curve being as represented. Now assume that there is an overall change in the climate of opinion so that all individuals think the normal rate is higher than previously. This will shift the L_a curve upward. What is the process whereby equilibrium is restored? Is it realistic to assume shifts in the L_a curve?

c. Given the speculative demand for money curve, what determines the extent to which a given change in the money supply for asset purposes will alter the interest rate?

d. How realistic is the liquidity trap?

e. Keynes criticized the classical economists for not recognizing that income is an important determinant of their interest theory. This same criticism can be made of Keynes' interest theory. Changes in the income level will alter the interest rate. Explain what happens to the rate of interest, *ceteris paribus,* when the level of income rises. [Note: The relationships involved in this question will become more apparent subsequently when we derive and analyze equilibrium for the economy as a whole.]

7. Compare Keynesian income-expenditure theory and the monetarist quantity theory with respect to each of the following:

a. The key variable that causes changes in aggregate expenditures.

b. Whether the theory is formulated in terms of money income or real income.

c. Whether the theory is short-run or long-run in nature.

d. The theoretical framework by which changes in the money supply affect economic activity. That is, compare the structure of the monetarist and Keynesian theory.

8. Explain fully Friedman's theory of the demand for money. In the process be sure to cover the following aspects of the demand for money function.

    a. The stability of the demand for money function. Is it stable or unstable compared to the Keynesian consumption and investment functions?

    b. The interest elasticity of the demand for money.

    c. Whether the demand for money is a demand for real money balances or nominal money balances.

    d. Justify the inclusion of each variable in the demand for money equation and tell whether it is positively or negatively related to the demand for money (that is, whether the partial derivative is positive or negative).

9. Explain in your own words what is meant by the "monetarist position." Be sure to give the policy implications of the monetarist position.

    a. Compare the policy implications of the monetarist position with the policy implications of the Keynesian theory.

    b. Is there strong empirical support for the monetarist position? Explain.

10. Explain and evaluate the role of monetarism in the Reagan administration. Why was it difficult to apply monetarism and supply-side economics at the same time?

A Self-Test

Completion Questions

1. There is (*an inverse, a direct*) relationship between the interest rate and the demand for money as a store of value; the (*lower, higher*) the interest rate, the greater the quantity of money demanded.

2. For equilibrium in the money market, the _____ must

    equal the _____ .

3. At equilibrium, if the total money supply is $300 billion and the transactions demanded for money—assume precautionary balances are included with the transactions balances—is $275 billion, the speculative demand for money must

    be _____ .

4. The total demand for money is a function of both the _____

    and the _____ .

5. As the level of income increases, the total demand for money curve—as a function of the interest rate—rotates to the (*right, left*) by the amount of

    _____ . When the income level falls, the total demand curve for money rotates to the (*right, left*).

6. If the income level is $315 billion and the ratio of L_t to Y is 1/3, the amount of

    money desired for transactions purposes is _____ .

7. Money is neutral in (*classical, Keynesian*) theory but not in (*classical, Keynesian*) theory.

8. Whereas the classical economists emphasized the _____ function of money, Keynes placed primary emphasis on the

   _____ function.

9. Keynes said there are three major motives for holding money: they are the

   _____, _____, and _____ motives. The

   _____ motive is a function of income and the _____ motive is a function of the interest rate.

10. The _____ demand for money is related primarily to the store-of-value

    function, whereas the _____demand is more closely related to the medium-of-exchange function of money.

11. The higher the interest rate, the more costly it is to hold (*money, bonds*) and consequently the smaller the amount of (*money, bonds*) held for (*transactions, speculative*) purposes.

12. Keynes' explanation of the negatively-sloped speculative demand for money curve is based on the premise that individuals and business executives have some

    idea about what constitutes a "normal" interest rate. If the _____ interest rate is above the normal rate, most people expect the most likely movement of the interest rate to be (*downward, upward*). Should this occur, they will realize a (*capital loss, capital gain*) on bonds—as well as interest income. Thus people will (*buy, sell*) bonds and hold less of their assets in the form of (*bonds, money*). On the other hand, if the current (*rate of interest, level of investment, amount of consumption*) is below the normal rate, most people think the interest rate will (*rise, fall*). If their expectations materialize, they will realize a (*capital loss, capital gain*). Accordingly, in this case, they will prefer to hold (*bonds, cash*). Note that the greater the deviation of the current rate above or below the normal rate, the more certain are the expectations that there will be a reversal; and of course, the more the switch from cash to bonds or bonds to cash.

13. A criticism of Keynes' explanation of the negative slope of the asset demand for money curve is that it implies people will hold (*no, all, part*) cash or (*no, all, part*) bonds, and this (*is, is not*) consistent with reality.

14. James Tobin's explanation of the inverse relationship between the interest rate

    and speculative demand for money is based on the _____ involved in holding bonds. The larger the portion of total assets held in the form of bonds, the (*less, greater*) the risk. To get people to undertake more risk, hold (*less, more*) bonds, it is necessary to pay them a higher _____.

True and False

_____ 1. The transactions demand for money reflects the medium-of-exchange function of money.

_____ 2. The store-of-value function of money is reflected in the speculative demand for money.

_____ 3. In expressing the transactions demand for money as a function of income, a straight line implies that the transaction velocity of money is constant.

_____ 4. The transactions demand for money will decline as income advances.

_____ 5. The lower the interest rate, the more money will be demanded for speculative purposes.

_____ 6. The precautionary motive relates to holding money balances to meet unforeseen contingencies.

_____ 7. Individuals and business firms desire money balances for speculative purposes because of uncertainty about future interest rates and prices.

_____ 8. If the transactions demand for money becomes interest elastic at high interest rates, we can take it for granted that the velocity of money increases.

_____ 9. Individuals may hold money, which yields little or no interest return, in preference to bonds because of uncertainty about future bond prices.

_____ 10. The basic explanation of the inverse relationship between interest rates and the asset demand for money hinges upon the expectations of individuals and business firms about the future value of liquid nonmoney assets.

_____ 11. Changes in expectations, depending upon their type, may cause movements along the liquidity-preference function or shifts of the entire function.

_____ 12. An asset is liquid if it can be sold in a very short period of time with little loss of value.

_____ 13. Money is the most liquid of all assets.

_____ 14. The classical quantity theory of money postulates that the level of production varies directly in proportion to changes in the money supply.

_____ 15. The Marshallian (or Cambridge) version of the quantity theory is merely an alternative formulation of the Keynesian theory of money.

_____ 16. The transaction demand for money function can be specified as $L_t = jY$.

_____ 17. Specifying the speculative demand for money function as $L_a = L_o - li$ implies that if the interest rate is zero, the demand for money for speculative purposes is also zero.

_____ 18. The total demand for money may be specified as $L = jY + L_o - li$ if we assume linearity.

_____ 19. If the money supply is a function of the interest rate, the monetary authorities have no control over its level.

_____ 20. All economists agree that the Keynesian theory of interest is the only true explanation of interest.

_____ 21. According to Keynes, the interest rate is determined by the relationship between the speculative demand for money and the total money supply.

_____ 22. If the demand for money function is infinitely elastic, monetary policy would not be effective in fighting inflation.

_____ 23. The income elasticity of demand for real money balances ranges from about 0.5 to 1.0.

_____ 24. Keynes made an error in stating that the demand for speculative balances is a function of the interest rate according to James Tobin's explanation of the speculative demand for money.

_____ 25. If the transactions demand for money increases, we can conclude that the rate of interest will also rise if all other things are held constant.

_____ 26. According to Keynes' explanation of the speculative demand for money, if the current market interest rate is above the normal rate of interest, society will want to hold the wealth solely in the form of money.

_____ 27. Keynes treated the money supply as exogenous when explaining how changes in the money supply affect aggregate demand.

_____ 28. Post Keynesians view money as an exogenous variable.

_____ 29. During the 1980s and early 1990s, the U.S. economy behaved as would be predicted by monetarism.

_____ 30. Monetarism helped pave the way for the new classical economics.

_____ 31. The new classical economics challenges every fundamental part of Keynesian thought.

_____ 32. The main social problem giving rise to the Keynesian revolution was inflation, while that giving rise to the monetarist counter-revolution was unemployment.

_____ 33. Keynesians and monetarists alike argue that output and changes in output can be explained in terms of the level and changes in the level of expenditures.

_____ 34. Monetarists argue that the modern quantity theory explains changes in both prices and money income, whereas the Keynesian income-expenditures theory explains only changes in real output.

_____ 35. The monetarists argue that changes in the money supply are the basic explanation of changes in real output, money income, and the price level.

_____ 36. Friedman argues that monetary influences have a smaller impact on economic activity than fiscal influences.

_____ 37. The demand for money function is the basic relationship for understanding how money affects the economy in the Keynesian model, while the consumption function is the basic relationship for this purpose in the monetarist theory.

_____ 38. Friedman's theory of the demand for money concentrates on how much money people want to hold, whereas Keynes' theory emphasizes the motives for holding money.

_____ 39. Friedman's definition of money is broader than the standard Keynesian definition.

_____ 40. Compared to the monetarists, Keynesians have a strong faith in the underlying stability of the economy.

_____ 41. In Friedman's analysis money yields utility like any other commodity.

_____ 42. Monetarists attribute the bulk of economic instability to government policy.

Multiple Choice

1. The liquidity trap implies that
   a. the money supply is infinite.
   b. monetary policy will be ineffective in this range.
   c. any increase in the demand for money for transactions purposes will reduce the rate of interest.
   d. the speculative demand for money is limited.

2. If the rate of interest increases, those people holding bonds will
   a. experience a capital gain on the bonds.
   b. experience a capital loss on the bonds.
   c. not be able to find a buyer should they decide to sell.
   d. experience neither a capital gain nor a capital loss.
   e. all of the above

3. In addition to the standard-of-value function of money, the classical economists emphasized the
   a. store-of-value function.
   b. standard-of-deferred payments function.
   c. the medium-of-exchange function.
   d. none of the above

4. To say that an asset is highly liquid means that
   a. people think it will maintain its value over time.
   b. it can readily be converted into cash with little loss of value.
   c. it can readily be converted into money but only at a sizable loss.
   d. it can be converted into money with little loss but only after an extended period of time.

5. The Cambridge version of the quantity theory
   a. emphasizes the supply of money.
   b. emphasizes the demand for money to hold.
   c. is entirely different from the Fisherian velocity approach.
   d. denies the full employment conclusion of classical analysis.
   e. none of the above

6. Which one of the following will probably have little effect on the transactions demand for money in most cases?
   a. the stage of development of credit institutions
   b. the frequency of receipts—that is, the pay period
   c. the rate of interest
   d. the rapidity with which money can be transported from one place to another

7. The total demand for money is a function of
   a. the interest rate and income.
   b. income only.
   c. interest rates only.
   d. liquidity preference.

8. The transactions demand for money has been described by which of the following functional relationships?
   a. $L_t = f(p)$
   b. $L_t = f(Y)$
   c. $L_t = f(p)$
   d. $L_t = L_t^\circ$
   e. $L_t = f(M^s)$

9. Which of the following specifications of the speculative demand for money was used throughout this chapter (linear form)?
   a. $L_a = -li$
   b. $L_a = L_o + li$
   c. $L_a = L_o (li)$
   d. $L_a = L_o - li$

10. If the supply of money is a function of the interest rate, then we would expect that
    a. the monetary authorities would have no power to control the money supply.
    b. an increase in interest rates would increase the money supply.
    c. a reduction in interest rates would increase the supply of money in circulation.
    d. investment would also be functionally related to the interest rate.

11. The total demand for money may be written in equation form as
    a. $L = f(Y,i) = jY + L_o - li$
    b. $L = f(Y) = L_o + jY$
    c. $L = f(i) = jY$
    d. $L = f(Y,i) = L_o + li + jY$

12. If the interest rate increases, the demand for money will
    a. not be affected.
    b. be affected but not possible to say if it will increase or decrease.

    c. decrease.
    d. increase.

13. Keynes' assumption that society views interest rates as having some *normal* level is
    a. a crucial part of his explanation of the speculative demand for money.
    b. tied up with the argument that the transactions demand for money is a function of income.
    c. not only unrealistic but also unnecessary because bond prices and interest rates are positively correlated.
    d. actually a part of the classical theory of employment and not Keynesian at all.

14. If the money supply is at least partly responsive to interest rates, we would expect that
    a. as the interest rate increases, the money supply would fall slowly.
    b. the demand for money would not be responsive to the interest rate.
    c. the money supply would expand mildly as the interest rate increases.
    d. the conclusions of the Keynesian theory of interest would be reversed.

15. Tobin's explanation of the negative slope of the speculative demand for money curve is based on the idea that
    a. as the current interest rate falls, people will buy bonds in the hope that they will realize a capital gain.
    b. people will take on more risk only if adequately compensated for doing so.
    c. there is an opportunity cost to holding money.
    d. there is a normal level of interest rates.

16. Of the three theories of interest so far discussed, the one which is *least likely* to be a true explanation of the rate of interest is
    a. Keynes' liquidity preference theory of interest.
    b. the loanable funds theory of interest.
    c. the classical theory of interest.
    d. all are equally good explanations.

17. The more interest elastic the demand for money function, the
    a. more effective monetary policy will be.
    b. more interest rates will fluctuate.
    c. less effective monetary policy will be in controlling inflation.
    d. greater will be the money supply.

18. If people expect interest rates to increase, they
    a. would sell bonds and hold money.
    b. buy bonds and reduce their money holdings.
    c. expect bond prices to remain unchanged.
    d. expect bond prices to rise.

19. Keynes argued that the interest rate is determined by the speculative demand for money and the money supply available for speculative purposes. A more complete liquidity preference theory would argue that the interest rate is determined by
    a. the total demand for money and total money supply.
    b. the speculative demand for money and transactions money supply.

c. the transactions demand for money and asset money supply.

d. the supply of loanable funds and total money supply.

20. Keynes denied the classical view that interest is the reward for saving and maintained that interest is

a. a useful concept but not measurable.

b. the reward for abstaining from consumption.

c. the reward for parting with liquidity.

d. indeterminate.

e. the reward for creating liquidity.

21. If the price of bonds is above the equilibrium price, one can conclude that

a. the money available to hold exceeds the demand for money as an asset.

b. the demand for money to hold as an asset exceeds the money available for this purpose.

c. interest rates will tend to fall.

d. bondholders will experience a capital gain.

e. none of the above

22. If the price of bonds is *below* the equilibrium bond price, we may conclude that

a. bondholders will realize a capital loss.

b. the interest rate will increase.

c. the demand for money exceeds the money supply.

d. the money supply is greater than the demand for money.

e. none of the above

23. The *interest elasticity* of the demand for money balances is between

a. −0.15 and −0.4 in the short run and −0.4 and −0.9 in the long run.

b. −0.5 and −0.9 in the short run and −0.9 and −1.5 in the long run.

c. −0.9 and −1.5 in the short run and −0.15 and −0.4 in the long run.

d. −2.0 and −4.0 for the post-World War II era.

24. The *income elasticity* of demand for money ranges from

a. 0.1 to 0.3.

b. 0.3 to 0.5.

c. 0.5 to 1.0.

d. 1.0 to 1.5.

e. 1.5 to 1.8.

25. The money multiplier can be expressed as

a. the reciprocal of the MPS.

b. the ratio of the M1 money supply to the M3 money supply.

c. the ratio of the changes in the M1 money supply to changes in the M2 money supply.

d. the ratio of the change in the money supply to the change in the monetary base.

e. none of the above

26. The money multiplier is approximately

a. 1.5

b. 2.0

c. 2.5

d. 3.0

e. 3.5

27. Economists swayed to the classical theory and monetarist theory of the Milton Friedman school
    a. view money as exogenous.
    b. view money as endogenous.
    c. think money is unimportant.
    d. none of the above
    e. all of the above

28. Post Keynesians argue that
    a. increases in the money supply result in increases in spending.
    b. there is no relationship between the amount of money in circulation and the demand for goods and services.
    c. it is increases in spending decisions by society that increase the money supply and not vice versa.
    d. the Federal Reserve cannot control the amount of reserves in the system.

29. Which one of the following relationships did not challenge the validity of monetarism during the 1981–1993 period?
    a. There was not a strong relation between the annual rate of growth of the money supply and the annual rate of growth of the nominal GDP.
    b. There was not a strong correlation between the rate of change of the money supply and rate of change of prices.
    c. The velocity of money (GDP/M1) was not stable and instead was very unstable.
    d. none of the above

30. Professor Milton Friedman argues that
    a. money has no effect on the economy and thus should be increased at a constant rate.
    b. money plays a less important role in controlling inflation than fiscal policy.
    c. money is the single most important determinant of changes in money income.
    d. too much attention is given to the possible disrupting effects of changes in the money supply.

31. The St. Louis Federal Reserve Bank supports
    a. the monetarist analysis.
    b. the Keynesian analysis.
    c. neither the monetarist nor the Keynesian analysis.

32. According to monetarists,
    a. money is the key variable causing changes in expenditures.
    b. changes in expenditures are primarily due to changes in autonomous consumption, investment, taxes, and so forth.
    c. real output will always be at the full-employment level.
    d. the basic way to reduce inflation is to set into motion a chain of events that reduces total output.

33. Friedman argues that the demand for money function
    a. is highly unstable and hence cannot be relied upon for policy purposes.

  b. is much more stable than the consumption function.

  c. always shifts to offset shifts in the consumption function.

  d. does not play a very important role in his theory.

34. Keynesians argue that the interest elasticity of the demand for money is
  a. low, while monetarists say it is high.
  b. unimportant in terms of affecting economic activity, while monetarists disagree.
  c. relatively high, while monetarists argue it is low.
  d. not a factor in determining if velocity is stable or unstable.

35. Monetarists argue that the demand for money
  a. is a demand for nominal money balances.
  b. is a demand for real money balances.
  c. is highly unstable.
  d. is highly interest sensitive.

36. In which of the following ways does Friedman's theory of the demand for money differ from Keynesian theory?
  a. Friedman concentrates on how much money people want to hold, while Keynes concentrates on the motives for holding money.
  b. Friedman uses a different definition of money than used in Keynesian analysis.
  c. Friedman's demand for money is less interest elastic than Keynes'.
  d. all of the above

37. Friedman argues that all the following are determinants of the demand for money *except*
  a. the distribution of income among different classes in society.
  b. the wealth of society.
  c. tastes and preferences of those holding wealth.
  d. the cost of holding money.

38. Modern monetarists maintain that instability in the economy
  a. arises from ineffective fiscal policies.
  b. arises from fluctuations in economic activity abroad.
  c. is due to Federal Reserve mismanagement of the money supply.
  d. is due to refunding the national debt.

39. Monetarists argue that
  a. there is a long and variable lag between changes in the money supply and its effect on the economy.
  b. the investment function is the major component of aggregate demand.
  c. the velocity of money is more unstable than the Keynesian multiplier.
  d. complete reliance on monetary policy is all that is needed to assure full employment without inflation.

40. Friedman argues that the monetary authorities should adopt a rule increasing the
  a. money supply at a rate of 3 to 5 percent a year.
  b. money supply at a rate equal to the rate of inflation.
  c. demand for money by 3 to 5 percent per year.
  d. rate of return on government bonds by 2 percent per year.

41. In Friedman's theory of the demand for money, the demand for nominal money balances will increase if there is
   a. a reduction in permanent income.
   b. an increase in the ratio of nonhuman wealth to human wealth.
   c. an increase in the rate of return on bonds and equities.
   d. an increase in the general price level.

42. Friedman argues that there is an inverse relationship between the demand for nominal money balances and
   a. the expected rate of change in the price level.
   b. the general price level.
   c. permanent income.
   d. none of the above

43. Which of the following is *not* a variable in Friedman's demand for money equation?
   a. tastes and preferences of the wealth-holding units
   b. the supply of money created by the Federal Reserve
   c. the general price level
   d. the rate of return on bonds and equities
   e. permanent income
   f. the ratio of nonhuman wealth to human wealth

44. For Friedman's demand for money function to be stable, it is necessary that
   a. the velocity of money be stable.
   b. the interest rate change very little.
   c. the income level grow by a constant amount per year.
   d. the money supply remain relatively constant.

45. Unlike Keynesians, Friedman believes that
   a. monetary policy is extremely effective.
   b. the interest elasticity of the demand for money is low.
   c. the expenditures multiplier is very stable.
   d. fiscal policy has been highly stabilizing since World War II.

46. Which of the following is *not* a major issue between the monetarists and Keynesians?
   a. whether changes in the money supply or changes in autonomous expenditures are more important in explaining short-run changes in output, employment, and the price level
   b. whether velocity is stable and thereby the demand for money function is also stable
   c. the responsiveness of the demand for money to interest rates
   d. the degree to which the Fed can control the money supply
   e. whether changes in the money supply will alter interest rates

47. Beryl Sprinkel, Chairman of the Council of Economic Advisers under President Reagan
   a. was a Keynesian.
   b. was a supply-sider.
   c. was a monetarist.
   d. none of the above

CHAPTER 12

Output, Employment, and Inflation

Key Concepts

Inflation (definition)
Keynes' "true inflation"
Creeping inflation
Suppressed inflation
Hyper-inflation
Demand-pull inflation
Cost-push inflation
Structural inflation
Phillips curve
MAP
TIP

Natural rate hypothesis
Friedman's natural rate of unemployment
Inflation-unemployment trade-off
Kennedy-Johnson wage-price guidelines
Nixon wage-price controls
Inflation "indexed" benefits
"Escalator" clauses in wage contracts
Money illusion
COLAS
Incomes policy
Productivity

Problems and Essays

1. *Demand-Pull Inflation.* Three major types (or theories) of inflation are analyzed
   in this chapter: demand-pull inflation, cost-push inflation, and structural inflation.
   This problem covers demand-pull inflation, which for both analytical and
   historical reasons should be first, problem 2 covers cost-push, and problem 3
   analyzes structural inflation. The demand-pull analysis of this problem is based on
   Figure 12–1. Aggregate demand and aggregate supply are in billions of dollars.

FIGURE 12–1

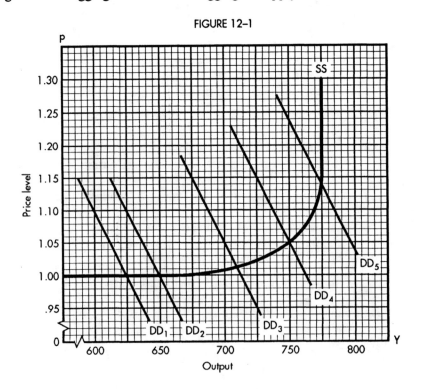

Output

a. Assume aggregate demand increases from DD_1 to DD_2. What is the effect on the general level of prices?

b. Assume aggregate demand increases successively from DD_2 to DD_3 to DD_4 to DD_5. Explain the effect of this change on the level of prices and output.

c. The inflation in this case is caused by increases in aggregate demand and is frequently referred to as demand-pull inflation. Explain in your own words what is meant by demand-pull inflation. Does demand-pull inflation alter the aggregate supply curve?

d. Suppose aggregate demand is at the level represented by DD_5 and the economy experiences a relatively mild recession such that aggregate demand falls back to DD_4. If prices are inflexible in the downward direction, would the price level and output fall to about 1.05 and $750 billion, respectively? Explain.

e. What does this model imply about the relationship between inflation and employment?

f. Does the above model imply that monetary and fiscal policies designed to alter aggregate demand could effectively control demand-pull inflation?

g. Classical economists envisioned, on the basis of their quantity theory of money, all inflation as being of the demand-pull type. In the classical view what was the major cause of inflation?

h. As we discovered in a prior chapter, a modern version of the quantity theory is espoused by members of the so-called Chicago School, the foremost exponent being Milton Friedman. What is the basic cause of inflation according to this modern quantity theory? [The student is urged to consult M. Friedman, "The Quantity Theory of Money—A Restatement," in M. Friedman, ed., *Studies in the Quantity Theory of Money* (Chicago: University of Chicago Press, 1956), pp. 3–21.]

i. What is the basic cause of inflation according to Keynesian theory?

2. *Cost-Push Inflation.* Figure 12–2 portrays an aggregate demand curve and four aggregate supply curves. At any one time only one supply curve is relevant, but by depicting several of them it may be possible to show the general nature of cost-push inflation. Study the diagram carefully.

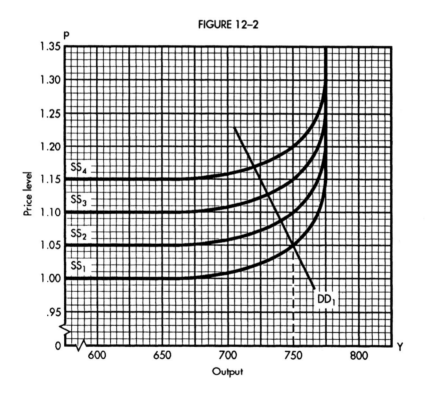

FIGURE 12–2

a. What is the equilibrium output and price level if we assume the relevant curves are SS_1 and DD_1? Is the economy at full employment?

b. Assume rising production costs cause the aggregate supply curve to shift upward from SS_1 to SS_2 to SS_3 to SS_4. Explain how this alters the price level, output level, and volume of employment.

c. What does this model imply about the relationship between cost-push inflation and unemployment? Is this the same conclusion as derived earlier from the model dealing with demand-pull inflation?

d. Does it appear from the above model that cost-push inflation can be effectively combated by changing aggregate demand? Would a policy of changing aggregate demand, through monetary and fiscal measures, to combat cost-push inflation have any effect on employment?

e. If aggregate demand is given as in Figure 12–2 and cost-push inflation ensues, unemployment will increase (according to this model). Assume there is nothing the government can do, or will do, to control the rising costs. Could the increasing unemployment be prevented by monetary and fiscal policies designed to increase aggregate demand? Illustrate your answer in Figure 12–2.

f. What are the basic causes of cost-push inflation?

3. *Structural Inflation.* Figure 12–3 contains aggregate-demand–aggregate-supply diagrams for two different industries (referred to as Industry A and Industry B). The demand and supply curves, price level, and output now refer to industries rather than the whole economy. Assume that initially equilibrium in both industries is given by the intersection of D_1 and S_1 (not DD_1 and SS_1 since these curves are no longer aggregates). In addition, assume that demand shifts from Industry B to Industry A, as indicated in the two diagrams, such that the increase in A is exactly equal to the reduction in B—thus *aggregate* demand does not change.

FIGURE 12–3

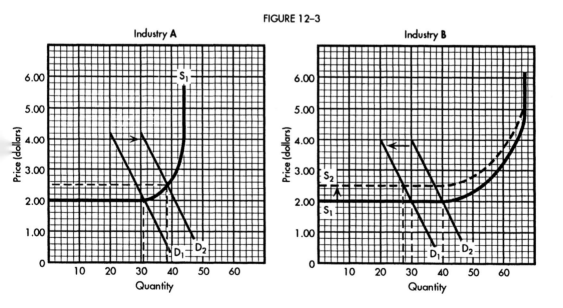

a. What conditions are necessary for structural inflation to occur?

b. Study Figure 12–3. Demand increased in Industry A by exactly the same amount as it declined in Industry B. Given the situation as depicted, did prices fall by the same amount in Industry B as they increased in A? What is the net effect of this shift in demand on the price level?

c. What effect did the shift in demand have on output and employment?

d. Suppose the higher wages and prices in Industry A cause organized labor to press for and obtain wage increases in Industry B—perhaps because of higher living costs. The increase in per unit costs in Industry B shifts the supply curve up to S_2. How does this affect output and employment?

  e. Evaluate the effectiveness of general monetary and fiscal policy in controlling structural inflation.

4. *Interdependence of Aggregate Demand and Aggregate Supply.* Since World War II, prices and costs in the United States have been more responsive to an increase in demand than to a reduction in demand. Prices and costs have risen when the economy is expanding but not fallen, or at least not fallen as much as they increased, with a contraction of economic activity. Explain and illustrate (in Figure 12–4 below) this downward inflexibility of prices (or, as some refer to it, the "nonreversibility of the price-output relationship") using aggregate demand and supply curves related to the price level.

FIGURE 12–4

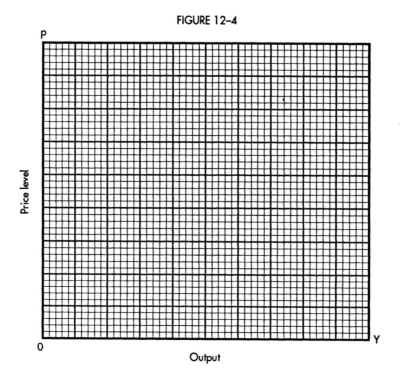

5. *The Phillips Curve.* Since the pioneering work of A. W. Phillips (1958), in which he set forth the relationship embodied in the Phillips curve, much theoretical and empirical attention has focused on the relationship between unemployment and money wages (and, correcting for productivity changes, inflation). This problem points out the nature and significance of the Phillips curve. The hypothetical Phillips curve (*PC*) illustrated in Figure 12–5 is the starting point for the questions below. The unemployment rate (*U*) is measured on the horizontal axis and the rate of change of money wages ($\Delta w/w$) on the vertical axis.

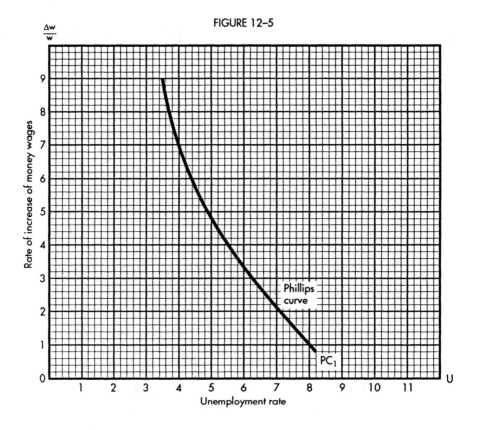

FIGURE 12–5

a. *Define* the Phillips curve.

b. *Trade-off.* What happens to money wages as unemployment declines? For example, let unemployment fall from 5 percent to 4 percent and explain what happens to money wages. Is the change in money wages always the same amount for each percentage decrease in the unemployment rate?

c. How would an increase in aggregate demand be reflected in this diagram?

d. Suppose labor productivity increases at 3.5 percent per year. How much inflation would this country experience if the unemployment rate is 5 percent?

e. Let labor productivity continue to increase at 3.5 percent per year. How much additional inflation must this country accept if the unemployment rate is reduced from 5 to 4 percent?

f. Given this Phillips curve, what is the lowest unemployment rate consistent with price level stability; that is, with no increase in prices at all?

g. Suppose full employment is defined to be 4 percent unemployment. If labor productivity increases at 3.5 percent, what rate of inflation would occur at the full-employment output level?

h. Assume unemployment is 4 percent. Now let there be an increase in labor productivity from 3.5 to 4 percent. What impact does this have on the rate of inflation?

i. What happens to the percentage increase in money wages at each unemployment level if the Phillips curve shifts inward toward the origin?

j. Figure 12–6 contains two Phillips curves showing the relationship between unemployment and inflation. Each curve was derived from a corresponding Phillips curve (not shown) relating the percentage change in money wages to the unemployment rate by subtracting the increase in productivity from the money-wage Phillips curve at each level of the unemployment rate. [For example, assume productivity is increasing at a 3.2 percent annual rate. If at the unemployment rate of 7 percent the percentage increase in money wages is 5.5 percent, the inflation rate would be roughly 2.3 percent (= 5.5 percent – 3.2 percent). If the increase in money wages is 8.2 percent at $U = 5$ percent on the money-wage Phillips curve, the inflation rate would be roughly 5 percent (= 8.2 percent – 3.2 percent). Using this approach we can derive all the point on the Phillips curve relating the unemployment rate to inflation.] Which Phillips curve is more representative of the U.S. situation at the present time?

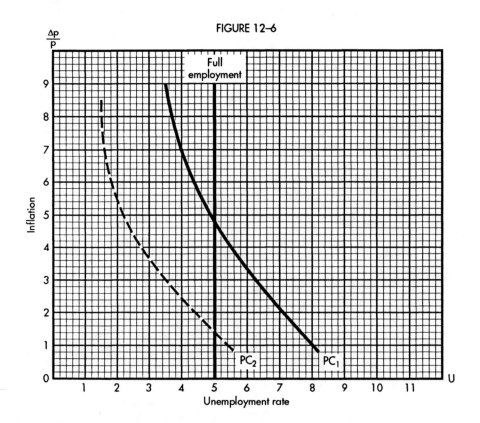

FIGURE 12–6

k. Suppose the Phillips curve is PC_1 and the inflation rate is higher than what is socially acceptable. Could the government rely on monetary and fiscal policy to reduce inflation without significantly increasing unemployment?

l. It is apparent that the country would be better off—in terms of the PC_1 inflation-unemployment trade-off curve—if the Phillips curve were closer to the origin. What measures could the government take to shift the curve inward toward the origin?

m. During the 1970s and 1980s, unlike the 1960s, the existence and/or stability of the Phillips curve came into question. Explain why this happened and its implications for government stabilization policy.

6. *Monetarist (Friedman) Criticism of the Phillips Curve—The Acceleration Thesis.* Although widely used, the Phillips curve has come under sharp attack by the monetarists (led by Friedman). These economists, with some exceptions, deny that there is any long-run permanent trade-off between money wages and unemployment, although they recognize the possibility of a short-run transitory relationship. Explain Friedman's criticism of the Phillips curve and indicate its significance for public policy.

7. *Incomes Policies.* Review briefly the post World War II history of U.S. wage-price controls including the Kennedy-Johnson guidelines of 1962–66, Nixon's wage-price control program (phases I–IV) of 1971–74, and Carter's voluntary program of 1978–79. Consider such points as:

a. the purpose of such controls.

b. guidelines for wage and price increases.

c. the machinery of the control program—how it was carried out.

d. the effectiveness of the controls in achieving their objectives.

e. the pros and cons of controls.

8. Explain fully the impact of inflation on the distribution of income and wealth. In the process be sure to indicate which groups in society suffer most from inflation.

9. Explain and evaluate the usefulness of a tax-based incomes policy (TIP) for controlling inflation. Be sure to distinguish between a TIP based on the *penalty* principle and one based on the *reward* principle.

10. *Micro Foundations of Aggregate Supply.* The aggregate supply function is a basic part of the Keynesian model. Answer each of the following questions in the order presented.

a. Define aggregate supply.

b. Derive the aggregate supply schedule from the microeconomic analysis of the firm assuming *pure competition*.

c. Derive the aggregate supply schedule from the microeconomic analysis of the firm assuming *imperfect competition*.

d. What determines the slope of the aggregate supply curve?

e. What factors cause shifts of the aggregate supply curve?

11. *The Natural Rate Hypothesis of Market Adjustment.* Assume the Keynesian-classical aggregate supply curve (*AS*) and classical long-run aggregate supply curve (*LRAS*), which is always located at the full-employment level of output, are as given in Figure 12–7. Assume further that the initial equilibrium is at point *A* with the price level at P_1 and income at Y_1.

FIGURE 12–7

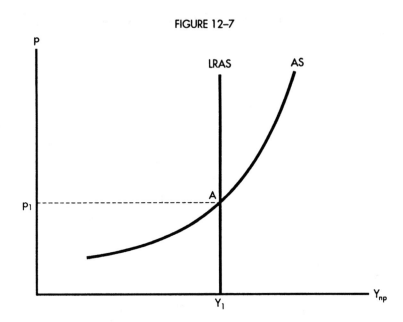

a. Explain and illustrate graphically the *natural rate hypothesis* adjustment process when there is an *increase* in the price level, with a corresponding increase in the money wage, and workers mistakenly believe there has been an increase in the real wage.

b. Now consider the opposite situation. Explain and illustrate graphically the *natural rate hypothesis* adjustment process when there is an equal *decrease* in the price level and the money wage and workers mistakenly believe there has been a decrease in the real wage.

c. What are the implications of the natural rate hypothesis for government policy designed to promote full employment and combat inflation if:

(1) prices and wages are highly flexible and thus adjust rapidly.

(2) prices and wages are flexible upward but sticky downward.

d. Does the U.S. historical record imply that prices and wages are highly flexible in both directions? Explain.

A Self-Test

Completion Questions

1. If price controls prevent prices from rising when inflationary forces are building up in the economy, we have (*creeping, hyper-, suppressed, true*) inflation.

2. The Phillips curve postulates (*a direct, an inverse*) relationship between the rate of unemployment and the _____.

3. The Phillips curve is basically related to (*demand-pull, cost-push*) inflation.

4. If the cause of inflation is "too much money chasing too few goods," we can conclude that the economy is experiencing (*structural, demand-pull, cost-push*) inflation; if it is wage increases that exceed productivity gains, the inflation is of the (*demand-pull, cost-push*) type.

5. Whereas the Kennedy-Johnson wage-price guidelines of 1962–66 were (*mandatory, voluntary*), the Nixon wage and price controls of 1971–74 were (*mandatory, voluntary*).

6. Suppose money wages increase at 6 percent per year and labor productivity increases at 3 percent. Inflation will be about _____ percent.

7. According to the Phillips curve, inflation (*may, may not*) occur simultaneously with an increase in unemployment.

8. In order for structural inflation to occur, there must be

   a. _____.

   b. _____.

   c. _____.

9. An increase in aggregate demand will cause a leftward (*shift of, movement along*) the Phillips curve. Wage and price controls are intended to cause a (*shift of, movement along*) the Phillips curve.

True and False

_____ 1. The Keynesian theory of the price level relates directly to microanalysis even though the idea of a general price level is a macro concept.

_____ 2. Like the classical economists, Keynes emphasized the medium-of-exchange function of money.

_____ 3. Keynes agreed with the classical economists that a change in the money supply would *directly* increase or decrease aggregate demand.

_____ 4. Marginal cost refers to the increase in total cost associated with producing one more, or one less, unit of output.

_____ 5. Higher wage demands may be a factor causing the general level of prices to rise before maximum capacity is attained.

_____ 6. To say that prices and costs are "inflexible" implies that they are responsive to changes in aggregate demand.

_____ 7. Oligopolistic market structures and labor's resistance to wage reductions are primary factors in making prices inflexible downward.

_____ 8. The Phillips curve shows how the balance of payments will deteriorate when inflation in the United States exceeds inflation in other nations.

_____ 9. From 1947 to 1978 American prices, as measured by the GDP price deflators, increased by roughly 175 percent.

_____ 10. Suppressed inflation implies that, should price controls be removed, prices would surge upward.

_____ 11. The demand-pull hypothesis of inflation implies that prices are pulled up by administered prices of oligopolistic firms.

_____ 12. Money policy is more effective in combating demand-pull inflation than in combating cost-push inflation.

_____ 13. All inflation prior to World War II was of the cost-push type.

_____ 14. Cost-push inflation implies that there can be inflation even if there is no excess demand.

_____ 15. Cost-push inflation implies that pure competition exists in the economy.

_____ 16. Inflation of the cost-push type is explained mainly by administered prices and excessive wage demands.

_____ 17. Monetary and fiscal policies are not very effective tools for fighting inflation that originates on the cost side.

_____ 18. If inflation is caused by cost-push forces, restrictive monetary policy aimed at controlling the inflation may cause a reduction in output and employment.

_____ 19. The structural inflation thesis implies that certain sectors may be experiencing falling demand for their products, and yet there may be inflation as long as the demand for some products is expanding.

_____ 20. For inflation to continue for a long period of time, there must be an increase in the money supply, regardless of which type of inflation is occurring.

_____ 21. Following the dropping of the World War II price controls, American inflation dropped sharply to less than 1 percent per year until 1949.

_____ 22. Historical data for the United States show a close correlation between the money supply and the price level. It also shows a close correlation between the money supply and output.

_____ 23. Friedman denies that there is a trade-off between unemployment and money wages over the long run.

_____ 24. If money wages increase by 6 percent per year, then prices must increase by at least 6 percent per year.

_____ 25. The Phillips curve shows that the unemployment rate cannot be affected by monetary and fiscal policy.

_____ 26. The Phillips curve shows that there is a trade-off between unemployment and inflation.

_____ 27. During phase II of Nixon's wage-price controls the guidelines were wage increases of 5.5 percent and price increases of 2.5 percent.

_____ 28. In _The General Theory_, Keynes ignored supply and dealt only with aggregate demand.

_____ 29. Measured by the GDP deflator, there has been no price deflation in any years since 1940.

_____ 30. The major problem associated with moving from the firm's supply curve to the economy's supply curve is that the firm's supply curve is in terms of one price and one product, whereas the economy's supply is in terms of an average price level and total output.

_____ 31. Keynes did not accept the classical view that firms normally operate under conditions of decreasing returns.

_____ 32. Prior to 1940 the main cause of inflation was war.

_____ 33. Keynes' theory of inflation starts with a change in the money supply, not a change in fiscal policy.

Multiple Choice

1. According to classical theory, inflation is primarily the result of
   a. aggregate demand exceeding aggregate supply.
   b. a sharply rising velocity of money.
   c. too much money in circulation.
   d. excessive union wage demand combined with administered prices.
   e. none of the above

2. When money no longer serves as a store of value due to price conditions in the economy, there is
   a. true inflation.
   b. creeping inflation.
   c. hyper-inflation.
   d. suppressed inflation.
   e. none of the above

3. The 1973–80 inflation in the American economy is explained best by the
   a. demand-pull hypothesis.
   b. cost-push hypothesis.
   c. structural hypothesis.
   d. combination of these three hypotheses.

4. The structural inflation hypothesis indicates that inflation is due mainly to
   a. changes in the structure of demand combined with inflexible wages and prices.
   b. excessive demand which pulls up prices.
   c. rising production costs.
   d. monopoly power of big business.

5. Modern price level theory implies that
   a. inflation is a matter of too much money following too few goods.
   b. the money supply is not a significant factor in inflation.
   c. increases in the money supply are the secondary results of changes in other factors which are the main cause of inflation.
   d. changes in the money supply are the cause of inflation.

6. The classical theory of inflation indicates that
   a. changes in the money supply are the basic cause of an inflationary process.
   b. increases in the money supply are secondary results of changes in other factors which are the major causes of inflation.
   c. the money supply is not a significant factor in inflation.
   d. inflation is due to administered prices of big business.

7. General monetary and fiscal measures
   a. are of little use in controlling structural inflation.
   b. will effectively control structural inflation.
   c. are highly effective in controlling cost-push inflation.
   d. will not be effective in controlling demand-pull inflation.
   e. none of the above

8. In considering the relationship between wage rates and employment, the classical economists did *not* assume
   a. the demand for labor was inversely related to the real wage.
   b. a change in aggregate money demand would result from a change in money wages.
   c. a direct link between money wages and prices.
   d. none of the above

9. The Phillips curve suggests that
   a. there is some level of unemployment that will keep the increase in money wages at a noninflationary rate.
   b. there is no inconsistency between a falling rate of unemployment and a falling rate of increase in money-wage rates.
   c. the productivity of labor has no bearing on the rate of increase in the price level.
   d. the relationship between wage increases, productivity, and unemployment is of only minor significance when considering the degree of inflation.
   e. none of the above

10. Prices, measured in terms of the GDP price deflators, increased in all the post-World War II recessions *except*
    a. 1948–49.
    b. 1953–54.
    c. 1957–58.
    d. 1960–61.
    e. 1969–70.
    f. 1973–75.
    g. 1980.
    h. 1981–82.
    i. 1990–91.

11. Between 1947 and 1991 prices in the United States, measured by the wholesale price index, increased about
    a. 100 percent.
    b. 200 percent.
    c. 300 percent.
    d. 400 percent.
    e. 500 percent.

12. Had President Nixon's wage-price controls been successful,
    a. there would have been suppressed inflation during the time they were in effect.
    b. the United States would not have been able to export as much as otherwise.
    c. it would have been necessary to expand the money supply at a faster rate.
    d. the "energy crisis" would never have happened.

13. If the Phillips curve relationship is accepted, then
    a. monetary and fiscal policies oriented to reducing unemployment will also reduce inflation.
    b. if there is no zone of socially acceptable combinations of inflation and unemployment, government policy must be designed to shift the curve inward.
    c. there cannot be any cost-push inflation.
    d. attempts by the government to improve the balance of payments will increase the rate of unemployment.

14. Friedman criticizes the Phillips curve by contending that
    a. the Phillips curve relationship exists only in the long run.
    b. the Phillips curve is highly stable and does not shift in and out over time.
    c. attempts to reduce unemployment by increasing the price level will lower interest rates.
    d. attempts to lower the unemployment rate by increasing the price level will merely accelerate the pace of inflation, while having no effect on the long-term natural rate of unemployment.

15. The accelerationist thesis argues that a rise in the price level will *not* permanently lower the rate of unemployment below the natural rate of unemployment because
    a. money wages cannot rise in the long run, whereas the price level can.
    b. first, the real wage cannot change significantly from inflation alone and, second, wage earners will bargain for money wages that take anticipated inflation into account.
    c. workers will continually suffer from the money illusion regardless of how rapidly price increases over time.
    d. the rising price level will reduce real aggregate demand and thereby increase the output level associated with full employment.

16. Friedman argues that the only way the unemployment rate can be permanently reduced is
    a. by structural changes that lower the natural rate of unemployment.
    b. by expansionary monetary and fiscal policies.
    c. by wage and price controls that prevent inflation.
    d. by the government setting up make-work projects.

17. The basic principle underlying the Kennedy-Johnson guideposts is that to be noninflationary,
    a. wage increases should not exceed the rate of inflation.
    b. wage increases should be no greater than the average annual increase in productivity for the economy as a whole.
    c. unemployment rates should be 5 percent or greater in all industries.
    d. wage increases in each industry should be equal to the increase in productivity in that industry.

18. There can be no doubt that the Nixon wage-price controls in effect during the years 1971–74
    a. reduced the rate of inflation below what it otherwise would have been.
    b. resulted in no inequities.
    c. has little effect on resource allocation since they did not foster scarcities in any sectors of the economy.
    d. none of the above

19. The Full Employment and Balanced Growth Act of 1978 made it a national goal to reduce inflation to no more than
    a. 1 percent annually within 5 years from passage of the act.
    b. 2 percent annually within 3 years from passage of the act.
    c. 3 percent annually within 5 years from passage of the act.

d. 4 percent annually within 3 years from passage of the act.

e. 5 percent annually within 3 years from passage of the act.

20. Between 1980 and 1985, the average annual rate of money wage increase was about
    a. 4 percent.
    b. 5 percent.
    c. 6 percent.
    d. 7 percent.
    e. 8 percent.

21. Indexing the personal income tax was designed to
    a. eliminate bracket creep.
    b. provide more government tax revenue.
    c. permit an increase in government expenditures.
    d. redistribute real income.
    e. none of the above

22. The Reagan administration's 1981 5–10–10 tax cut (proposed initially as a 10-10-10 cut) was presented to the Congress and public as a
    a. Keynesian policy to increase aggregate demand.
    b. supply-side measure to increase aggregate demand.
    c. monetarist measure to stimulate the economy.
    d. supply-side measure to increase productivity and production.

23. Measured by the CPI, the rate of inflation in 1994 was about
    a. 5.0 percent.
    b. 4.2 percent.
    c. 3.5 percent.
    d. 2.7 percent.

24. In *The General Theory*, Keynes concentrated on aggregate demand because
    a. in the short run it is aggregate demand that drives the economy.
    b. at the time he was writing this book the problem was not supply but insufficient demand.
    c. none of the above.
    d. both *a* and *b*.

25. During the 1980s, U.S. manufacturing productivity increased at an average annual rate of about
    a. 2.0 percent.
    b. 3.0 percent.
    c. 4.0 percent.
    d. 4.5 percent.
    e. 5.5 percent.

26. A major reason for the rapid U.S. inflation during the 1970s was
    a. OPEC I and OPEC II.
    b. highly restrictive monetary policy.
    c. moderately tight fiscal policy.
    d. a sharp appreciation of the U.S. dollar.

27. The micro foundation of Keynes' aggregate supply
    a. assumes firms seek to maximize profits.
    b. is developed in terms of expected values.
    c. develops the aggregate supply schedule from a series of aggregate supply prices.
    d. expresses profits and proceeds in nominal terms.
    e. all of the above

28. Considering the period 1750–1987, it is apparent that
    a. before 1940 wars were the major cause of inflation.
    b. historically inflation has not been the norm.
    c. prices have gone down, as well as up, for long time periods.
    d. all of the above

29. The major causes of the drop in inflation from 1981 to 1986 are
    a. the recession of 1981–82.
    b. appreciation of the U.S. dollar.
    c. falling crude-oil prices.
    d. all of the above.
    e. none of the above

30. The problem with the standard version of the Phillips curve and the monetarists' accelerationist critique is that they do not take into account
    a. money wage rate changes and employment.
    b. monetary and fiscal policy.
    c. factors that influence demand.
    d. expected inflation and the bargaining strength of workers.
    e. all of the above

31. During the time period 1975–79 and 1980–85, the rates of money wage increase on an average annual basis were
    a. 3.1 and 5.1 percent, respectively.
    b. 5.1 and 6.8 percent, respectively.
    c. 6.8 and 7.9 percent, respectively.
    d. 7.9 and 6.0 percent, respectively.
    e. 6.0 and 7.5 percent, respectively.

32. The average annual unemployment rate during 1980–85 was roughly
    a. 8.0 percent.
    b. 9.0 percent.
    c. 7.0 percent.
    d. 6.0 percent.
    e. 5.0 percent.

33. Between 1980 and 1985, the annual rate of
    a. inflation increased.
    b. money wage increase slowed from about 9 to 3 percent.
    c. unemployment increased.
    d. interest rates increased.
    e. none of the above

34. The real value of the average weekly wage of American workers
    a. was about 10 percent higher in 1994 than in 1973.
    b. was about 20 percent higher in 1994 than in 1973.
    c. was about 10 percent lower in 1994 than in 1973.
    d. was about 20 percent lower in 1994 than in 1973.

35. Paul Ormerod argues that the
    a. Phillips Curve has no validity.
    b. over the years 1960–93, the U.S. has experienced three different Phillips Curves.
    c. Phillips Curve for 1985–93 lies below the Phillips Curve for 1960–70.
    d. Phillips Curve for 1974–84 is almost flat.

CHAPTER 13   **Productivity and Growth**

Key Concepts

Economic growth
Determinants of economic growth
Post-Keynesian theory
Productive capacity
Classical model of economic growth
Static analysis
Dynamic analysis
Average productivity of labor
Capacity-creating effects of investment
Harrod's theory of growth
Domar's theory of growth
Average capital-output ratio
Marginal capital-output ratio
Average productivity of capital
Marginal productivity of capital
Capital-saving technological change
Endogenous Growth Theory

Capital-deepening technological change
Neutral technological change
Social costs of economic growth
Potential social average productivity
of investment
Dual nature of investment
Domar's required rate of growth
"Forward looking" aspect of Domar's
analysis
"Backward looking" aspect of Harrod's
analysis
Accelerator
Warranted rate of growth
Actual rate of growth
Natural rate of growth
Productivity crisis
Convergence hypothesis

Problems and Essays

1. A major objective of all countries, whether developed or developing, has been that
of optimum economic growth. Discuss economic growth with respect to each of
the following:

   a. Meaning of economic growth.

   b. Measurement of economic growth.

   c. Determinants (sources) of economic growth.

d. Benefits and costs (private and social)—and thus desirability—of economic growth.

e. The growth record of the United States during the post-World War II period.

f. The U.S. productivity crisis.

2. "Government expenditures should be limited to those that are absolutely necessary because the more the government spends, the more private citizens must reduce their consumption." Do you agree with this assertion? If so, why? If not, why? What bearing does economic growth have on your answer?

3. Explain how infrastructure investment may affect the rate of economic growth?

4. *Classical Theory of Economic Growth.* For both historical reasons and because of renewed current interest, it is desirable to have a general understanding of the classical model of economic growth, a model developed largely by David Ricardo and J. S. Mill but which owes much to other classical economists as well.

a. What are the basic propositions on which the classical model rests?

b. What is the conclusion of the classical model and how did the classical economists reach this conclusion?

c. The classical economists did not incorporate technological progress in their model. What happens to the conclusion when this defect is corrected?

5. *Domar's Theory of Economic Growth—Algebraic Formulation.* Domar's model is based on a two-sector economy in which aggregate demand is composed of consumption and investment; it excludes government and the foreign sector. The symbols utilized below are defined as follows:

$$\Delta Y_c = \text{change in productive capacity}$$
$$\Delta Y_d = \text{change in aggregate demand}$$
$$I = \text{net investment per income period}$$
$$(\text{sigma}) \ \sigma = \text{potential social average productivity of investment (API)}$$
$$(\text{alpha}) \ \alpha = \text{marginal (and average) propensity to save}$$

a. Complete the following equations to derive Domar's required rate of income growth. The change in productive capacity is given by:

(1) $\Delta Y_c =$ _____.

The change in aggregate demand is equal to:

(2) $\Delta Y_d =$ _____.   (Note: As the price level is assumed constant, this expression also represents the increase in actual output.)

The equilibrium rate of growth, or "fundamental equation," is the one which causes aggregate demand (and thus actual output) to increase by an amount equal to the increase in productive capacity; that is, such that $\Delta Y_c = \Delta Y_d$ in each income period. The equilibrium rate is:

(3) _____.

Equation (3) can be solved to obtain the required rate of growth of net investment. Multiply both sides by a:

(4) _____.

Divide both sides by I:

(5) _____.   (The required rate of growth of net investment. This rate insures that actual potential output increases by the same amount in each period.)

b. The rate of growth of income and output, $\Delta Y/Y$, must equal the rate of growth of investment, $\Delta I/I$; the growth rates of both output and investment must equal $\alpha\sigma$. Prove this statement by completing the following equations. In equilibrium, capacity and aggregate demand must grow at the same rate. Thus:

(1) $\Delta Y_c = \Delta Y_d$
The change in capacity equals:
(2) $\Delta Y_c = $ _____ .
Therefore, in equilibrium the change in demand must equal:
(3) $\Delta Y_d = $ _____ .
In equilibrium, investment equals:
(4) $I = $ _____ .
Substitute (4) into (3):
(5) $\Delta Y_d = $ _____ .
Divide through by Y:
(6) $\dfrac{\Delta Y}{Y} = $ _____ .   (The above statement is verified.)

c. Explain the dual role played by investment in Domar's theory of growth. What paradox does this imply about investment?

d. If α is 0.15 and σ is 0.35, what is the rate of income growth required to maintain full employment over time?

6. *Domar's Theory of Economic Growth—Numerical Illustration.* The three following numerical illustrations of Domar's theory are designed to show both the important relationships and to illustrate what happens to the economy when actual increases in net investment differ from the required rate. The first example assumes that investment increases at the required rate; the second, that investment increases faster than the required rate; and the third, that investment increases at less than the required rate. Study each illustration carefully.

Assume the economy is initially in equilibrium with actual output (aggregate demand) equal to potential output of $200 billion. In addition, assume that $\alpha = 0.20$ and $\sigma = 0.25$; the required growth rate, $\Delta I/I = \Delta Y/Y$, is thus 5 percent. Given these assumptions, the capital stock, productive capacity, aggregate demand, consumption, net investment, and changes in net investment must be initially as indicated in the table below (all figures in billions).

a. *Investment increases at the required rate.* In this example investment is assumed to expand at the equilibrium rate of 5 percent. Note that the capital stock (column 2) must be $800 billion at the beginning of the first year in order for productive capacity to equal $200 billion (as assumed in this example). Aggregate demand (column 4) must also be $200 billion since the economy is assumed to be initially in full capacity equilibrium. Consumption is initially $160 billion, which can be determined by multiplying the marginal propensity to consume $(1 - \alpha)$ times income (since Domar assumes the average and marginal propensities to consume and save are equal, there is no autonomous consumption). Finally, investment must be $40 billion to offset saving of that amount.

(1)	(2)	(3)	(4)	(5)	(6)	(7)
	Capital	Productive	Aggregate		Net	Change in Net
Year	Stock	Capacity	Demand	Consumption	Investment	Investment
	K	$Y_c = \sigma K$	$Y_d = C + I$	$C = (1 - \alpha)Y_d$	$I(= \Delta K)$	ΔI
1	$800.00	$200.00	$200.00	$160.00	$40.00	———
2	840.00	210.00	210.00	168.00	42.00	$2.00
3	( )	( )	( )	( )	( )	( )
4	( )	( )	( )	( )	( )	( )
5	( )	( )	( )	( )	( )	( )

(1) Complete the columns in the above table for K, Y_c, Y_d, C, I, and ΔI. [Note: Start with year 2. The capital stock (column 2) increases to $840 billion because net investment, which equals the change in the capital stock (ΔK), in year 1 is $40 billion (see column 6). Productive capacity (column 3) of year 2 expands to $210 billion; the change in productive capacity equals the product of σI, which is $10 billion. The accretion to aggregate demand (column 4) and consumption (column 5) cannot be determined until the behavior of investment is analyzed. As investment (column 6) is assumed to augment at the required rate of 5 percent, total investment increases to $42 billion (40 plus 5 percent of 40 is 42), and the change in investment (column 7) is 2. It is now a simple matter to find the values for aggregate demand and consumption. The change in aggregate demand (ΔY_d) equals ΔI times $1/\alpha$, the latter expression being the multiplier. Thus aggregate demand enlarges by $10 billion (2 times 5), and total aggregate demand expands to $210 billion (column 4). To find the increase in consumption (column 5) for year 2, multiply the MPC (which is 0.8) times the change in aggregate demand; total consumption expands to $168 billion at the beginning of year 2. Now start over and complete the columns for the remaining years.]

(2) Did aggregate demand and productive capacity expand by the same amount in each year?

(3) What is the basic conclusion, derived from this numerical illustration, about equilibrium and disequilibrium?

b. *Actual investment exceeds the required rate.* In this illustration everything is the same as in the preceding case, except that the actual increase in investment is greater than the required rate of growth. Assume that investment increases at 6 percent per year.

(1) Year	(2) K	(3) Y_c	(4) Y_d	(5) C	(6) I	(7) ΔI
1	$800.00	$200.00	$200.00	$160.00	$40.00	———
2	840.00	210.00	( )	( )	( )	($)
3	( )	( )	( )	( )	( )	( )
4	( )	( )	( )	( )	( )	( )
5	( )	( )	( )	( )	( )	( )

(1) Complete the table for years 2, 3, 4, and 5. (Use the same approach as in the preceding part of this problem.)

(2) Is aggregate demand growing by the same amount as, less than, or more than the increase in productive capacity?

(3) When the actual increase in net investment is greater than the required rate (as in this example), what general conclusion can be stated about the impact on the economic system?

c. Investment increases at less than the required rate. In this case assume the actual increase in investment is 3 percent.

(1) Year	(2) K	(3) Y_c	(4) Y_d	(5) C	(6) I	(7) ΔI
1	$800.00	$200.00	$200.00	$160.00	$40.00	————
2	840.00	210.00	( )	( )	( )	($)
3	( )	( )	( )	( )	( )	( )
4	( )	( )	( )	( )	( )	( )
5	( )	( )	( )	( )	( )	( )

(1) Complete the table for years 2 to 5.

(2) Is aggregate demand growing by the same amount as productive capacity?

(3) In this case investment is growing but at a slower rate than required for equilibrium. What are the implications of this situation for the economic system?

7. *Domar's Theory of Economic Growth—Graphic Representation.* **Figure 13–1** illustrates Domar's growth model graphically. The figure is basically the Keynesian saving-investment diagram, except that the long-run saving function is utilized, with capital-output curves superimposed at the appropriate levels of income. Assume the economy is initially at equilibrium at income Y_1; thus at Y_1 aggregate demand equals productive capacity. Keep in mind that the *I* curves represent net investment only; it is net investment that is relevant to changes in productive capacity.

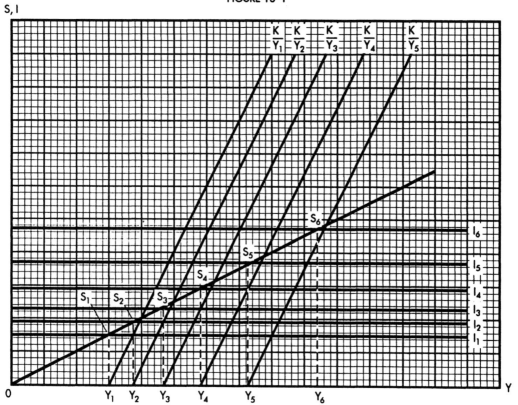

FIGURE 13-1

a. Explain fully the significance of the *K/Y* curve. What is its slope, and how does it relate to the productivity of capital?

b. How will an increase or decrease in the average productivity of capital alter the *K/Y* curve?

c. In year 1, net investment is I_1 and output is Y_1. By how much does net investment of year 1 increase productive capacity?

d. By how much will aggregate demand have to increase to utilize the increase in capacity?

e. If we assume the saving function is stable, an increase in demand must derive from an expansion of investment. Is there any automatic mechanism to insure that investment increases enough to increase aggregate demand by the necessary amount? By what amount must investment expand to have equilibrium at full capacity in year 2?

f. Suppose that investment increases to I_2, so that equilibrium is attained at full-capacity output in year 2. What is the change in capacity, and by how much would aggregate demand and investment have to increase to have full-capacity equilibrium in year 3?

g. What must happen to the absolute increase in investment from one period to the next if equilibrium at full capacity is to be maintained over time (if we assume the K/Y and saving function remain unchanged)?

h. Explain what will happen if net investment does not rise fast enough from one period to the next to realize full-capacity equilibrium; that is, net investment increases at less than the required rate.

i. Study the diagram to see what will happen if the absolute increase in net investment from one period to the next is greater than the required amount.

j. Up to this point it has been assumed that the productivity of capital and saving functions remain constant. If there is a secular fall in the propensity to save, would it still be necessary for net investment to increase over time in order for growth to occur? Is this realistic?

k. If the saving function is constant, what impact would a secular rise in the productivity of capital have on the required rate of growth and the magnitude that investment must grow from one period to the next to realize full-capacity equilibrium? Shift the K/Y curve in the appropriate manner to determine the answer to this question.

8. *Harrod's Theory of Economic Growth.* Like Domar, Harrod developed his growth theory assuming a closed economy with no government. There are many ways in which the two models are similar but there are some basic differences as well.

The symbols used below are defined as follows:

G_w = the warranted rate of growth
C_r = desired capital requirement (or accelerator)
s = the long-run propensity to save (s = APS = MPS, *ex ante* and *ex post*)
G = actual rate of growth
C = actual capital requirement (or accelerator)
G_n = natural rate of growth

a. Harrod distinguishes between three growth rates, each represented by an equation. Complete the equations below for the growth rates indicated:
  The equation for the *warranted* rate of growth is:

(1) _____ = _____.
The equation for the *actual* growth rate is:
(2) _____ = _____.
The equation for the *natural* growth rate is:
(3) _____ = _____.

b. What is the meaning of each growth rate and how does one differ from the other?

c. What is the difference between C_r and C?

d. Prove, by substituting in the appropriate expressions, that both the warranted and actual growth rate can be condensed to:

$$\frac{I}{Y} = \frac{S}{Y}$$

In what manner, then, do the two views of growth differ?

e. Solve the following problems:

(1) If the APS = 0.16 and the desired K/Y ratio is 4, what is the equilibrium growth rate?

(2) If the desired K/Y ratio is 3, what must be the APS to obtain an equilibrium growth rate of 6 percent per year?

(3) If the APS = 0.12 and the growth rate is 4 percent per year, what is the value of the K/Y ratio?

f. Harrod argues that any divergence between the actual and warranted growth rates will have serious consequences for the economy.

(1) What happens when the actual exceeds the warranted growth rate? Illustrate this situation in Figure 13–2.

FIGURE 13–2

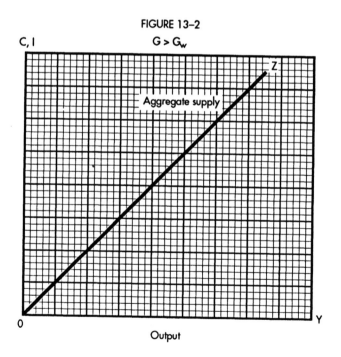

(2) What is the impact on the economic system when the actual rate is less than the warranted growth rate? Illustrate this situation in Figure 13–3.

FIGURE 13–3

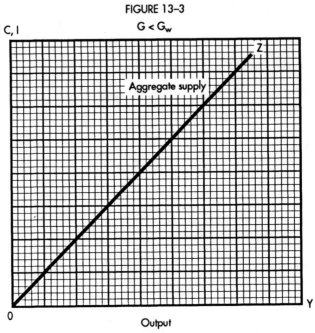

g. The preceding question deals with the divergences between G and G_w. However, the natural rate of growth must be considered as well.

(1) Explain what occurs when the natural exceeds the warranted growth rate.

(2) Explain what changes occur in economic activity when the natural rate falls short of the warranted rate of growth.

h. For equilibrium with full employment of both capital and labor, all three growth rates must be equal. Suppose, however, that the actual growth rate equals the warranted rate but is less than the natural rate of growth. What will happen under these circumstances?

9. Although the approach is different, it can be demonstrated that, for all practical purposes, Domar's required rate of growth is equivalent to Harrod's warranted rate. Complete the following equations to show this formal equivalence.

Domar's required rate of growth is equal to:

(1) $\dfrac{\Delta I}{I} =$ _____.

Harrod's warranted growth rate is:

(2) $G_w =$ _____.

But Harrod's s is basically the same as Domar's α; both equal the APS and MPS. Substitute α for s in the equation (2):

(3) $G_w =$ _____.

It is also apparent that $C_r = 1/\sigma$; C_r is the capital-output ratio (marginal and average) and σ is the productivity of capital (marginal and average). One must be the reciprocal of the other. Substitute $1/\sigma$ in equation (3):

(4) $G_w =$ _____.

Simplify the right side of equation (4) by dividing α by $1/\sigma$:

(5) $G_w =$ _____.

Thus the two growth rates are formally equivalent.

10. Compare and contrast the growth theories of Harrod and Domar with respect to the following points:

a. Similarities.

b. Differences.

c. Implications.

d. Limitations.

e. Merits.

11. Assume the government is concerned with increasing the *actual* rate of growth. Harrod's formula, $G = s/C$, indicates that for a nation to increase its actual growth rate, it must either increase the propensity to save, reduce the K/Y ratio, or both. What measures could a nation employ to (1) increase the saving ratio and (2) to decrease the K/Y ratio?

12. *Neoclassical Growth Theory.* Robert Solow developed a growth theory, based on neoclassical assumptions, that challenged the instability conclusion of the Harrod-Domar model.

a. Explain fully Solow's Neoclassical Growth Model.

b. How does Solow's model differ from the Harrod-Domar model?

c. What is the "convergence hypothesis"?

13. *Endogenous Growth Theory.* A third type of growth theory covered by your text is the Endogenous Growth Theory developed by Paul Romer and Robert Lucas.

a. Explain fully the Endogenous Growth Theory.

b. How does this theory differ from the Harrod-Domar theory?

c. How does this theory differ from the Neoclassical Growth Theory?

A Self-Test

Completion Questions

1. The demand side of Domar's growth theory is (*the same as, different from*) the factors affecting demand in Keynesian income theory.

2. If investment exceeds the required rate, aggregate demand (*exceeds, is less than*) aggregate supply. Producers will (*decrease, increase*) investment in order to (*increase, decrease*) productive capacity. In other words, there is a capital (*surplus, shortage*). But when businessmen (*decrease, increase*) investment, they only cause demand to (*exceed, fall short of*) capacity more in each successive period—the capital (*surplus, shortage*) becomes more and more severe. The result is secular (*deflation, inflation*). The system (*does, does not*) move back to equilibrium as the disequilibrium becomes (*more and more, less and less*) severe.

3. If investment falls short of the required rate, aggregate demand (*exceeds, is less than*) aggregate supply, and producers will (*reduce, increase*) investment more and more in each successive period. In this case secular (*deflation, inflation*) occurs.

4. If the APS = 0.12 and the potential social average productivity of investment is 0.40, the required rate of growth is _____ percent per year.

5. If the APS is 0.12 and the K/Y ratio is 3, the warranted growth rate is _____ percent per year.

6. If the K/Y ratio is 4, the APS must be _____ to obtain an actual growth rate of 7 percent per year.

7. If the APS is 0.20 and the growth rate is 4 percent per year, the equilibrium K/Y ratio is _____.

8. Domar's required rate of growth is equal to the _____ times _____. Harrod's warranted growth rate is equal to _____ divided by _____. Domar's required rate of growth (*is, is not*) basically the same as Harrod's warranted growth rate.

9. Domar and Harrod both assume that the average capital-output ratio (*is, is not*) equal to the marginal capital-output ratio.

10. If the capital-output ratio is 5, the average productivity of capital is _____.

11. In Domar's model, if net investment remains constant from one income period to the next, aggregate demand (*will, will not*) grow and capacity will (*increase, decrease, remain constant*) continually. Investment and income (*must grow, do not have to grow*) for productive capacity to be continually utilized.

12. Both Harrod and Domar are concerned with the necessary conditions under which (ex ante, ex post) saving and investment are (*equal, unequal*) over time. Investment is treated (*the same, differently*) in the two models. Domar looks (*backward, forward*) in that he is concerned with how much income will have to (*increase, decrease*) in the coming income period to (*equal, exceed, fall short of*) the (*increase, decrease*) in productive capacity caused by net investment of the (*last, present, coming*) income period. Harrod looks (*backward, forward*) in that he is concerned with whether income has (*increased, decreased*) sufficiently in the (*past, present, coming*) period to induce enough (*investment, consumption*) expenditures to offset saving in the (*past, present, coming*) income period.

13. Harrod emphasizes (*induced, autonomous*) investment, whereas Domar emphasizes (*induced, autonomous*) investment.

14. Harrod and Domar treat saving (*the same, differently*). Both assume that the average propensity to save (*is, is not*) equal to the marginal propensity to save. This implies that the average propensity to consume is (*equal, not equal*) to the marginal propensity to consume.

15. In Harrod's model both (G_w, $G_w \times C_r$, C_r) and (G, $G \times C$, C) equal the propensity to save—both marginal and average. Therefore, if G exceeds G_w, then C (*exceeds, is less than, is equal to*) C_r; if G is less than G_w, then C (*exceeds, equals, is less than*) C_r.

16. When G exceeds G_w, the actual increase in investment is (*greater, less*) than the intended increase. In other words, aggregate demand is (*greater, less*) than aggregate supply. Output has (*increased, decreased*) but aggregate demand has increased (*faster, slower, by the same amount*). The (*shortage, surplus*) of capital, which results because (*ex post, ex ante*) is less than (*ex post, ex ante*) investment in each successive period, induces business executives to (*increase, decrease*) investment. This (*does, does not*) restore equilibrium because the additional investment (*increases, decreases*) the actual rate of growth so that it (*equals, exceeds*) the warranted rate more and more in each successive income period. Thus the economy will continuously experience stronger and stronger (*equilibrating, inflationary, deflationary*) pressures until something happens to alter the relationship between the actual and warranted growth rates. The (*same, opposite*) occurs when the actual rate of growth is less than the warranted rate.

17. If the natural rate of growth is less than the warranted rate, the actual rate of growth will usually be (*equal to, greater than, less than*) the warranted rate because the natural rate is the (*ceiling, minimum*) rate. The actual rate (*can, cannot*) exceed the natural rate except for very short periods of time.

18. Whereas Harrod's warranted rate of growth represents the full employment of (*labor, capital*), his natural growth rate denotes a condition of full employment of (*labor, capital*). Domar (*did, did not*) make a distinction between full employment of capacity and the full employment of labor.

19. The average annual increase in U.S. non-farm productivity was _____ percent for 1950–59, _____ percent for 1960–69, _____ for 1970–79, and _____ for 1980–89.

True and False

_____ 1. In Domar's theory, only when the change in investment equals the required rate of change is the economic system in equilibrium without inflation or deflation.

_____ 2. Whenever net investment takes place, the level of output must grow in order for the entire productive capacity to be continuously utilized.

_____ 3. Added productive capacity from net investment will be put to use whether aggregate demand increases or not.

_____ 4. Domar's required rate of growth is the rate at which aggregate demand must grow over time to equal increases in productive capacity.

_____ 5. To have equilibrium in Domar's model, the amount of investment in the present period must be less than the saving of the past period.

_____ 6. Domar can be criticized for placing too much emphasis on the accelerator, while Harrod goes to the opposite extreme and places too much emphasis on autonomous investment.

_____ 7. If the actual growth rate exceeds the warranted rate, aggregate supply exceeds aggregate demand.

_____ 8. Harrod's analysis indicates that the actual must equal the warranted rate of growth for the economy to be in equilibrium.

_____ 9. It is not possible for the actual and warranted rates of growth to be equal while the economy is experiencing continual unemployment.

_____ 10. Economic growth is basically concerned with an increase in the economy's productive potential and the extent to which productive capacity is used.

_____ 11. Economic growth is a goal to be achieved in its own right.

_____ 12. In the past 25 years the United States has realized an increase in its real output of about 2.4 percent per year.

_____ 13. The long-run historical rate of growth of the United States is about 3.6 percent.

_____ 14. A question frequently raised today is not whether economic growth is desirable but whether a continuation of growth is possible.

_____ 15. Some social costs of economic growth are pollution, despoliation of the countryside, destruction of wildlife, and the rapid exhaustion of vital natural resources.

_____ 16. Doomsday models of economic growth assert that if drastic changes are not made in production and consumption, there will be a sudden economic collapse.

_____ 17. Classical economists argued that nations could always grow at a rapid rate because of continued technological progress.

_____ 18. Among other things, the classical model of economic growth is based on the idea that profits will always be large enough to justify additional investments.

_____ 19. One way for the U.S. to increase productivity would be to undertake a massive program of infrastructure investment.

Multiple Choice

1. In Domar's theory of economic growth, the increase in capacity is equal to
   a. net investment times the average productivity of investment.
   b. the amount of net investment in any specific income period.
   c. the average propensity to save times net investment.
   d. the reciprocal of the average propensity to save times the change in net investment.
   e. none of the above

2. According to Domar's theory, the change in aggregate demand is given by
   a. net investment times the marginal propensity to save.
   b. net investment of an income period times the average productivity of investment.
   c. the change in net investment times the reciprocal of the marginal propensity to save.
   d. the average productivity of capital times the average propensity to save.

3. A major distinction between the theories of Keynes and Domar is that
   a. Keynes' assumes changes in investment will have a multiplier effect on aggregate demand, while Domar's rejects the multiplier.
   b. Domar's theory fails explicitly to recognize that net investment increases capacity, while Keynes worked capacity changes into his model.
   c. Domar argues that the economy always grows at a full-employment equilibrium rate, whereas Keynes rejected this notion.
   d. Keynes did not consider the impact of net investment on productive capacity, whereas Domar did.
   e. none of the above

4. Recognizing that net investment increases capacity, Domar wants to
   a. determine the rate of income growth that will utilize the increase in capacity over time.
   b. determine the cause of the increase in capacity over time.
   c. determine the rate at which capacity should grow over time.
   d. none of the above

5. It can be argued that a shortcoming of Domar's model is that he
   a. fails to consider the autonomous net investment that increases capacity.
   b. uses an average capital-output ratio that should be disaggregated into a capital-output ratio for each industry.
   c. puts too much emphasis on changes in aggregate demand.
   d. none of the above

6. The dual role of investment in Domar's model is that
   a. investment not only increases capacity but adds to the stock of capital equipment.
   b. investment increases aggregate demand when it increases, and decreases aggregate demand when it decreases.
   c. part of the investment goes to replace capital used up in production, while part of it increases capacity.
   d. all net investment increases capacity, but only increases in investment raise aggregate demand.
   e. none of the above

7. Domar's model implies that
   a. not only must investment increase over time, but it must increase by increasing amounts in order for full employment to be maintained.
   b. if net investment remains constant, neither capacity nor aggregate demand will grow.

    c. there will be no problem of aggregate demand keeping up with productive capacity.

    d. none of the above

8. Which of the following is not emphasized by Domar's model of economic growth?

    a. Capital accumulation is a very important element in the growth process.

    b. An advanced economy must grow to avoid a continually increasing volume of unemployed labor and capital.

    c. The path of growth is a perilous one—a razor's edge.

    d. Equilibrium growth is quite likely to occur automatically.

    e. none of the above

9. Harrod's warranted rate of growth is the rate of advance which

    a. leaves entrepreneurs satisfied that they have made the correct past decisions and are prepared to continue the same rate of advance.

    b. keeps *ex ante* investment equal to *ex ante* saving.

    c. is determined when the marginal propensity to save is divided by the desired capital requirement.

    d. none of the above

    e. all of the above

10. If Harrod's actual rate of growth exceeds the warranted rate,

    a. the economy will move in the direction of stagnation because the actual increase in the capital stock is greater than that desired by entrepreneurs.

    b. the economy will stagnate because the actual increase in the capital stock is less than the increase desired by entrepreneurs.

    c. the economy will experience an inflationary spiral because businessmen desire a greater increase in the capital stock than actually occurred and therefore will increase investments in each successive period.

    d. the economy will experience deflation because business executives desire a smaller increase in the capital stock than occurred and will therefore cut back on investment in each successive period.

11. Harrod's natural rate of growth is that growth rate which

    a. keeps entrepreneurs satisfied that they have made the best decisions and will continue to make similar decisions in the future.

    b. insures that there is no excess capacity.

    c. the economy automatically tends to experience.

    d. is allowed for by population increases and technological advances.

    e. none of the above

12. Over the long run, the maximum possible rate of growth is given by

    a. the warranted growth rate.

    b. the natural growth rate.

    c. the actual growth rate.

    d. none of the above

13. If the annual rate of increase in the labor force is 1.5 percent and the annual rate of increase in productivity of labor is 3 percent, the natural rate of growth is

    a. 1.5 percent.

    b. 3 percent.

c. 4.5 percent.
d. impossible to determine from information given

14. If the actual and warranted growth rates are the same, one can conclude
    a. that the natural rate of growth equals the actual and warranted rates.
    b. that the natural rate must be below the two other rates.
    c. that the natural rate is probably above, if not equal to, the actual and warranted rates.
    d. none of the above

15. If the natural rate of growth exceeds the warranted rate, Harrod argues that the economy will generally experience
    a. inflation because the actual growth rate will exceed the warranted rate most of the time.
    b. inflation because the warranted rate will exceed the actual rate most of the time.
    c. deflation because the actual rate of growth will be inadequate.
    d. deflation because the warranted rate of growth is excessive relative to the actual and natural rates.
    e. none of the above

16. Domar and Harrod differed about which one of the following?
    a. The importance of investment in the growth process.
    b. The use of a Keynesian framework of analysis.
    c. The central problem of growth is to keep intended investment continually equal to a growing volume of planned saving.
    d. The way they look at the investment process.

17. In terms of material well-being, the most meaningful measure of economic growth available is
    a. monetary GDP.
    b. real GDP.
    c. real per capita output.
    d. per capita income in monetary terms.

18. Economic growth may allow the government to increase its expenditures
    a. only if private consumption is reduced.
    b. even though private consumption increases.
    c. only if private consumption remains unchanged.
    d. none of the above

19. Over the past 150 years, U.S. GDP in constant prices increased at an average rate per year of approximately
    a. 3 percent.
    b. 5.5 percent.
    c. 2.5 percent.
    d. 3.5 percent.
    e. 4.5 percent.

20. Over the past 150 years, U.S. per capita GDP in constant prices has increased at an average annual rate of about
    a. 3.5 percent.

    b. 2.7 percent.
    c. 2.0 percent.
    d. 3.8 percent.
    e. 1.7 percent.

21. From 1970 to 1993 the average annual rate of growth of the United States was about
    a. 4.2 percent.
    b. 3.8 percent.
    c. 3.2 percent.
    d. 2.4 percent.

22. According to the classical model of economic growth, a country will ultimately
    a. grow at an increasing rate.
    b. attain a stationary state.
    c. run out of natural resources and hence no longer support life.
    d. make so much pollution that people will not be able to exist.

23. The doomsday models of economic growth conclude that
    a. the country will gradually reach a long-run stationary state.
    b. given no change in production or consumption, the economic system will collapse.
    c. there will be a nuclear war that destroys all life on planet Earth.
    d. the classical growth model is totally without foundation.

24. The doomsday models of economic growth may generally be criticized because
    a. they give insufficient attention to technological progress.
    b. they fail to adequately recognize that new resources appear over time.
    c. they fail to build a price mechanism in the model.
    d. all of the above

25. Which one of the following is not a possible major explanation of the slowdown in U.S. productivity since 1950?
    a. a slowdown in the pace of capital formation
    b. an increase in the percentage of less experienced teenagers and women in the labor force
    c. a shift in the composition of real GDP from goods to services
    d. a decline in research and development expenditures
    e. excessive regulation of business
    f. none of the above

26. The average annual increase in U.S. productivity during 1973–93 was about
    a. 3.0 percent.
    b. 2.0percent.
    c. 1.1 percent.
    d. 0.6 percent.

27. Lester Thurow argues that the decline in American productivity is due to
    a. the decline in the "blue collar" workforce and sharp increase in the "white collar" workforce.
    b. the deterioration in U.S. technology.
    c. a decline in the educational and skill levels of the American workforce.
    d. a dwindling of natural resources.

28. What percentage of the U.S. average annual growth rate was accounted for by rising productivity, as opposed to labor and capital, during the period 1973 to 1992?
    a. 10 percent
    b. 15 percent
    c. 20 percent
    d. 25 percent
    e. 30 percent

29. In every year from 1974 to 1993, the American economy
    a. was at full employment.
    b. grew by at least 3 percent.
    c. produced at a level below its potential output.
    d. experienced inflation of over 5 percent.
    e. experienced rising unemployment.

30. In general, there is a close positive correlation between the growth of worker productivity and
    a. the rate of inflation.
    b. the balance of trade deficit.
    c. the real incomes of workers.
    d. none of the above
    e. all of the above

31. According to the text, the crisis in productivity has been due to
    a. military Keynesianism.
    b. the decline in the nation's stock of non-military public capital.
    c. a slowdown in the rate of growth of equipment per worker.
    d. all of the above
    e. none of the above

32. In order to increase productivity growth, the U.S. must have more and better investment in
    a. capital.
    b. people.
    c. research and development.
    d. all of the above
    e. none of the above

33. Which of the following growth theories posits a razor-edge state of equilibrium?
    a. Neoclassical growth theory
    b. Harrod-Domar growth theory
    c. Endogenous growth theory
    d. none of the above

34. Which of the following growth theories brings technological change, innovation, institutions, international trade, and education into the analysis as endogenous factors of the growth process?
    a. Harrod growth theory
    b. Domar growth theory
    c. Classical growth theory
    d. Endogenous growth theory

CHAPTER 14   Business Cycles and Forecasting

Key Concepts

Business cycles (or fluctuation)
Forecasting
Forecasting error
National Bureau of Economic Research (NBER)
Cyclical upswings vs. cyclical downswings
Recession
Depression
Amplitude of a cycle
Turning point
Conference board
Survey of Current Business

Juglar cycle
Kondratieff cycle
Kitchin cycle
Hicksian constrained business cycle
W. Stanley Jevons' "sunspot theory"
Schumpeter's innovation theory of the cycle
Kalecki's political business cycle
Underconsumption theories of the cycle
Overinvestment theories of the cycle— monetary causes
Overinvestment theories of the cycle— nonmonetary causes

Problems and Essays

1. Discuss each of the following aspects of the business cycle:

    a. Definition of a business cycle.

    b. How the business cycle can be measured.

    c. Number and duration of average cycle in the United States.

d. Relationship between business cycle and inflation.

2. Explain what happens during a business cycle to turn an expansion (upswing) into a contraction (downswing) according to:

a. Wesley C. Mitchell.

b. J. R. Hicks.

c. John Maynard Keynes.

3. Distinguish between the basic cause(s) of the business cycle according to theories based on the following:

a. External (exogenous) shocks.

b. Internal (endogenous) forces—underconsumption theories—overinvestment theories.

4. Discuss economic forecasting relative to each of the following:

  a. What is economic forecasting?

  b. What is the purpose of forecasting?

  c. Reaction of individuals and businesses to the forecasts.

  d. Alternative methods of forecasting:

    (1) Extrapolation method.

    (2) Consensus method.

    (3) Economic indicators method (leading, coincident, and lagging indicators).

    (4) Econometric models.

  e. The effectiveness of economic forecasting.

A Self-Test

Completion Questions

1. During the period from 1854 to 1987, the United States experienced _____ business cycles. The duration in months of the average expansion was about

   _____, while that of the average contraction was about _____.

2. The average length of the Juglar cycle is _____ years. This compares

   with _____ years for the Kondratieff long-wave cycle. The Kitchin major

   cycle includes _____ minor Kitchin cycles, where each of the minor

   cycles is an average of _____ months in duration.

3. Wesley C. Mitchell argued that business cycles are inherent in (*barter, money-using*) market economies which are (*profit-, nonprofit-*) oriented. He also maintained that the typical business cycle is (*noncumulative, cumulative*), (*nonrepetitive, repetitive*) and contains forces that automatically transform one phase of the cycle into the next phase.

4. Mitchell said there are two basic reasons why a cyclical expansion comes to an end. These are:

   a. _____

   _____.

   b. _____

   _____

   _____.

   Mitchell argued that ultimately these two forces would produce a crisis which would entail (*increasing, decreasing*) debt (*liquidation, accumulation*) and eventually cause the economic boom to become a (*recession, steady expansion*).

5. Historical explanations of the business cycle have often been divided into exogenous and endogenous theories. (*Exogenous, Endogenous*) explanations state that the business cycle is caused by external shocks such as wars and bad harvests. (*Exogenous, Endogenous*) explanations make business cycles an inherent part of the economy, relying on such explanations as the multiplier-accelerator model, expectations, and so forth. Most of the endogenous explanations are based on a (*profit-oriented, non-profit-oriented*) economy.

6. List the two broad categories into which pre-Keynesian theories of the business cycle can be divided:

   a. _____

   b. _____

7. Keynes believes that the major explanation of a collapse in economic activity is a sudden drop in the (*MEC, consumption function*), after which liquidity preference

(*increases, decreases*) sharply. Even when interest rates begin to (*increase, fall*), the MEC will remain (*low, high*) and hence (*impede, stimulate*) economic expansion. Outside intervention by the government could change the result, but to do so, it must (*increase, decrease*) the MEC.

True and False

_____ 1. The business cycle is the wavelike movement over time of the overall level of economic activity.

_____ 2. By definition, a recession is said to occur whenever real GDP increases by less than 2 percent.

_____ 3. A recession becomes a depression when unemployment increases above 9 percent and real GDP drops for two quarters.

_____ 4. Since 1790, the United States has experienced over 40 recessions.

_____ 5. During the recession of 1981-82, the United States experienced not only a longer contraction than on average, but also a greater drop in real GDP than during any recession since the 1930s.

_____ 6. According to Wesley C. Mitchell, profits are the key factor that determines when an expansion or contraction will occur.

_____ 7. One of Mitchell's key statistical findings is that during the recovery and early phase of cyclical expansions, costs of production rise more rapidly than prices of goods and services.

_____ 8. According to Hicks, actual output cannot exceed the ceiling growth of output except for short periods of time.

_____ 9. Thomas Malthus explained the business cycle in terms of an excess of demand.

_____ 10. John A. Hobson developed an overinvestment theory of the business cycle.

_____ 11. Overinvestment theories attribute the cause of an investment boom and ultimate collapse of the economy to either monetary or nonmonetary factors.

_____ 12. Frederick A. Hayek developed a monetary overinvestment theory of the cycle.

_____ 13. Keynes visualizes a boom period as being caused to a greater extent by consumer spending than by investment.

_____ 14. Keynes did not classify his analysis of the cycle as being an overinvestment theory.

_____ 15. Michael Kalecki argued in the early 1940s that once governments had the power to "control" the business cycle, the business cycle might be caused by political factors. In this respect, he pointed to the opposition of the business community to continued deficit spending and of the general public to prolonged periods of high unemployment.

_____ 16. Economic forecasting aims basically at determining what will happen to the economy, or certain strategic economic variables, over a specified future period of time.

_____ 17. Forecasting is probably more of an art than a science.

_____ 18. Forecasts may be very useful, but they must be interpreted with great care and with a wide margin of error.

_____ 19. Measured by the official unemployment rate the recession of 1990–91 was relatively mild.

Multiple Choice

1. Which of the following researchers conducted extensive investigations of the business cycle under the auspices of the NBER?
   a. John Maynard Keynes.
   b. Wesley C. Mitchell.
   c. Alfred Marshall.
   d. W. Stanley Jevons.
   e. Michael Kalecki.

2. A publication dealing extensively with business cycle developments is the
   a. *Survey of Current Business.*
   b. *Federal Reserve Bulletin.*
   c. *Monthly Labor Review.*
   d. *Employment and Earnings.*

3. The NBER measures the business cycle
   a. from trough to peak to trough.
   b. from peak to trough to peak.
   c. from peak to trough.
   d. from trough to peak.
   e. none of the above.

4. The NBER defines a recession as an interval during which
   a. money GDP has dropped for at least 4 quarters in a row.
   b. real GDP has dropped for at least 2 quarters in a row.
   c. real GDP has dropped for at least 4 quarters in a row.
   d. money GDP has dropped for at least 2 quarters in a row.
   e. unemployment has increased above 6 percent and real GDP has dropped 2 percent.

5. During the post-World War II era, the average expansion has been
   a. longer than during the period before World War II.
   b. shorter than during the period before World War II.

    c. about the same duration as before World War II.

    d. two years in duration.

6. During the post-World War II era, the average contraction has been
    a. longer than during the period before World War II.
    b. shorter than during the period before World War II.
    c. about the same duration as before World War II.
    d. two years in duration.

7. The number of recessions experienced by the U.S. between 1945 and 1995 is

a. four.	*e.* eight.
b. five.	*f.* nine.
c. six.	*g.* ten.
d. seven.	*h.* eleven.

8. The worst U.S. recession since the 1930s, measured by the unemployment rate, was that of

a. 1948–49.	*f.* 1973–75.
b. 1953–54.	*g.* January 1980–July 1980.
c. 1957–58.	*h.* 1981–1982.
d. 1960–61.	*i.* 1990–91.
e. 1969–70.	

9. Which of the following is *not* a common characteristic of Wesley C. Mitchell's business cycle during a recession phase of the cycle?
    a. Prices drop or begin to increase less rapidly.
    b. Wages and other costs of production tend to decline.
    c. Money and credit become increasingly easier.
    d. Profits drop, perhaps ultimately becoming losses.
    e. Recovery starts in some sector due to a greater drop in costs than in prices.
    f. Real GDP begins to increase at an increasing rate.

10. Professor J. R. Hicks argued that the magnitude of fluctuation of business cycles is
    a. unconstrained by any economic factors.
    b. constrained by ceilings and floors set by the interactions of the accelerator and multiplier.
    c. not a relevant way of measuring the severity of business cycles.
    d. determined by the laws established by the government.

11. In the Hicksian business cycle model, the ceiling is determined by the
    a. rate of growth of the full-employment labor force plus the rate of growth of labor productivity.
    b. growth rate of the labor force plus the rate of inflation.
    c. rate of growth of real GDP and rate of increase of labor's productivity.
    d. none of the above.

12. In the business cycle developed by Hicks, if the growth rate of the fully employed labor force is 1.5 percent and productivity is increasing at 2.5 percent, the ceiling rate of growth of real GDP is
    a. 1.5 percent.
    b. 2.5 percent.
    c. 3.5 percent.
    d. 4.0 percent.
    e. 4.5 percent.
    f. indeterminate.

13. In the Hicksian business cycle model, the floor below which output cannot fall during a downswing is determined by the
    a. fact that the decrease in induced investment associated with the accelerator becomes less and less and that at some point consumption associated with the multiplier ultimately begins to exceed output.
    b. accelerator becoming larger as the downswing continues and the multipliers getting smaller and smaller.
    c. induced investment becoming greater than autonomous investment, thereby altering the multiplier and hence the income level.
    d. government policies affecting the minimum wage, price controls, and other direct interferences with the forces of supply and demand.

14. In Keynes' *General Theory*, cycles are caused by
    a. changes in government policy.
    b. changes in aggregate demand.
    c. wars and bad harvests.
    d. extremely tight credit conditions.

15. The sunspot theory is an external explanation of the business cycle attributable to
    a. Alfred Marshall.
    b. W. Stanley Jevons.
    c. Thomas Malthus.
    d. Wesley C. Mitchell.
    e. Joseph A. Schumpeter.

16. Joseph Schumpeter developed an external theory in which the business cycle is caused by
    a. wars and crop failures.
    b. the interaction of the multiplier and accelerator.
    c. innovations.
    d. sunspots.

17. The monetarists, as represented by Milton Friedman,
    a. see government policy designed to achieve the goals of full employment and price-level stability as a major cause of cyclical fluctuations.
    b. do not believe in the business cycle since they argue the economy is always at full employment.

     c. argue that the business cycle is much less severe since 1914 because the Federal Reserve System has been effectively stabilizing the economy.

     d. argue that the business cycle is caused by underconsumption.

18. Overinvestment theories of the business cycle attribute the collapse of prosperity to
     a. excessively high interest rates which reduce the need for investments already underway and, hence, lead to excess production.
     b. excessive investment resulting in excessive production and, hence, a general glut.
     c. business making the wrong types of investment during cyclical expansions.
     d. government interference in the operations of the market system.

19. Underconsumption theories of the business cycle typically attribute the collapse of prosperity to
     a. consumer spending not keeping up with production and thereby causing a general glut of goods to occur.
     b. investment growing much faster than consumption and thereby not leaving enough goods for consumers to purchase.
     c. a decrease in saving and investment.
     d. government taxes being so high that they do not leave consumers sufficient money to purchase goods and services.

20. Which of the following is *not* associated with developing a nonmonetary overinvestment theory of the business cycle?
     a. Michel Tugan Baranowsky
     b. Arthur Spietoff
     c. Gustav Cassel
     d. Frederick A. Hayek

21. In *The General Theory,* Keynes argues that the business cycle is due primarily to
     a. fluctuations in the MEC.
     b. government policies.
     c. changes in consumer expenditures.
     d. the unequal distribution of income.

22. Among the things desired of economic forecasts is information about the
     a. cyclical turning point and the magnitude of change.
     b. changes in government policy.
     c. magnitude of drop and duration of past recessions.
     d. none of the above.

23. Which of the following is *not* a method of economic forecasting?
     a. extrapolation (of the present into the future)
     b. using a consensus of opinions by business and financial experts
     c. relying heavily on leading economic indicators
     d. using an econometric model of the economy
     e. none of the above

CHAPTER 15 Managing the Macroeconomy in a Global Setting

Key Concepts

Incomes policy
Policy indicators (guides)
Lags—inside lags vs. outside lags
Functional finance budget philosophy
Countercyclical finance budget philosophy
CED formula flexibility (or automatic balance) budget philosophy
Full-employment budget
High-employment budget
Mundell-Fleming condition

Congressional Budget and Impoundment Control Act of 1974
Congressional Budget Office
"Nature of Economic Thinking"
"Crowding-out" effect
Fiscal stagnation
GDP gap
Disintermediation
Full-employment surplus
Full-employment and Balanced Growth Act of 1978
Reaganomics
Gramm-Rudman-Hollings Act

Problems and Essays

Monetary policy, fiscal policy, and incomes policy are three major policy instruments (tools) at the disposal of governments to achieve the policy objectives of full employment, optimum economic growth, and reasonable price level stability. We should recognize, of course, that these instruments are not equally effective and that typically they cannot be used alone to achieve the policy objectives. Moreover, all these policy instruments have shortcomings, and under certain circumstances none of them may be effective. The first problem/essay question deals with various aspects of monetary policy, while the second covers fiscal policy. Incomes policy was considered in a prior chapter. The third problem/essay question explores the relative effectiveness of monetary and fiscal policy under alternative conditions. The fourth and fifth problems/essay questions extend the analysis by using the *IS-LM* model to analyze an economy at full employment and the crowding-out effect.

The above questions deal with a closed economy. The sixth problem/essay question extends the analysis of monetary and fiscal policy to an open economy.

1. *Monetary Policy.* Review the meaning of monetary policy and the general (direct) and selective (indirect) controls through which monetary policy operates. Then, answer the questions below.

  a. What is an economic *indicator* (or policy guide)?

b. What are two important requirements of a good monetary policy indicator?

c. Discuss the relative merits of the money supply and interest rates as a guide to monetary policy. Which one is preferred by monetarists and which by Keynesians?

d. Explain the problem associated with *lags.* Distinguish between *inside lags* and *outside lags.*

e. Discuss the relative impact and fairness of monetary policy on different groups in the economy.

f. Critically analyze the relative advantages and disadvantages of monetary policy and fiscal policy (1) as tools for promoting full employment and price level stability and (2) in terms of the speed and flexibility with which they affect economic activity. [Note: You may want to skip this question for now and return to it after you have completed the other problem/essay questions in this chapter.]

2. *Fiscal Policy.* Before answering the subquestions below, review the meaning of fiscal policy and the mechanism(s) by which it affects economic activity. In your review be sure to bring in the Congressional Budget and Impoundment Control Act of 1974.

a. Define and contrast each of the following budget philosophies:

(1) Functional finance budget.

(2) CED formula flexibility (or automatic balance) budget.

(3) Countercyclical budget.

(4) Full-employment budget.

b. Compare actual and full-employment federal government receipts, expenditures, and budget balances. Use data provided in the *Economic Report of the President*. How meaningful is the full-employment budget as a guide for government fiscal policy?

c. Discuss the problems and limitations associated with fiscal policy.

d. Should congress give the president authority to raise and lower, within limits, tax rates for fiscal policy purposes? Why or why not?

3. *Effectiveness of Monetary Policy and Fiscal Policy.* The *IS-LM* model can be utilized to illustrate the conditions under which monetary and fiscal policies will and will not be effective. Answer the questions below on the basis of Figure 15–1. [Note: It is not possible to consider fiscal and monetary policy without bringing the government sector into the model. Therefore, assume the *IS* curve represents equality between $I + G + X$ and $S + T + M$. Note also that the answers provided in this section have many qualifications. Two of the important ones should be noted at the outset. First, it is assumed that monetary policy affects economic activity only by causing changes in the interest rate and thereby increasing or decreasing investment. In reality, changes in the interest rate may have a small effect on consumption and other components of aggregate demand. Just as important, monetary policy may shift the investment function and hence the *IS* curve by altering the availability of funds. Second, fiscal policy may affect the supply of money and hence the *LM* curve. These two qualifications show that it is highly simplistic to assume that fiscal policy affects only the *IS* curve and monetary policy only the *LM* curve.]

a. *Monetary policy.* Assume the money market equilibrium curve is initially LM_1 and the commodity market equilibrium curves are IS_1, IS_2, and IS_3. Now let the money supply increase so that the *LM* curve shifts to LM_2. For simplification, it is assumed, as is typically done, that monetary policy affects only the *LM* curve.

   (1) Explain the effect of this increase in the money supply on the interest rate and income level assuming the commodity equilibrium curve is IS_1. Is monetary policy effective in this range?

   (2) Is monetary policy effective if the commodity equilibrium curve is IS_2? Why or why not?

FIGURE 15–1

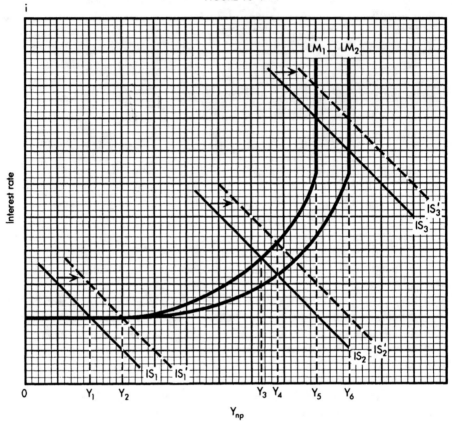

(3) Assume the commodity equilibrium curve is IS_3. How effective is monetary policy in this range?

b. *Fiscal policy.* Now assume that the money market equilibrium curve remains at LM_1 and that the *IS* curves are initially IS_1, IS_2, and IS_3. Assume further that the government increases its purchases or reduces taxes so that the three *IS* curves shift as indicated in Figure 15–1. For simplification it is assumed fiscal policy affects the *IS* curve only.

(1) How effective is fiscal policy if the income level is Y_1?

(2) Evaluate the effectiveness of fiscal policy if the income level is Y_3. Explain.

(3) Assume the income level is given by the intersection of LM_1 and IS_3. Is fiscal policy effective in this range? Why or why not?

c. In discussing the relative effectiveness of fiscal policy and monetary policy above, it was assumed that the investment function is not completely interest inelastic. Suppose the investment function is highly interest inelastic.

(1) What can be said about the slope of the IS curve?

(2) If the IS curve is highly interest inelastic, will this change the conclusion concerning the effectiveness of fiscal policy?

(3) What does a highly interest inelastic IS curve imply for the effectiveness of monetary policy? Why?

d. Assume the IS and LM curves are initially IS_2 and LM_1 in Figure 15–1 and that the government wants to foster a substantial increase in income because unemployment is relatively high. Under the circumstances, might it be desirable to finance an increase in government purchases of goods and services with an increase in the money supply? Study Figure 15–1 before answering this question.

4. IS-LM *Analysis for a Full-Employment Economy.* Up to this point it has been assumed that the country is producing at an output level below full employment— there are unemployed resources. Hence an increase in aggregate demand could, via the production function, stimulate greater production of goods and services. By the same token, the price level has been held constant so changes in demand were reflected in changes in real output. We now analyze the effects of shifts of the *LM* and *IS* curves when the country is at full employment and therefore cannot expand output. Although the analysis can be very complicated, concern here is only with the major considerations.

   Figure 15-2, which contains two *IS-LM* models, should be used as the basis for answering the questions below. In both parts of Figure 15-2 the economy is assumed to be in the intermediate range—since this is typically the more realistic position—of the *LM* curve. The full-employment output level is labelled Y_f. Since less than full employment takes us back into the world covered in earlier problems, it is assumed here that the *IS* and *LM* curve shifts outward from the origin (to the right). [Assume throughout this problem that the money supply is autonomous.]

   a. *Full employment and shifts of the* LM *curve.* Assume the monetary authorities increase the money supply so the *LM* curve shifts outward from LM_1 (the solid line) to LM_2 (the dashed line) as illustrated in part A of Figure 15-2.

      (1) Explain how the increase in the money supply affects the *equilibrium* levels of the interest rate and income. [Hint: Even though aggregate supply cannot increase from the full-employment level Y_f, *ex ante* aggregate demand can increase.]

      (2) Would the same sequence of events have been set into motion if there had been a reduction of the demand for money instead of an increase in the money supply?

   b. *Full employment and shifts of the* IS *curve.* Now consider what happens if the expansion of demand is due to a change in the real, as opposed to money, sector of the economy. This is illustrated in part B of Figure 15-2 by the outward shift of the *IS* curve (which includes government and foreign trade) from IS_1 (the solid line) to IS_2 (the dashed line). Full employment is again indicated by Y_f.

      (1) Explain how the outward shift of the *IS* curve affects aggregate demand and the process by which equilibrium is restored at full employment Y_f.

What are the new equilibrium interest rate and income levels? [Note: For the new equilibrium i and Y_{np}, it makes no difference whether the outward shift arises from an autonomous increase in I, G, X, or an autonomous decrease in saving, taxes, and imports. However, it does matter if one is concerned about the change in the composition of aggregate demand.]

FIGURE 15–2

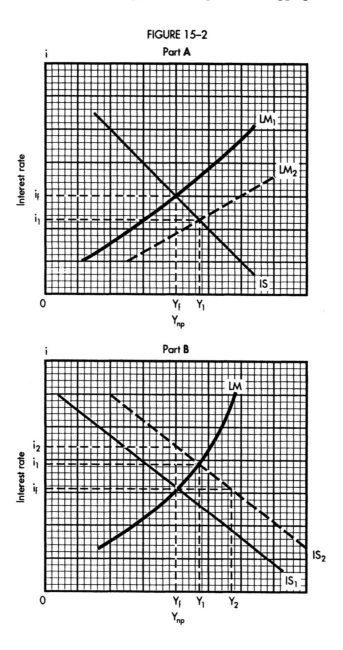

Part A

Part B

(2) Compare this situation with that in the question above.

5. *Crowding-Out Effect.* There has been much discussion and controversy surrounding what is often referred to as the crowding-out effect. This problem illustrates, given varying assumptions, the nature and significance of this effect. Three of the possible alternative interpretations of crowding out are considered. In all cases the initial step is an increase in government demand associated with expansionary fiscal policy. The money supply is held constant throughout.

   a. Explain what is meant by the crowding-out effect.

   b. What, in general, is the position of monetarists and Keynesians with respect to the magnitude of the crowding out effect?

   c. Crowding out—interest rate effect only. Consider, first, a simple interpretation of crowding out wherein the wealth effect of tax changes and or selling bonds to the public is neglected and the price level is held constant. Using the *IS-LM* model, explain under what circumstances the crowding-out effect associated with an expansionary fiscal policy will be complete.

   d. Crowding out—interest rate and wealth effects. Continue to hold the price level constant but now allow wealth to vary. Explain and illustrate graphically the crowding-out effect using Figure 15–3. Assume the increase in government expenditures is financed by selling bonds to the public.

   e. Crowding out—interest rate and price level effects. In this case, assume the wealth effect is zero, but let the price level be flexible. Explain and illustrate graphically the crowding-out effect using Figure 15–4.

   f. Other combinations. Numerous other combinations are possible, including combining the interest rate effect, wealth effect, and price level effect. However, the above examples serve to show the basic nature and implications of the crowding-out argument.

FIGURE 15–3

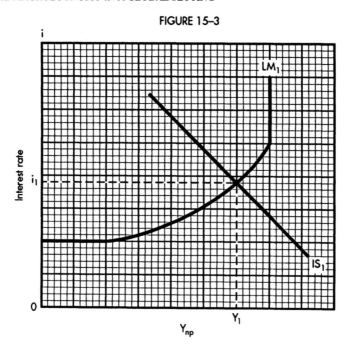

FIGURE 15–4

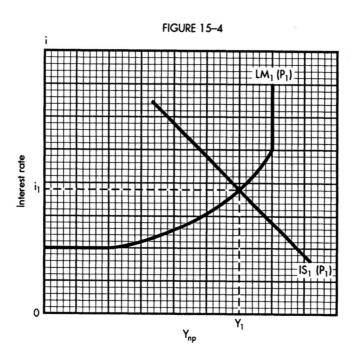

6. *Fiscal and Monetary Policy in an Open Economy.* This problem analyzes the economic effects of monetary and fiscal policy using the complete *IS-LM-BP* model. Part *a* deals with the effects of the two policies when exchange rates are pegged and thus not allowed to fluctuate in response to changes in the supply of and demand for foreign exchange. Part *b* goes through the same analysis under a flexible exchange rate system. In each case we first consider expansionary policies and then consider restrictive policies. In all cases, international financial capital is assumed to be highly, but not completely, responsive to the spread between domestic and foreign interest rates.

   a. *Monetary and fiscal policy with fixed (pegged) exchange rates.*

      (1) *Expansionary monetary and fiscal policy.*

         (a) *Fiscal policy.* Explain and illustrate graphically, using the *IS, LM* and *BP* curves as depicted in Figure 15–5, how an increase in government purchases and cut in taxes will affect domestic income, interest rates, and foreign income. Assume the exchange rate does not change and that financial capital flows are highly-mobile internationally.

FIGURE 15–5

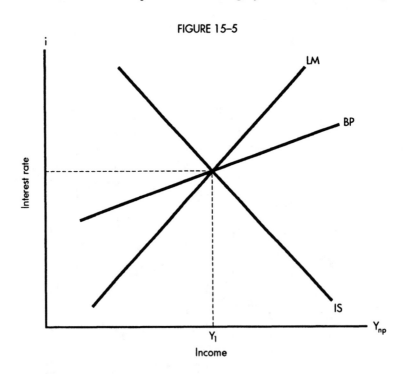

(b) *Monetary policy.* Explain and illustrate graphically, using the *IS, LM,* and *BP* curves as depicted in Figure 15–6, how an expansionary monetary policy will affect domestic income, interest rates, and foreign income. Assume the exchange rate does not change and that financial capital flows are highly-mobile internationally.

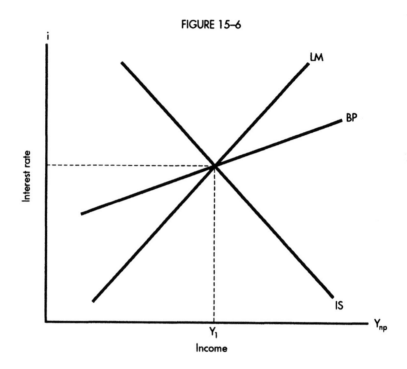

FIGURE 15–6

(2) *Restrictive monetary and fiscal policy.* Now reproduce the above diagrams on your own paper—so you get use working with the graph—and analyze the impact of *restrictive* fiscal policy and restrictive monetary policy on domestic interest rates and high international capital mobility.

b. *Monetary and fiscal policy with flexible (freely fluctuating) exchange rates.*

(1) *Expansionary monetary and fiscal policy.*

(a) *Fiscal policy.* Explain and illustrate graphically, using the *IS, LM,* and *BP* curves as depicted in Figure 15–7, how an increase in government purchases and a cut in taxes will affect domestic income, interest rates, and foreign income. Now assume exchange rates are flexible. Continue to assume financial capital flows are highly-mobile internationally.

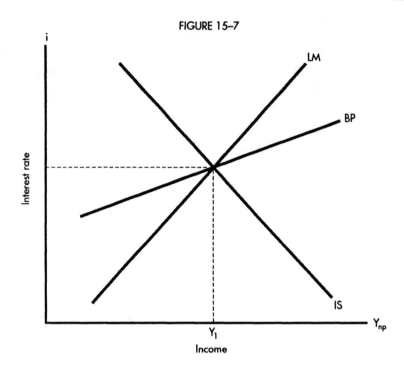

FIGURE 15–7

(b) *Monetary policy.* Explain and illustrate graphically, using the *IS, LM,* and *BP* curves as depicted in Figure 15–8, how an expansionary monetary policy will affect domestic income, interest rates, and foreign income. Assume exchange rates are fully flexible and that financial capital flows are highly-mobile internationally.

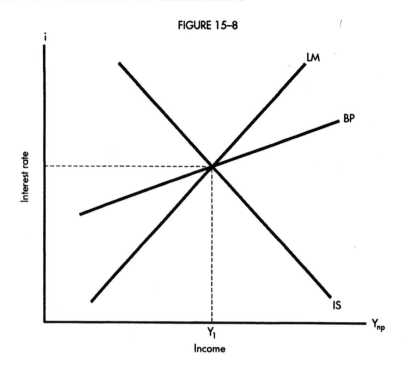

FIGURE 15-8

(2) *Restrictive monetary and fiscal policy.* Reproduce Figures 15-7 and 15-8 on your own paper and analyze the impact of *restrictive* fiscal policy and *restrictive* monetary policy on domestic interest rates and income. Do each one separately, first fiscal policy and then monetary policy. Continue to assume flexible exchange rates and high international capital mobility.

7. Identify and explain the major causes of the Great Depression. Are any of them applicable to the U.S. today? Discuss.

A Self-Test

Completion Questions

1. If the economy is in the liquidity trap, monetary policy will be (*effective, ineffective*). An expansion of the money supply will shift the *LM* curve to the (*right, left*) and (*will, will not*) alter income. Income (*increases, decreases, remains constant*) because (*investment, consumption, the interest rate*) does not fall and thereby stimulate (*consumption, government purchases, investment*).

2. If the *IS* and *LM* curves intersect in the intermediate range, an increase in government purchases (*will, will not*) have a full multiplier effect on income. This is because as income advances, the (*speculative, transactions*) demand for money (*increases, decreases*), leaving (*more, less*) money for (*speculative, transactions*) purposes; the result is (*an increase, a decrease, no change*) in the interest rate and (*an increase, a reduction, no change*) in investment. An expansion of the money supply (*will, will not*) increase income by (*increasing, reducing*) the interest rate and thereby (*increasing, decreasing, having no effect on*) investment. Accordingly, in the intermediate range both monetary and fiscal policy are (*effective, ineffective*).

3. If the commodity-equilibrium curve intersects the money-equilibrium curve in the classical range—where the *LM* curve is completely vertical—fiscal policy (*can, cannot*) increase income. An increase in government purchases will cause the interest rate to (*advance, decline*) to the point where it (*increases, chokes off*) investment equal to the increase in government purchases; the net effect will be (*positive, negative, zero*). An increase in the money supply will be (*effective, ineffective*) as it provides more money for transactions and speculative purposes, thereby (*increasing, reducing*) the interest rate and (*reducing, increasing*) investment expenditures such that the income level (*remains unchanged, advances, declines*). This assumes that investment (*is, is not*) completely interest inelastic. Accordingly, in this range (*fiscal, monetary, neither*) policy is completely effective and (*fiscal, monetary, neither*) policy is completely ineffective.

4. Suppose the investment function is completely interest inelastic. This implies that the *IS* curve is completely (*vertical, horizontal*). Under these circumstances, (*monetary, fiscal*) policy could still be effective, but (*monetary, fiscal*) policy would be ineffective (*regardless of, depending on*) where the *IS* curve intersects the *LM* function.

True and False

_____ 1. If the *LM* curve is completely vertical, fiscal policy will be ineffective in increasing employment.

_____ 2. In relating monetary policy to the *IS-LM* model, one should recognize that even if the investment function is interest inelastic, monetary policy may still be effective in terms of the availability of funds thesis.

_____ 3. If the investment function is completely interest inelastic, fiscal policy is more effective than otherwise.

_____ 4. Keynesians believe that changes in the money supply directly affect aggregate demand; monetarists believe changes in the money supply affect economic activity indirectly via the impact that changes in the stock of money have on interest rates.

_____ 5. An economic indicator is an economic variable that the monetary authorities use to assist them in determining when to make policy changes.

_____ 6. Monetarists are more inclined to use interest rates than the money supply as an economic indicator.

_____ 7. A good economic indicator should be subject to control by the Federal Reserve authorities and, when changed, have a significant impact on total spending.

_____ 8. Those who prefer the money supply as an economic indicator often argue that the Fed cannot control interest rates very well in the short run.

_____ 9. Throughout the 1950s and 1960s the Fed relied largely on interest rates as the economic indicator with little attention given to the money supply.

_____ 10. Between 1965 and 1977 the annual percentage change in the M1 definition of the money supply ranged from 2.5 to 9.2 percent; between 1948 and 1965 the range was about -1.4 to 5.6 percent.

_____ 11. According to the monetarists, the money supply should be increased at a constant rate of between 3 and 5 percent during cyclical expansions and 1 to 3 percent during cyclical contractions.

_____ 12. The inside lag associated with monetary policy is the interval between the time when action is needed and the time when action is actually taken by the Fed; the outside lag is the interval between the time the Fed takes action and the time that the action affects employment and the price level.

_____ 13. It is generally agreed that a tight money policy has a greater adverse impact on large businesses than small businesses because the latter rely more heavily on internal financing.

_____ 14. A tight money policy has a greater adverse impact on investment in inventories than on investment in housing and plant construction.

_____ 15. Due to the monetarist counter-revolution, the prevalent pre-1970 view that fiscal policy is more powerful than monetary policy is no longer as widely held.

_____ 16. Since 1949 the federal government of the United States has run a surplus in approximately two-thirds of the years.

_____ 17. Under the leadership of Walter Heller, chairman of the Council of Economic Advisers during the Kennedy administration, fiscal policy targets were cast in terms of the full-employment budget.

_____ 18. From 1970 to 1980, the full-employment budget typically had a smaller deficit and larger surplus than the actual budget. Hence, the full-employment budget implied that government taxes and expenditures have been less expansionary than implied by the actual budget balance.

_____ 19. The Congressional Budget and Impoundment Control Act of 1974 requires that the Congress look at the total federal budget, not just component parts, when making spending proposals and appropriations.

_____ 20. The Congressional Budget Office, created in 1974, serves the Congress in a way similar to how the Council of Economic Advisors serves the president.

_____ 21. One recommendation often made to give fiscal policy the same speed and flexibility as monetary policy is for Congress to give the Federal Reserve System the authority to raise and lower tax rates within limits of plus or minus 5 percent.

_____ 22. Keynes argued that the purpose of economic thinking was basically to have an organized and orderly method for thinking about particular problems.

_____ 23. Fiscal policy is ineffective in the classical range, while monetary policy is ineffective in the Keynesian range (of the *LM* curve).

_____ 24. Both monetary and fiscal policy are totally ineffective in the intermediate range of the *LM* curve.

_____ 25. The crowding-out effect of interest rate changes is smaller the less responsive investment is to the interest rate, all other things constant.

_____ 26. Some economists argue that the crowding-out effect may be substantially greater in the intermediate range of the *IS-LM* model than implied by interest rate changes because of the wealth effect and changes in the price level.

_____ 27. The greater the crowding-out effect, the greater the effectiveness of fiscal policy in affecting economic activity.

_____ 28. A frequently used definition of a recession is that real GDP drops two quarters in a row.

_____ 29. Fiscal policy was widely employed during the Truman-Eisenhower administrations.

_____ 30. Throughout the 1960s, a widely used definition of the "full-employment surplus" was the federal government budget surplus generated at full employment (defined to have 4 percent unemployment) with a fixed level of expenditures and tax rates.

_____ 31. In the author's view, the validity of competing macroeconomic theories can be readily determined by econometric testing.

_____ 32. As their policy guide, monetarists prefer to use interest rates, whereas Keynesians prefer to use the money supply.

_____ 33. Since 1984 the rate of inflation has been "modest" even though the *M*1 money supply has grown rapidly.

_____ 34. The worsening distribution of income and wealth during the 1920s was a major cause of the Great Depression of the 1930s.

Multiple Choice

1. In the liquidity trap
   a. both monetary and fiscal policy are highly effective.
   b. monetary and fiscal policy are ineffective.
   c. monetary policy is ineffective and fiscal policy is effective.
   d. fiscal policy is ineffective and monetary policy is effective.

2. If the *IS* curve and the *LM* curve are in the classical range—where the *LM* is completely vertical—the economy
   a. must be at full employment.
   b. cannot possibly be at full employment.
   c. may or may not be at full employment.
   d. is using all its money for speculative purposes.
   e. none of the above

3. The 1964 and 1981 tax cuts
   a. had no effect on the *IS* curve.
   b. shifted the *IS* curve to the left.
   c. shifted the *LM* curve to the right.
   d. shifted the *IS* curve to the right.
   e. none of the above

4. If the *IS* curve intersects the *LM* curve in the intermediate range, and investment is not completely interest inelastic, fiscal policy
   a. will be more effective if it is used by itself.
   b. will be ineffective.
   c. will be more effective if it is combined with an expansionary monetary policy.
   d. should not be utilized to stimulate the economy because it will cause the interest rate to rise.
   e. none of the above

5. Assume the *IS* curve and *LM* curve intersect at the full-employment level of output. Now let there be an increase in autonomous investment. We now have a situation where
   a. aggregate demand exceeds aggregate supply and will result in inflation.
   b. aggregate demand is less than aggregate supply, thereby increasing interest rates.
   c. prices will fall until equilibrium is restored at full-employment output.
   d. the demand for money will decline and thereby cause the *LM* curve to shift outward.

6. Assume the *IS-LM* model yields equilibrium at full employment. Now let the government reduce taxes. There will be, among other things, a
   a. fall in the price level that reduces the demand for money and thereby causes the *LM* curve to rotate outward.
   b. reduction in the output level to an extent that unemployment increases above the socially desired level.
   c. rise in prices that increases the demand for money and thereby causes the *LM* curve to rotate upward until equilibrium is at full-employment output.
   d. rise in the level of prices that causes the *IS* curve to shift outward and induces even more inflation.

7. Monetarists in general argue that the "best" economic indicator is
    a. the price level.
    b. interest rates.
    c. the rate of economic growth.
    d. the money supply.
    e. none of the above

8. Monetarists often argue that
    a. the Fed has good control over the money supply but not interest rates.
    b. the price level is not related to changes in the money supply.
    c. the money supply should be decreased over time at a fixed rate of 3 to 5 percent.
    d. the Fed has good control over interest rates but not the money supply.

9. From 1980 to 1987 the M_1 definition of money increased continually on an annual basis within a range of about
    a. 2.5 to 4.5 percent.
    b. 0.9 to 16.9 percent.
    c. 0.5 to 3.5 percent.
    d. 6.5 to 9.5 percent.

10. President Reagan's 1981 tax cut was primarily intended to
    a. stimulate aggregate demand.
    b. promote a more equal distribution of income.
    c. increase productivity and output.
    d. increase interest rates.

11. To determine the full-employment budget balance, it is necessary to estimate
    a. the economy's potential full-employment output level.
    b. the federal tax revenue that the full-employment output level will generate.
    c. the amount of expenditures at full employment.
    d. none of the above
    e. all of the above except d

12. Compared to the actual federal budget deficit since 1975, the full-employment budget deficit has typically been
    a. about the same.
    b. much larger.
    c. much smaller.
    d. about half the time above and half the time below.

13. In the classical range
    a. monetary policy and fiscal policy are equally effective.
    b. monetary policy and fiscal policy are both totally ineffective.
    c. monetary policy is effective and fiscal policy is ineffective.
    d. fiscal policy is effective and monetary policy is ineffective.

14. In the classical range, an increase in government expenditures causes the
    a. interest rate to increase and thereby crowds out an equal amount of private expenditures.

     b. level of private expenditures to increase by more than the increase in government expenditures.

     c. income and employment to decline.

     d. investment level to increase as businesses have more funds available for investment.

15. If we assume the price level is constant and the wealth effect is zero, crowding out would be complete only if the *IS* curve intersects the *LM* in the classical range; it would be partial in the intermediate range and zero in the Keynesian range. If the assumptions of zero wealth effect and a fixed price level are dropped, crowding out may be complete even in the intermediate range. This is because the increase in government expenditures or reduction in taxes, which shifts the *IS* curve outward, sets into motion forces that

     a. increase society's wealth and hence the demand for money and thereby causes the *LM* curve to rotate upward by an amount sufficient to intersect the new *IS* curve at the same income level.

     b. increase the price level, thereby causing the *IS* curve to shift part way back due to the negative Pigou effect and the *LM* curve to rotate upward due to the reduction in real money balances, these combined changes resulting in a new equilibrium at the original income level.

     c. cause the *IS* curve and *LM* curve to both shift further outward to the right.

     d. none of the above

     e. both *a* and *b*

16. Crowding out due to Friedman's wealth effect arises because to finance the deficit, the government

     a. issues new bonds which increase people's wealth and thereby society's demand for money and hence causes the *LM* curve to shift inward.

     b. prints money which thereby causes the *LM* to shift inward.

     c. raises taxes on business, thereby reducing the wealth of business and hence their investment.

     d. issues new bonds which discourage the public from spending as much as they originally planned.

17. Crowding out due to the price level effect arises because the expansionary fiscal policy

     a. results in lower prices and hence businesses cut back on investment.

     b. pushes up the price level which results in a negative Pigou effect and reduces the real money supply.

     c. pushes up the price level and thereby results in a negative Pigou effect combined with an increase in the real money supply.

     d. none of the above

18. In the post-World War II era, fiscal policy was first "accepted" on a systematic basis by the

     a. Truman administration.

     b. Eisenhower administration.

     c. Kennedy administration.

     d. Johnson administration.

     e. Nixon administration.

  f. Ford administration.
  g. Carter administration.
  h. Reagan administration.
  i. Bush administration.
  j. Clinton administration.

19. Over the past 140 years, the average annual U.S. inflation rate has been about
  a. 1.0 percent.
  b. 1.5 percent.
  c. 2.0 percent.
  d. 2.5 percent.
  e. 3.0 percent.

20. From 1970 to 1990, the average annual rate of inflation in the United States was about
  a. 2.5 percent.
  b. 4.5 percent.
  c. 6.5 percent.
  d. 8.5 percent.
  e. 10.5 percent.

21. The Gramm-Rudman-Hollings Act was designed to
  a. yield a federal government balanced budget by the year 1991.
  b. protect American industries adversely affected by import competition.
  c. cut down the flow of illegal aliens to the United States.
  d. hold the increase in defense expenditures at the rate of inflation.
  e. none of the above

22. Which of the following is not one of the philosophical precepts of the Reagan "revolution"?
  a. Big government is desirable because it can promote growth and national defense.
  b. Free trade is the best policy.
  c. Decision making should be made at the lowest government level possible.
  d. Cutting taxes is anti-inflationary.
  e. Cutting tax rates will increase total tax receipts.

23. Which of the following is not one of the four pillars of Reaganomics?
  a. Cut taxes.
  b. Cut government outlays.
  c. Deregulate the economy.
  d. Promote a stable monetary policy.
  e. Return to an international Gold Standard.

24. Under Reaganomics (1981–88), federal spending as a percentage of GDP annually averaged about
  a. 17 percent.
  b. 19 percent.
  c. 21 percent.
  d. 23 percent.
  e. 26 percent.

25. During President Reagan's eight years in the White House, the U.S. national debt, which was at about $910 billion in 1980, increased to about
    a. $1.2 trillion (by the end of 1988).
    b. $1.6 trillion (by the end of 1988).
    c. $2.3 trillion (by the end of 1988).
    d. $2.6 trillion (by the end of 1988).
    e. $3.1 trillion (by the end of 1988).

26. Expansionary fiscal policy in an open economy with pegged exchange rates and highly-mobile capital flows will cause
    a. a reduction in domestic interest rates and domestic income.
    b. an increase in domestic interest rates and a drop in domestic and foreign income.
    c. no change in domestic interest rates but an increase in domestic income.
    d. an increase in domestic interest rates, domestic income, and foreign income.

27. Expansionary monetary policy in an open economy with pegged exchange rates and highly-mobile financial capital will
    a. have no lasting effect on domestic interest rates and domestic income.
    b. increase domestic income and interest rates.
    c. increase interest rates, encourage a capital inflow, and decrease domestic income.
    d. lower domestic interest rates, increase domestic income, and reduce foreign income.

28. Expansionary fiscal policy in an open economy with flexible exchange rates and highly-mobile capital flows will
    a. have no effect on domestic income since the exchange rate will neutralize the expansionary fiscal policy effect.
    b. reduce domestic interest rates, lower domestic income, and not affect foreign income.
    c. result in higher domestic interest rates and income and higher foreign income.
    d. lower domestic interest rates and increase domestic income.

29. Expansionary monetary policy in an open economy with flexible exchange rates and highly-mobile financial capital will
    a. raise domestic interest rates, increase domestic income, and lower foreign income.
    b. raise domestic interest rates and lower domestic and foreign incomes.
    c. lower domestic interest rates and increase domestic and foreign incomes.
    d. lower domestic interest rates, increase domestic income, and not affect foreign income.

30. The Mundell-Fleming condition says that
    a. for devaluation to be effective, the sum of the elasticities of the domestic demand for imports and the foreign demand for exports must exceed unity.
    b. with fixed exchange rates and high capital mobility, monetary policy will not affect domestic income.
    c. monetary policy is more effective with pegged exchange rates and high capital mobility.
    d. freely-fluctuating exchange rates make it difficult to use monetary and fiscal policy to promote full employment and economic growth.

31. October 29, 1929, often referred to as "Black Tuesday," is the day
    a. President Hoover died.
    b. the Gold Standard was abandoned.
    c. Lord John Maynard Keynes proposed using fiscal policy to end the Great Depression.
    d. the stock market crashed.
    e. none of the above

32. After the Great Depression started, real output did not regain its 1929 level until
    a. 1933.
    b. 1936.
    c. 1937.
    d. 1940.

33. Monetarists of the Friedman school argue that the Great Depression was caused by
    a. excessively tight fiscal policy.
    b. inappropriate tight Federal Reserve monetary policy.
    c. the collapse of the Gold Standard.
    d. excessively easy Federal Reserve monetary policy.
    e. excessively easy fiscal policy.

34. Which one of the following is not a major factor that allegedly caused the Great Depression?
    a. expansionary monetary policy
    b. expansionary fiscal policy
    c. increased concentration of income and wealth during the 1920s
    d. a farm depression throughout the 1920s
    e. a rise in real interest rates as a result of prices dropping during the 1920s

CHAPTER 16   The Rebirth of Classical Economics

Key Concepts

Adaptive expectations	Random walk
Risk vs. uncertainty	Reaganomics
Index of consumer sentiment	Supply-side economics
Laffer curve	Theory of rational expectations
Natural rate of unemployment	Theory of continuous market clearing
Nominal business cycle model	Insider trading
Real business cycle model	New classical economics

Problems and Essays

1. The new classical economics, as opposed to the orthodox classical theory, is based on two theories: the theory of rational expectations (the new ingredient) and the theory of continuous market clearing (a basic premise of orthodox classical economics).

   a. Explain the *theory of rational expectations.*

   b. How do "rational expectations" differ from "adaptive expectations"?

   c. How do rational expectations differ from the survey technique of determining expectations?

d. What are the macroeconomic policy implications of the theory of rational expectations?

e. Explain the *theory of continuous market clearing,* including a clear statement of the relationship between Walrasian general equilibrium theory and the theory of efficient markets.

f. What are the macroeconomic policy implications of the theory of continuous market clearing? How do supporters of the continuous market clearing theory reconcile its policy implications with the fact that the business cycle does exist? What is the role played by "information lags" and misinformation?

g. Evaluate the new classical economics. What are its strengths and weaknesses?

2. New classical economics has two models for understanding the business cycle, the *nominal* business cycle model and the *real* business cycle model.

a. Explain how economic fluctuations are accounted for using the *nominal* business cycle approach.

b. Explain how economic fluctuations are accounted for using the *real* business cycle approach.

c. Compare the two approaches. Does one do a better job than the other in explaining the U.S. business cycle?

3. Supply-side economics provided the basic theoretical underpinning for the initial Reagan administration economic recovery program.

a. Explain the meaning of supply-side economics and explain the role played by the following:

(1) Say's Law of markets.

(2) Tax rates and incentives to work, save, and invest.

(3) Laffer's curve.

(4) Hostility toward big government.

    b. In what respects is supply-side economics similar to the orthodox classical theory of employment?

    c. In what respects is supply-side economics a fundamental part of Keynesian economics?

    d. Evaluate supply-side economics. What are its strengths and weaknesses?

    e. How will tax cuts reduce inflation according to supply-siders?

4. Figure 16–1 illustrates the typical Laffer curve, showing the relationship between tax receipts and marginal tax rates. Tax receipts are on the vertical axis and tax rates on the horizontal axis.

FIGURE 16–1

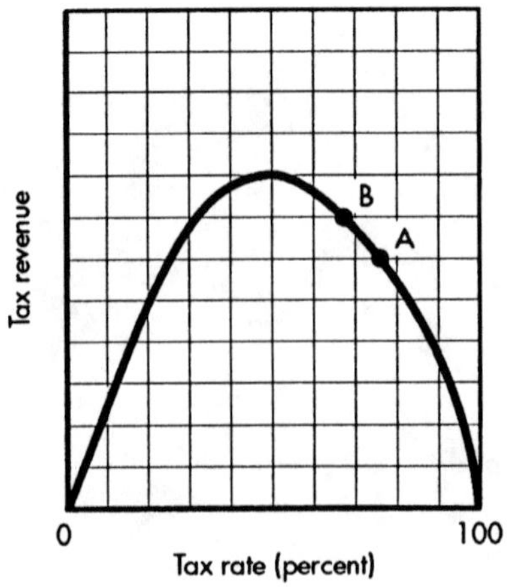

a. Explain the relationship between tax receipts and tax rates portrayed by the curve.

b. Explain the theoretical rationale for there being two different tax rates that produce the same amount of tax receipts.

c. Explain clearly why a reduction in tax rates from point A to point B results in an increase in government tax receipts.

d. What is the tax "wedge"?

e. What factors could cause the Laffer curve to shift up or down?

f. Evaluate the Laffer curve with respect to its theoretical validity, shape, and usefulness for government policy.

A Self-Test

True and False

_____ 1. In the efficient market theory, a market is efficient when the price in that market is based upon all available information about the item being traded.

_____ 2. An "efficient market" processes all information about the market instantaneously.

_____ 3. The new classical economics, like the older orthodox classical theory, implies that the economy will typically operate at less than full employment.

_____ 4. The new classical economics maintains that the business cycle would not occur if there were no information lags and no misinformation.

_____ 5. While monetarists disagree with the basic relationships and policy implications of the Keynesian income-expenditures model, they accept the role played by aggregate demand in determining GDP, employment, and the price level in the short run.

_____ 6. Unlike the monetarists, new classical economists largely reject the Keynesian approach and accept the pre-Keynesian classical approach.

_____ 7. Supply side economists assume upward sloping supply curve.

Multiple Choice

1. According to the theory of rational expectations, expectations are formed on the basis of
   a. adaptive expectations.
   b. survey techniques.
   c. individual rationality.
   d. none of the above

2. The theory of rational expectations says that in forming their expectations, people
   a. use all available relevant information and use such information efficiently.
   b. never make any errors.
   c. have no knowledge of the economic models that governments use to promote economic objectives.
   d. rely heavily on survey techniques.

3. The rational expectations theory says that the probable results of government policies are already taken into account by people in forming their expectations and hence government macroeconomic policies
   a. will seldom be effective.
   b. can achieve their objectives only if the government systematically fools the people.
   c. can achieve their objective only if the policy is unanticipated.

   d. will cause greater fluctuations in output and employment than would otherwise occur.
   e. all of the above

4. The theory of continuous market clearing maintains not only that all markets grope to equilibrium in a very short time, but also that
   a. wages and prices are inflexible in the downward direction.
   b. efficient markets process all relevant information almost instantaneously.
   c. full employment will seldom be achieved.
   d. all of the above

5. According to the new classical economics, the business cycle, which implies periodic unemployment, occurs because of
   a. tight monetary policy.
   b. restrictive fiscal policy.
   c. monopoly in the product and resource markets.
   d. information lags and misinformation.
   e. all of the above

6. Which of the following is not, according to critics, a major weakness of the new classical economics?
   a. The assumption that markets clear continuously.
   b. Rational expectations theory assumes people know more about how the economy works than is the case.
   c. The cost of obtaining and interpreting information may, in some instances, be less than the perceived benefit.
   d. Expectations are rooted in habits and are not typically modified very rapidly in response to economic changes.
   e. Rational expectations applies only to situations involving "risk" and not "uncertainty"—that is, to a world in which economic events are repetitive in logical time and not nonrepetitive in historical time.
   f. The explanation of the business cycle has no empirical support and fails to recognize that people often do not understand what is happening in different markets and the economy overall.
   g. none of the above

7. Which of the following is a basic feature of supply-side economics?
   a. Tax rates must be reduced to increase incentives to work, save, and invest.
   b. Laffer curve.
   c. Say's law of markets.
   d. Hostility toward big government.
   e. all of the above

8. The Laffer curve postulates that for the United States, a cut in tax rates
   a. will stimulate consumption and investment and thereby tax receipts.
   b. is undesirable because it will reduce government tax revenue.
   c. will create a large and persistent federal government deficit, thereby increasing interest rates and crowding out private investors.
   d. have no significant effect on the business cycle.

9. Critics of the new classical economics school maintain that
    a. markets are perfectly competitive.
    b. the assumption of continuous market clearing is essentially the same as the assumption that markets are purely competitive.
    c. most sellers are unable to influence their prices.
    d. none of the above
    e. all of the above

10. New classical economics assumes that
    a. all economic agents behave rationally.
    b. all markets for goods and services are efficient.
    c. an expansion of business investment generates additional saving.
    d. big business exerts market pressure in determining the prices for their products.
    e. both (a) and (b) above

11. New classical economics maintains that instability in the economy is due to
    a. instability of the investment function.
    b. misguided policies of the central government.
    c. the basic instability of a market economy.
    d. shifting consumer and business expectations about inflation.
    e. none of the above

12. Advocates of the real business cycle theory maintain that business fluctuations begin with
    a. a contraction of investment.
    b. irrational consumers and investors.
    c. a basic inability of the market to clear continually.
    d. a monetary surprise and are perpetuated by misinformed economic agents.
    e. an anticipated monetary change.

13. The real business cycle theory postulates that business fluctuations are caused by
    a. sharp changes in the money supply.
    b. random supply and demand shocks.
    c. misguided government policies.
    d. the irrational decisions of consumers and investors.
    e. none of the above

14. The supply side revolution of the late 1970s and 1980s
    a. had no effect on government policy during the 1980s.
    b. postulated that a cut in taxes would lower saving and lower investment.
    c. has lost a large part of its credibility.
    d. became even stronger during the mid-1990s.

CHAPTER 17 The New Keynesian Macroeconomics

Key Concepts

New classical economics
New Keynesian economics
Rational expectations
Continuous market clearing
  principle

Credit rationing theory
Mark-up pricing
Menu costs
Efficiency wage theories
Dual labor markets

Problems and Essays

1. Compare the economic theory of the new Keynesian economics with that of the new classical economics. In the process be sure to cover, among other things, their positions with respect to:

   a. the assumption of rational expectations.

   b. the assumption of continuous market clearing.

   c. the effectiveness of macroeconomic policy.

2. Figure 17–1 portrays the Keynesian-Classical aggregate supply/aggregate–demand model with the price level measured on the vertical axis and real income on the horizontal axis. Note that in addition to the aggregate demand function (AD) there are two Keynesian-classical aggregate supply curves (AS_1 and AS_2) and a classical long run aggregate supply ($LRAS$) curve. Assume the economy is in equilibrium with AS_1 equal to AD at the natural level of income (Y_n) with the price level at p_1 and that the actual price level equals the expected price level. Now assume a supply shock, perhaps due to a huge jump in the price of OPEC crude oil or to a reduction of the capital stock, shifts the Keynesian-Classical aggregate supply curve up to AS_2. What is the process of adjustment to equilibrium according to the new Keynesian economics?

FIGURE 17–1

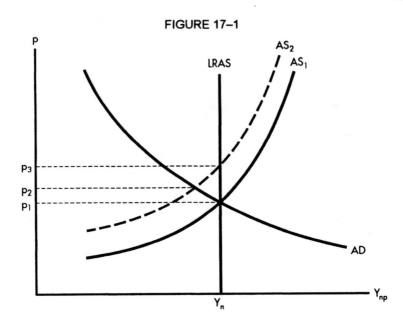

3. Over the past few years there has been much talk about using government policies to promote zero inflation. Explain how disinflationary policies will affect output and employment according to the new classical economics and new Keynesian economics and then compare the results.

4. Explain the "efficiency wage theories" of involuntary unemployment.

   a. If valid, what effect do these theories have on the labor market?

b. What are the four major explanations of efficiency wages according to new Keynesian economics?

c. Does empirical evidence support the efficiency wage theories?

5. Explain the "credit rationing theory."

a. What is the role played by financial institutions? Explain.

b. Instead of withholding loans that involve high risk, why don't financial institutions merely charge a higher interest rate to cover the higher risk?

A Self-Test

Completion Questions

1. New (*classical, Keynesian*) economics concludes that macroeconomic policy is ineffective. New (*classical, Keynesian*) economists believe this conclusion derives from their assumption of continuous market clearing and (*not, also*) their assumption of rational expectations.

2. New classical economics maintains macroeconomic policy is effective only when it is (*anticipated, unanticipated*) because only in this case are there expectational errors which may cause output to (*equal, differ from*) its natural level. However, since expectational errors (*are, are not*) corrected very rapidly, the effectiveness of macroeconomic policy will be (*permanent, temporary*).

True and False

_____ 1. When the continuous market clearing assumption is replaced with the assumption of sticky wages and prices, macroeconomic policy may then be effective.

_____ 2. New Keynesian economics postulates that markets are highly competitive and clear continuously.

_____ 3. For new classical economics, involuntary unemployment is a serious problem.

_____ 4. Lester Thurow argues disinflationary policy will reduce output and increase unemployment because overlapping three-year indexed labor contracts make it difficult to slow nominal wage increases.

_____ 5. New classical economics maintains that macroeconomic policy will typically be highly effective in promoting growth and employment.

_____ 6. New Keynesian economics maintains that expectations are not rational but the market typically does clear continuously.

_____ 7. The only difference between the new Keynesian economists and new classical economists is that the latter relay on Say's law to ensure full employment.

_____ 8. The mark-up equals the firm's profit margin per unit of output.

_____ 9. Empirical data shows that periods of unemployment may last for several years.

_____ 10. The new Keynesian efficiency wage theories make a lot of sense in theory but have only very weak empirical support.

_____ 11. Credit rationing theory implies financial institutions are not extending enough credit to generate a sufficient amount of investment to promote full employment.

Multiple Choice

1. The basic difference between new Keynesians and new classical economists is not about
   a. how well the quantity theory works in theory but in practice.
   b. the interest elasticity of the saving function but rather the investment function.
   c. the assumption of continuous market clearing but rather about how expectations are formed.
   d. how expectations are formed but rather about the assumption of continuous market clearing.

2. The natural rate hypothesis argues that supply and demand shocks
   a. may cause substantial unemployment for long periods of time.
   b. affect money wages and prices in a manner that restores equilibrium at full employment fairly rapidly.
   c. cannot have any effect on prices but can permanently increase or lower money wages.
   d. cannot have a lasting effect on money wages but can permanently alter prices.
   e. none of the above

3. New Keynesians believe wage and price rigidity is traceable to
   a. irrational expectations.
   b. insufficient aggregate demand.
   c. the market system clearing too frequently and too rapidly.
   d. institutions and microeconomic imperfections in the economy.
   e. none of the above

4. Which of the following is a significant source of wage and price rigidity according to the Keynesian economics?
   a. shifts of the aggregate demand curve
   b. government policies to increase competition
   c. increases in wages in other nations
   d. labor union contracts
   e. none of the above

5. Which of the following have not been cited as causes of wage and/or price rigidities?
   a. labor union contracts
   b. equity considerations
   c. wage imitations
   d. business contract with suppliers of intermediate products
   e. prices being fixed by contracts between manufacturers and retailers
   f. none of the above

6. Which of the following does not promote sticky prices and/or sticky nominal wages?
   a. overlapping three-year indexed labor contracts
   b. contracts between suppliers and producers
   c. menu costs
   d. mark-up pricing
   e. none of the above

7. Letting p = price, mc = marginal cost, ac = average cost, m = the mark-up, the mark-up equation is
   a. $p = m + mc$.
   b. $p = m - ac$.
   c. $p = m(ac)$.
   d. $p = m + ac$.
   e. $p = m - mc$.

8. Studies by George A. Akerloff and Brian G. M. Main and by Hal Sider showed that, during the period 1959–82, laid-off workers were unemployed on average, even when economic activity was increasing,
   a. for 3–4 months.
   b. for 6–8 months.
   c. for 9–12 months.
   d. for 12–16 months.
   e. for 15–20 months.

9. Efficiency wage theories argue firms will pay a wage rate above the rate that clears the labor market because they believe the higher wage will
   a. increase productivity and thus profits.
   b. entice more workers into the marketplace.
   c. increase goodwill.
   d. none of the above
   e. all of the above

10. According to new Keynesians, efficiency wages higher than the equilibrium wage
   a. may cause employees to work more diligently and do less shirking on the job.
   b. will minimize turnover costs.
   c. serve as a device to get highly-qualified workers into the applicant pool.
   d. are a gift to workers that will get them to be more productive.
   e. all of the above

CHAPTER 18   Post Keynesian Economics

Key Concepts

Post Keynesian economics
Walrasian law (theory)
Neoclassical synthesis
Planned excess demand
Planned excess supply
Walrasian auctioneer
Tatonnement
False trading

Say's principle
Effective demand failure
Real, historic time
"Notional"
Minsky's financial instability theory
Hedge finance vs. speculative finance
"Village fair" perspective
"Wall Street" perspective

Problems and Essays

1. Post Keynesian economics disputes the validity of Walrasian economics and raises serious objections to the neoclassical synthesis.

   a. Explain fully the meaning and essential features of Post Keynesian economics.

   b. How does Post Keynesian economics differ from Walrasian economics?

   c. How does Post Keynesian economics differ from neoclassical synthesis?

2. Explain the roles played by "uncertainty" and "expectations" in Post Keynesian economics. Are these concepts used the same way in Keynesian economics and in the new classical economics? Discuss.

351

3. Post Keynesians place heavy emphasis on the role of institutions in determining human behavior.

   a. Identify and explain the major institutions that determine human behavior according to the Post Keynesian economists.

   b. Why are these institutions so important for understanding the economy?

   c. Do these institutions play the same role and have the same importance in classical economics? Explain.

   d. Do these institutions play the same role and have the same importance in neoclassical economics? Explain.

4. Explain fully Hyman Minsky's "financial instability" hypothesis and then answer the following questions:

   a. How does it differ from:

      (1) Walrasian theory.

      (2) Keynes' original contribution (in *The General Theory*).

(3) the neoclassical synthesis.

b. How does the "village fair" perspective differ from the "Wall Street" perspective and which is fundamental to Minsky's argument? Why?

c. Why is the economy subject to periodic breakdowns?

d. How does a business cycle boom develop and subsequently lead to a recession?

e. What is the role played by monetary and fiscal policies? Explain fully.

A Self-Test

Completion Questions

1. Hyman Minsky's financial instability hypothesis posits that the economy is (*stable, unstable*), (*does, does not*) necessarily tend to full employment, and that neoclassical theory is (*consistent, inconsistent*) with the historical behavior of the economy. Moreover, Minsky believes that neoclassical theory (*leaves out, includes*) too many vital elements of the original Keynesian theory.

2. Walrasian theory (*relies on, refutes*) the existence of economic stability and competition.

3. In the (*Post Keynesian, Walrasian*) model, prices are determined by the basic impersonal forces of the market.

4. Say's principle and Say's Law (*are, are not*) the same.

5. Hedging and speculation (*are, are not*) the same thing and are done by (*different, similar*) groups of people.

6. According to Keynes, fluctuations in (C, I, G) spending are primarily causes of economic instability. Minsky says most Keynesians fail to recognize that the instability of (C, I, G) is caused, as (*Keynes, Walras*) argued, by instability in the (*financial, real*) market. This (*financial, real*) market instability arises because of changes in the relationship between the present value and cost of (*capital, consumer*) goods.

7. According to Minsky, the (*complexity and sophistication of, additional government controls over*) the present financial system makes for (*greater, less*) instability of (*investment, consumption*) than originally envisaged by Keynes.

8. Minsky argues that for a business cycle boom to develop, the (*demand price for capital goods, rate of interest, marginal efficiency of capital*) must (*exceed, be less than*) the supply price of capital. This will (*discourage, stimulate*) investment and the investment will (*reduce, generate*) profits. The (*high, low*) profits provide the funds needed to pay off debts and increase dividends, resulting in favorable conditions for additional investment, and thereby increase the (*demand price, interest rate*) for more new capital. As the boom continues, further borrowing to undertake additional (I, C, G) occurs, leading to (*an increase, a decrease*) in the debt/asset ratio and correspondingly a relative (*increase, decrease*) in (*speculative, hedge*) financing of investment. This sequence ultimately causes a (*financial, real*) crisis and a recession. If it were not for the Federal Reserve, big government, and the built-in stabilizers, the result would be a major depression.

True and False

_____ 1. New classical economists, like Post Keynesians, believe expectations play a major role in economic activity.

_____ 2. Walras' law and Post Keynesian theory are essentially the same.

_____ 3. Tatonnement refers to the economy's groping to equilibrium.

_____ 4. Real, historic time is incorporated in static analysis.

_____ 5. Post Keynesians believe prices are set by the impersonal forces of the market.

_____ 6. Post Keynesians stress the role of institutions because they view human behavior as being largely determined by institutions.

_____ 7. Since Post Keynesians are concerned about the income distribution, they do not believe money plays a central role in the economy.

_____ 8. Minsky's model explains why the economy experiences financial crises and why these crises threaten to start a full-blown debt deflation process leading to great economic instability.

_____ 9. According to Post Keynesians, the neoclassical synthesis fails to incorporate Keynes' ideas about how financial factors affect capitalism.

_____ 10. A key point of Minsky's argument is that economic instability is due largely to financial instability, and this financial instability is even greater today than in the 1930s because of the increased complexity and sophistication of the financial system.

_____ 11. Minsky says the village fair perspective is useful for explaining instability of the economy.

_____ 12. Unlike the village fair perspective, which views the economy as a "real exchange" economy, the Wall Street perspective centers on monetary cash flows and their effect on the economy.

_____ 13. There is reasonably strong empirical support for the new Keynesian efficiency wage arguments.

Multiple Choice

1. Post Keynesian economics is based on all of the following *except* that
   a. industrial society is in a process of continual change.
   b. public policy should be designed to accommodate such change.
   c. economic performance can be improved by government policy.
   d. markets always clear if prices and wages are fully flexible.

2. Post Keynesian economics is founded on the belief that
   a. the Walrasian general equilibrium theory is the micro foundation for macroeconomic theory.
   b. the market system will automatically promote full employment.
   c. equilibrium prices will automatically balance the excess demands and excess supplies of all goods and services.
   d. there is no false trading—that is, trading of goods and/or services at nonequilibrium prices.
   e. None of the above are generally valid.

3. Walrasian tatonnement refers to
   a. the economy groping to general equilibrium.
   b. a system in which there is no equilibrium possible.
   c. making changes in government economic policy to offset distortions in the economy.
   d. none of the above

4. Say's principle, as the term is used by Robert Clower, says that buyers always
   a. plan to finance their purchases of goods and services by drawing down their savings.
   b. pay for their purchases by borrowing money so they can realize an interest return on their own money.
   c. plan to finance purchases through the sale of goods and/or services.
   d. none of the above

5. Post Keynesian economics views the economy as
   a. being at rest with full employment in real, historic time.
   b. an ongoing process which takes place in real, historic time.
   c. in equilibrium at a point in time.
   d. operating in a static and timeless situation.

6. Post Keynesian economics views uncertainty
   a. as a fundamental feature of the economy.
   b. as being of only minor significance.
   c. as being nonexistent.
   d. as desirable because it reduces the role played by expectations.

7. According to Post Keynesian economics, instability in the economy is
   a. temporary and of minimal importance.
   b. due to random external shocks.
   c. is endemic to the economic system.
   d. no problem since it always remains at the same level of intensity.

8. Post Keynesian economics postulates that human behavior is determined by
   a. humans acting rationally, as assumed by the classical theory.
   b. government policy.
   c. the social, cultural, and economic institutions of society.
   d. instinct.

9. The school of thought that stresses the role of institutions in human behavior is
   a. classical theory.
   b. monetarist theory.
   c. neoclassical theory.
   d. Post Keynesian theory.

10. The institutions of major concern to Post Keynesian economists are
    a. money and financial institutions.
    b. modern large corporations.
    c. trade unions.
    d. none of the above
    e. all of the above except d

11. The neoclassical synthesis approach to the economy says that, although there will
    be a lag, the economy will move to full employment if
    a. wages and prices are fully flexible.
    b. government monetary policy keeps investment from shifting erratically.
    c. the Fed adopts Friedman's monetary rule.
    d. exchange rates are not permitted to change.

12. The neoclassical synthesis denies
    a. the validity of the classical theory as a theory *per se.*
    b. that the Keynesian revolution was a revolution in theory, although it was in
       policy.
    c. the need for government policy to promote full employment.
    d. that the Keynesian theory is a valid theory.

13. Hyman Minsky's financial instability hypothesis rejects the neoclassical synthesis theory because it ignores
    a. vital parts of Keynes' argument that the fact that economic instability has occurred more frequently than can be explained by the neoclassical theory.
    b. that wages and prices are reasonably flexible, and hence it is not needed.
    c. the effectiveness of monetary and fiscal policy.
    d. the fact that investment is highly stable.

14. Minsky argues that investment is potentially even more unstable today than during Keynes' time because of
    a. the greater complexity and sophistication of the financial system.
    b. increasing government regulation of banking since the 1930s.
    c. massive government borrowing in the financial markets.
    d. increased international capital movements.

15. Minsky believes that the proper way to understand how the modern economy works is
    a. in terms of the Wall Street perspective.
    b. in terms of the village fair perspective.
    c. by analyzing the system of markets and prices.
    d. by understanding the destabilizing effects of government policy.

16. On the basis of his financial instability hypothesis, Minsky argues that
    a. the economy will experience minor fluctuations by the instability caused by government financial operations.
    b. the economy will move into an inflation that results in continued hyperinflation.
    c. the government has no role to play in stabilizing the economy.
    d. the economy will periodically experience financial crises and recessions.

17. According to Minsky, the reason the U.S. economy does not experience long and major depressions any longer is that
    a. the economy is inherently stable.
    b. the Fed, big government, and the automatic built-in stabilizers put a floor under the economy.
    c. aggregate demand is highly responsive to aggregate supply.
    d. big business stabilizes the economy.

18. Which one of the following is not a conclusion that emerges from Minsky's financial instability hypothesis?
    a. The economy is not self-regulating and therefore must be managed if the objectives are to be realized.
    b. Market capitalism has forces within it that generate financial and output crises.
    c. Although the financial markets are somewhat unstable, the economy overall is highly stable and approximates the competitive model very well.
    d. Federal Reserve action to combat a serious financial crisis causes inflation.
    e. Government policy to promote growth should manipulate consumption and not investment.

Answers

Answers to the problems and self-tests are provided below. Brief answers have also been included for those essay questions to which the answer could be summarized in a concise statement or two without misleading the student. No attempt has been made to give summary statements for those discussion questions requiring longer answers. It is expected that the student will consult class notes and the textbook being used in the course to obtain answers to such discussion topics. [Note that some of the essay questions are intended to stimulate the student's own thinking on a controversial topic; for these questions simple responses do not exist.]

Warning: The answers to essay questions provided here are merely the starting point for investigation. Students should develop extensive answers on the basis of the workbook, class lectures, outside readings, and the course text.

CHAPTER 1 Overview of Macroeconomics

A Self-Test

Completion Questions

1. macro
2. microeconomics
3. behavior of human beings
4. full employment, optimum economic growth, reasonable price level stability, and balance-of-payments equilibrium

True and False

1. True; 2. False; 3. True; 4. True; 5. True; 6. True; 7. True.

Multiple Choice

1. *c*; 2. *e*; 3. *e*; 4. *c*; 5. *a*; 6. *c*; 7. *a*; 8. *d*; 9. *d*; 10. *c*; 11. *b*; 12. *c*; 13. *b*; 14. *e*; 15. *c*; 16. *b*; 17. *d*; 18. *c*; 19. *d*; 20. *d*; 21. *d*; 22. *d*; 23. *c*; 25. *c.*

CHAPTER 2 Measuring the Economy's Performance

Problems and Essays

4. Let Y be real income, C be consumption, I investment, and S saving.
   (1) $Y = C + I$ (Source of income)
   (2) $Y = C + S$ (Disposition of income)

Subtracting C from both sides of equations (1) and (2) gives:
(3) $Y - C = I$
(4) $Y - C = S$.
Therefore:
(5) $I = S$.

5. Adding the government, the first two equations become (assume there are no transfers):
(1) $Y = C + I + G$ (Source of income)
(2) $Y = C + S + TX$.   (Disposition of income)
Subtracting C from both sides of equations (1) and (2) gives:
(3) $Y - C = I + G$
(4) $Y - C = S + TX$.
Therefore:
(5) $I + G = S + TX$.

6. This step involves adding foreign trade to the model. The approach is the same as for problems 4 and 5 above.
(1) $Y = C + I + G + X - M$
(2) $Y = C + S + TX$
(3) $Y - C = I + G + X - M$
(4) $Y - C = S + TX$
Therefore:
(5) $I + G + X - M = S + TX$.
Or by rearranging:
(6) $I + G + X = S + TX + M$.

13. a; e; f; g; h; k; m; n; o; p; q; r; t; w [yes]; x, and z, are not included in GDP.

14. Price Indices
a. 90.9; 76.4; 100.0; 123.6; 127.3; 145.4; 200; 272.7; 318.2; 336.4; 372.7.
b. 2339.4; 2795.6; 3110.8; 3381.3; 3776.8; 4405.2; 4895.1; 5343.4.
c. Divide GDP in current prices by GDP in 1987 prices.

16. a. Output increases as N increases (and vice versa).
b. The upward shift implies that one or more of the determinants of the production function have increased, and further that the marginal productivity of labor has increased for all levels of employment. The major factors which may account for such a change are improved natural resources, capital accumulation, and technological change. [Assume throughout this analysis that an upward shift of the production function is accompanied by an increase in the slope of the function at each possible level of employment and vice versa.]
c. An improvement in the quality of natural resources, capital, and technology will shift the function upward and thus increase the marginal product of labor at all employment levels; a deterioration in the quality of natural resources, capital, and technology will produce the opposite results. Changes in population will have no direct effect on the production function and marginal product of labor curves. An increase in the stock of capital, like an increase in quality, will shift the production function upward and increase the marginal product of labor. An

increase in the average level of education will shift the production function upward; a decrease will shift it downward.

A Self-Test

Completion Questions

1. are
2. flow, stock
3. declines
4. flow
5. *ex post*
6. disinvestment
7. *ex post.*
8. gross investment minus replacement investment
9. replacement
10. Identity, Identity, behavior, behavior, identity
11. the value of capital goods used up in the process of production
12. purchases for resale or for further processing
13. personal income, disposable income
14. all taxes, other than the corporate profit tax, paid by business firms
15. be passed on to the consumer in the form of a higher price
16. includes taxes which the individual must pay
17. changes in the price level
18. dividing, index of prices
19. capital equipment used up during the income period
20. economy's potential for producing goods and services
21. *a.* quantity and quality of labor
    b. the quantity and quality of natural resources
    c. the quantity and quality of capital
    d. the level of technology
    e. the standard number of hours worked per year
22. *a.* the quantity and quality of natural resources
    b. the quantity and quality of capital equipment
    c. the level of technology
23. extent to which all resources are utilized
24. then, if
25. postulate assumptions, use logic to arrive at the correct conclusion, test the conclusion against the real world
26. observe relevant facts and events, formulate hypotheses, test the hypotheses

True and False

1. False; 2. True; 3. True; 4. False; 5. False; 6. False; 7. False; 8. True;
9. True; 10. True; 11. False; 12. False; 13. False; 14. False; 15. False;
16. True; 17. True; 18. False; 19. True; 20. False; 21. True; 22. True;
23. False; 24. True; 25. False; 26. False; 27. True; 28. False; 29. False;

30. True; 31. False; 32. True; 33. True; 34. True; 35. False; 36. True; 37. True; 38. True; 39. False; 40. True; 41. True; 42. False; 43. False; 44. False; 45. False; 46. False; 47. True; 48. True.

Multiple Choice

1. *d*; 2. *b*; 3. *c*; 4. *a*; 5. *c*; 6. *e*; 7. *a*; 8. *b*; 9. *d*; 10. *b*; 11. *a*; 12. *e*; 13. *e*; 14. *c*; 15. *b*; 16. *a*; 17. *b*; 18. *e*; 19. *e*; 20. *b*; 21. *c*; 22. *c*; 23. *a*; 24. *d*; 25. *c*; 26. *e*; 27. *a*; 28. *a*; 29. *d*; 30. *a*; 31. *c*; 32. *d*; 33. *d*; 34. *d*; 35. *d*; 36. *c*; 37. *b*; 38. *d*; 39. *c*.

CHAPTER 3   The Classical System

Problems and Essays

1. *a.* Output increases as N increases (and vice versa).
   b. The upward shift implies that one or more of the determinants of the production function have increased, and further that the marginal productivity of labor has increased for all levels of employment. The major factors that may account for such a change are improved natural and human resources, capital accumulation, and technological change. [Assume throughout this analysis that an upward shift of the production function is accompanied by an increase in the slope of the function at each possible level of employment and vice versa.]
   c. An improvement in the quality of natural resources, capital, and technology will shift the function upward and thus increase the marginal product of labor at all employment levels; a deterioration in the quality of natural resources, capital, and technology will produce the opposite results. Changes in population will have no direct effect on the production function and marginal product of labor curves. An increase in the stock of capital, like an increase in quality, will shift the production function upward and increase the marginal product of labor.

2. *a.* Diminishing marginal productivity gives a negatively sloped MP_L curve, and profit maximization requires that entrepreneurs employ additional units of labor up to the point where the real wage equals the MP_L. As the real wage increases and decreases, the volume of employment will vary according to the MP_L. Accordingly, these two concepts require that the demand curve for labor be negatively sloped and the same as the MP_L curve.
   b. An increase in the money wage or a decrease in the price level will increase the real wage (and vice versa). An increase in the money wage or a decrease in the price level reduces the quantity of labor demanded (and vice versa).
   c. (1) The demand curve for labor will shift outward to the right.
       (2) The volume of labor demanded increases (from 75 to 105).
       (3) The marginal product of labor would decline and thus the demand curve for labor would shift toward the origin.

    d. The aggregates are basically a summation of each firm's production function and demand curve for labor. Nonetheless, aggregation problems exist.

3. *a.* This theory relates to the irksomeness or disutility of work. For some people a low real wage will offset the disutility of working, whereas others require a high real wage. The higher the real wage, the greater the number of workers who offer their services because the utility of the wage offsets, or more than offsets, the disutility of working. This assumes no money illusion.

    b. The quantity of labor supplied increases as the real wage increases (and vice versa).

    c. An increase in the money wage or a decrease in the price level will increase the quantity of labor supplied (and vice versa).

    d. No. However, if the demand curve is constant, an outward shift of the supply curve will necessitate moving out on the production function so that the new labor market equilibrium is associated with a higher output (and vice versa).

    e. Population changes and changes in workers' attitude with respect to their willingness to work are the major factors causing shifts in the supply curve of labor.

4. *a.* $N = 75$, $w/p = 4000$; No; Yes.

    b. No. Competition among workers for jobs will reduce the money wage and thus the real wage until equilibrium is attained.

    c. No. Competition among employers (for workers) would force up the money wage and thus the real wage until equilibrium is attained.

    d. w/p increases (to 4670), N increases (to 90), Y increases (to 570). Yes.

    e. w/p decreases, N increases, Y increases.

5. *a.* The classical theory of aggregate demand is basically Say's Law—supply creates its own demand—combined with the classical theory of interest.

    b. (1) $i = 6$ percent, $S = 60$, $I = 60$.

        (2) At any point other than equilibrium, there is either an excess supply (if the interest rate is above the equilibrium interest rate) or excess demand (if the rate is below the equilibrium rate) for investable funds. The former will reduce the incentive to save (as not all funds can be lent out at a rate of return) and increase the incentive to invest until equilibrium is attained; the latter will increase the incentive to save (as the rising interest rate on funds lent to others makes saving more profitable) and reduce the incentive to invest (because of the high cost of investment funds) until equilibrium is attained.

        (3) The saving curve will shift to the right, i will fall, S and I will increase. The opposite will result if consumers decide to save less at all interest rates.

        (4) The investment demand curve will shift inward, i will fall, S and I will decrease. If business executives decide to invest more at each rate, the opposite will occur.

    c. The classical theory of interest guarantees that saving (nonconsumption of current income) will not cause inadequate aggregate demand since the interest theory guarantees that investment will always exactly offset saving. Thus leakages from and inputs into the income stream are the same.

d. The classical theory of aggregate demand insures that unemployment cannot result because of inadequate aggregate demand; it implies that there cannot be overproduction of *all* commodities.

6. *a.* The classical theory of the price level is given by the quantity theory of money. It can best be explained in terms of the equation of exchange, $MV = pY$. Basically V and Y were held constant and p became a function of M. One version says there is a direct and proportional relationship between M and p; an increase (decrease) in M results in a proportional increase (decrease) in p. A more reasonable version posits the same direct relationship but indicates that changes in p will usually be less than in proportion to changes in M.

b. If MV is constant, there is an inverse relationship between p and Y ($p = MV/Y$)—the rectangular hyperbola illustrates this point. $MV = \$800$.

c. As MV is constant, the larger output can be sold only with a lower price level—money becomes more valuable in terms of purchasing power. $p = MV/Y$, and thus an increase in Y necessarily reduces p with a constant MV.

d. If we assume V remains constant, an increase in the money supply will shift the MV curve outward and, with a given Y, increase the price level. A reduction in M will have the opposite effect.

e. An increase in V has the same effect on the price level as an increase in M. Thus in this case the price level would increase as the MV curve shifts outward.

7. *a.* (1) $w/p = \$4000$, $N = 75$.
   (2) $Y = 400$.
   (3) $p = 2$.
   (4) $w = \$8000$.

   b. (1) The marginal product of labor increases at all employment levels. The size of the shift can be determined by computing the new marginal-product-of-labor schedule.
   (2) $w/p = \$4,670$, $N = 90$, $Y = 570$, $p = 1.4$ (approximately); and $w = \$6,538$ (approximately).

   c. If the supply curve shifts outward, w/p declines, N increases, Y increases, and p decreases. For an inward shift of the supply curve, the opposites result.

   d. (1) $MV = 250 \times 4 = 1000$.
   (2) $p = 2.5$, $w = \$10,000$.
   (3) No, because full employment prevails. [Note: Although there would be no lasting effect, there would be a short period of adjustment. The increase in the price level would temporarily lower the real wage and thereby create a mild excess demand for labor. The original real wage would be restored, however, as employers bid up the money wage in their quest for additional workers.]

8. *a.* $MP_L = \$9,000$ when N is 10 and then, $\$8,000$, $\$7,000$, $\$6,000$, $\$5,000$, $\$4,000$, $\$3,000$, $\$2,000$, $\$1,000$, respectively.

   c. $MV = \$600$ billion at all levels of Y and p.
   $p = 6$ when Y is 100, and then 3, 2, 1.5, 1.2, 1.0, 0.86, 0.75, and 0.67, respectively.

   d. (1) $N = 50$, $w/p = \$5,000$, $Y = \$350$, $p = 1.71$ (approximately), $w = \$8,550$ (approximately).

9. *a.* (1) $w/p = \$6,000$; $N = 50$ million; $Y = \$400$ billion; $p = 3$; $w = \$18,000$.
   (2) (a) p falls from $p = 3$ to $p = 2$.
       (b) The new real wage is $w/p = \$18,000/2 = \$9,000$. Since the initial real wage was $6,000, the new real wage exceeds the old one.
       (c) Yes. The quantity of labor demanded is 20 million, while the quantity supplied is 80 million. Thus, at this wage rate there is unemployment of 60 million workers. If we compare the quantity demanded at real wage $9,000 with the equilibrium employment, there are 30 million workers unemployed.
       (d) Yes, because if money wages are not allowed to fall, as is assumed here, competition among workers obviously cannot force down the money wage. [Actually, the real wage will fall slightly because p will rise a little due to the lower output, but the point is that the real wage will remain above the equilibrium real wage and hence there will be unemployment.]
       (e) Y falls to $190 billion. [It is for this reason that p may expand a little.]
   (3) With fully flexible money wages, the system adjusts to full employment. With inflexible money wages, there may be equilibrium at less than full employment.
b. (1) About $270 billion.
   (2) $N = 30$ million will produce $Y = \$270$ billion.
   (3) The answer to this question could be very misleading. Since the money wage is fully flexible downward (by assumption), the real wage could end up at $4,000, and hence by definition of the supply curve there is no unemployment. However, at this point it is well to recognize that both money wages and prices tend to be inflexible downward. If we recognize this, the real wage remains above the equilibrium level and generates some unemployment. If, for example, the real wage ended up at $8,000, there would be unemployment of 40 million with employment being 20 million less than at the equilibrium level.

[*Warning*: The above answers are necessarily simplified. They are intended only to point out the general aspects and conclusions of the classical model. Several qualifications and analytical problems have been passed over with no mention at all. These would necessarily have to be covered if a more advanced treatment were desired.]

A Self-Test

Completion Questions

1. agreed
2. value of the incremental output, cost of the additional workers
3. *a.* The wage is equal to the marginal product of labor
   b. The utility of the wage is equal to the marginal disutility of labor.
4. involuntary
5. competition among employers for workers will bid up the money wage rate and thus increase the real wage until equilibrium is restored

6. fall, shift inward, fall
7. Say's Law, the classical theory of interest
8. supply creates its own demand
9. the relative scarcity of savings will force the rate upward, thereby increasing the incentive to save, as well as reducing the incentive to invest, until equilibrium is restored
10. the money spent on goods and services is equal to the money received from the sale of goods and services
11. medium of exchange
12. in proportion to changes in the money supply
13. reduce the real wage by cutting the money wage rate
14. *a.* the mass unemployment of the 1930s—the Great Depression
    b. the development of an alternative theory by Keynes
15. full employment, less than full employment
16. *a.* workers do not leave the labor market if the real wage declines due to a rising price level
    b. workers cannot determine the real wage, and thus the volume of employment by the money wage bargains because money wages cannot move independently of the price level

True and False

1. False; 2. True; 3. False; 4. True; 5. False; 6. True; 7. True; 8. False; 9. False; 10. True; 11. True; 12. True; 13. True.

Multiple Choice

1. *d;* 2. *a;* 3. *d;* 4. *b;* 5. *c;* 6. *a;* 7. *d;* 8. *b;* 9. *c;* 10. *c;* 11. *b;* 12. *d;* 13. *e;* 14. *a;* 15. *a;* 16. *e;* 17. *b;* 18. *a.*

CHAPTER 4   The Keynesian System

Problems and Essays

4. *a.* At $1,400 billion aggregate supply equals aggregate demand. Up to that level, output is rising; beyond $1,400 billion, output is falling.
    b. $1,400 billion.
    c. If output is $1,800 billion, aggregate supply exceeds aggregate demand. Inventories will accumulate, ultimately causing producers to cut back on production, not only to reduce their inventories to the desired level but also to satisfy the lower level of demand. Production at this level is not profitable.
    d. If output is $800 billion, aggregate demand exceeds aggregate supply. Inventories are being depleted as business executives attempt to satisfy demand

from accumulated stocks. As production is profitable, business executives will expand production, not only to restore inventories to the desired level but also to satisfy the higher demand.

e. Equilibrium output increased to $1600 billion. Output increased by twice as much as the autonomous increase in aggregate demand.

f. Equilibrium output fell to $1,200 billion. Output fell by twice as much as the autonomous reduction in aggregate demand.

g. Because it is generally assumed that the price level is constant, i.e., the analysis is in constant prices.

h. Inflationary gap; $200 billion.

i. Deflationary gap; $100 billion.

5. a. (1) The aggregate demand curve implies that there is a relationship between the price level and aggregate demand. It shows the output level that will be demanded at various price levels during the period under consideration. Note that the relationship between output demand and the price level is probably much less than that implied by the graph. Conceptually, the aggregate demand curve related to the price level is the "summation" of the demand curves for each individual product, the quantity demanded of the individual product being expressed as a function of the price of the product.

(2) The negative slope of the aggregate demand curve implies that as the price level falls, there is an increase in either consumption, government purchases, investment, or net exports, or a combination of these items. There are three basic reasons why the aggregate demand curve may be downward sloping; they are the real balance effect, interest rate effect, and trade balance effect.

The real balance effect postulates that a change in prices alters the real purchasing power of a given amount of money and thereby consumption (and ultimately investment) expenditures. For example, a fall in the price level will increase the purchasing power of money and thereby consumption. The opposite happens for an increase in the price level. [An argument related to the real balance argument is referred to as the "Pigou Effect." A. C. Pigou argued, contra Keynes, that changes in the price level alter consumption. Pigou recognized that a decline in the price level would cause a corresponding reduction in the prices of most business assets and consumer durables. However, it will not reduce the "price" of currency or government bonds. Hence those people holding currency and government bonds realize an increase in their net worth, and this increase in their net worth causes them to increase their consumption; people have to save less to have a certain amount of purchasing power in the future. Thus the Pigou effect also leads to a negatively-sloped demand curve. Note that, as the classical economist denied the existence of a liquidity trap, there is always some price level low enough to generate a level of aggregate demand that will insure full employment. Most economists believe that, while theoretically possible, the Pigou effect would be relatively insignificant. It requires many qualifications. [The interested student should read, A. C. Pigou, "The Classical Stationary State," *Economic Journal*, December

1943, pp. 345–51, and "Economic Progress in a Stable Environment," *Economica*, August 1947, pp. 180–88, reprinted in AEA, *Readings in Monetary Theory* (Homewood, Ill.: Richard D. Irwin, Inc., 1951).]

The *interest rate effect* (or Keynes effect) builds on the real balance effect. Keynes doubted that a decline in the price level would have any direct effect on aggregate demand by increasing C, I, or G; however, he agreed that a falling price level might cause an indirect increase in aggregate demand—up to a point—by increasing the real value of money. If, e.g., the money supply is initially $150 billion and the price level falls by one-half, the purchasing power of this amount of money becomes $300 billion. Thus, as the price level falls, the increase in the real money supply set into motion forces that cause interest rates to decline and thereby stimulates investment and purchase of big ticket consumer durable goods. (See Keynes, *The General Theory*, Ch. 19.)

The *trade balance effect* refers to the impact of a change in the domestic price level on domestic exports and imports when world prices are constant—or at least do not change by as much as domestic prices. A decrease in domestic prices relative to world prices increases domestic exports, reduces domestic imports, and thereby improves the trade balance part of aggregate demand. An increase in domestic prices relative to foreign prices has the opposite effect—it reduces the quantity of aggregate demand.

While not of equal importance, the real balance effect, interest rate effect, and trade balance effect should be combined to explain why the aggregate demand curve is negatively sloped. If prices increase the reverse happens. Note that there are many qualifications to the three arguments.

(3) A change in any components of aggregate demand—consumption, investment, government purchases, exports and imports—not due to a change in the price level will shift the aggregate demand curve.

b. (1) In general terms, the aggregate supply curve is basically a summation of the industry supply curves. It shows the price level associated with various levels of output up to the maximum output that the existing stock of land, labor, capital, and technology can produce. It is a short-run concept because all factors are assumed given except labor. The positive slope is explained as follows: Assume there is an unexpected increase in the price level. Seeing an increase in the price of the product they are producing, producers perceive it to be a relative price increase and, expecting more profits, increase production. This causes an increase in the demand for labor and hence an increase in money wages. Seeing money wages increase more than they expected, workers mistakenly believe the real wage has increased and thereby offer to work more hours. The result is that both producers and workers end up having a money illusion and respond to a rising price level by increasing output and employment. Everything is the reverse for a falling price level. Note that producers and workers end up having a money illusion because they do not know and/or cannot accurately forecast the price level.

[The basic Keynesian explanation for the rising price level as output expands—for the upward climb of the curve—is the diminishing marginal product of labor as employment increases. Given the money wage, the shape of the aggregate supply curve is a reflection of diminishing returns to labor. When all labor is fully employed, the aggregate supply curve becomes vertical, signifying that no further increase in output is possible; at this point any increase in demand will merely raise the price level by a proportionate amount. Although the basic shape of the supply curve is given by the diminishing productivity of labor, many economists, including Keynes, have pointed out other considerations that may cause the price level to rise as output expands. The more important factors are the nonhomogeneity of variable resources, bottlenecks that arise because not all industries are capable of expanding at the same rate, and increased pressure by organized labor for higher wage rates. However, as we shall see later, the latter consideration may cause shifts in the supply curve.]

(2) Changes in the expected price level, the natural resource base, capital stock, and technology are the major factors. A decrease in the expected price level or an increase in the natural resource base, capital stock, or technology will shift the aggregate supply curve outward and downward. The opposite changes shift the supply curve upward and inward.

[The basic Keynesian explanation is as follows: As the aggregate supply curve is derived from the production function and cost-of-production function, it follows that anything causing the production function to shift will also shift the aggregate supply curve. Thus an increase in capital or technological advance will cause the curve to shift downward and probably also shift the full-employment output level to the right. A deterioration of technology or the capital stock would have the opposite effect. Second, a change in the money wage (or other costs of production) will cause shifts in the supply curve; if the money wage rate increases, the supply curve will shift upward and vice versa. Third, an improvement in the quality of labor through education, retraining, and so forth may cause the supply curve to shift downward. It should also be noted that an increase in the labor force will tend to shift the vertical section of the supply curve to the right so that a higher output is possible. Fourth, the imposition of (or an increase in) excise taxes, or any other consideration which raises the firms' marginal cost curves, will shift the aggregate supply curve upward (and vice versa).]

(3) The classical model yielded a conclusion that full employment was the normal state of the economy. As long as the production function and labor supply curve remain unchanged, full employment output will be the same at all price levels.

c. The approximate equilibrium values are $p = 1.1$ and $Y_{np} = \$720$ billion.

(1) At $p = 1.5$ the quantity of aggregate demand is less than that of aggregate supply and hence producers cannot sell all of their output. Prices will fall—if we assume fully flexible prices—until this imbalance is removed. As prices fall, consumers increase their purchases and producers cut back on production.

(2) At $p = 0.75$ the quantity of aggregate demand exceeds that of aggregate supply. Consumers will bid up prices until the excess demand is eliminated. As prices increase, production will be expanded and the quantity demanded will drop.

(3) No, equilibrium may be at less than full employment—there is nothing in the model to guarantee that full employment will generally prevail.

d. The aggregate demand curve shifts outward and, in this case, increases the price level, output, and (via the production function) employment. Note that, had the *AD* curve intersected *AS* in the portion that is (almost) parallel to the horizontal axis, *p* would not have changed while Y_{np} and *N* would have increased. Had *AD* intersected *AS* in the portion of the *AS* curve that is completely vertical—which would be the case beyond the point $p = 2.5$, Y_{np} = $880—*p* would increase while Y_{np} and *N* would not change. Thus, your answer depends on where the *AD* curve intersects the *AS* curve.

e. The *AS* curve will shift upward, thereby increasing the price level and reducing output. Note that the extent of reduction in output depends on how sensitive *AD* is to the price level.

f. An increase in the money supply should indirectly increase aggregate demand and thereby increase prices and output.

A Self-Test

Completion Questions

1. productive capacity of an economic system is utilized
2. productive capacity is assumed to be fixed
3. the economy's capacity changes over time
4. *ex ante*
5. accumulated assets, current income, borrowing, printing money
6. excess, draw down, inventories, increase, expanded, replace, inventories, higher, is
7. deficiency, inventories, accumulate, is not, cut back
8. is not, decisions to produce, decisions to spend, different, different
9. deficiency, exceeds
10. inflationary
11. shifts, movements along, remains unchanged
12. spending units, producing

True and False

1. True;   2. False;   3. True;   4. True;   5. True;   6. False;   7. True   8. False
9. False;   10. True;   11. False;   12. False;   13. False.

Multiple Choice

1. *b;*   2. *c;*   3. *d;*   4. *b;*   5. *a;*   6. *d;*   7. *b;*   8. *c;*   9. *d;*   10. *a;*   11. *a;*   12. *e;*
13. *a;*   14. *a;*   15. *b;*   16. *a;*   17. *a;*   18. *c.*

CHAPTER 5   Money and Interest in the Keynesian System and the International Economy

Problems and Essays

5. *a.* (1) 6 percent. It is where the asset money demand equals the amount of money available to hold as an asset.

   (2) At 9 percent the money supply available to hold ($60 billion) exceeds the asset demand for money ($40 billion). If we assume no change in consumption or investment, the full amount of the excessive supply of asset money will be used to purchase securities. The increased demand for bonds will force up the price of bonds and reduce the rate of interest. This continues until equilibrium is restored.

   (3) In this case the demand for cash ($80 billion) exceeds the money supply available to hold as an asset ($60 billion). Consumers and business firms want to hold more money than they are currently holding. Again, if we assume no change in consumption and investment, people try to obtain the additional cash by selling bonds. This reduces bond prices and increases the interest rate until equilibrium is restored.

   (4) Probably not. The money supply curve should be tipped slightly away from the vertical axis, indicating that at most rates of interest the money supply is slightly interest elastic. However, at a relatively high interest rate the curve would probably become completely interest inelastic. The commercial bank, due to the fractional-reserve requirement, can increase the money supply by creating demand deposits and will do so as long as they can make loans, and so forth. It is only when the banking system becomes "loaned up" that most of the changes in the money supply become autonomous in that it requires action by the Federal Reserve authorities before the money supply can increase further. However, the zero interest elasticity in the money supply does not alter the conclusions of the analysis.

b. (1) Before full adjustment has taken place, the supply of money to hold as an asset exceeds the asset demand for money. The demand for bonds will increase, causing bond prices to rise and the interest rate to fall until the new equilibrium is attained. The new equilibrium interest rate is 4 percent. For a reduction in the asset money supply, the process is just the opposite.

   (2) Before the full adjustment has occurred, the L_a exceeds $M^0{}_a$. To obtain more cash, bonds are sold. Bond prices decrease and the interest rate increases until equilibrium is restored at a higher level of the interest rate. Yes, shifts in the speculative demand for money curve are realistic. The curve, in reality, is never still and shifts up or down as the climate of opinion, wealth of the economy, and so forth changes.

c. It depends on the interest elasticity of the asset demand curve. The more interest inelastic the L_a curve, the more a given change in the asset money supply will alter the interest rate; the more elastic the L_a curve, the less a change in M_a^0 will alter the rate of interest. In the liquidity trap, there is no change in the interest rate whatsoever.

    d. There is controversy over whether the liquidity trap is theoretically possible. Most economists accept the theoretical existence of the liquidity trap but question its practical relevance. In the last 50 years, the only time when the United States may have been in the trap was during the 1930s.

    e. This can be answered with two different analytical techniques, both of which amount to exactly the same thing. First, think in terms of Figure 5–2. As income rises, more money is needed for transactions. If we assume the total money supply is constant, the additional transactions money must come from asset balances. As this occurs, there is less money left for speculative purposes and the interest rate advances. The second approach will be covered in Chapter 11. In essence it says that, as income advances, the *total demand* for money, which includes a transactions demand as well as the liquidity preference demand, increases because more money is desired for transactions. As this occurs, the interest rate rises. Either approach can be used and both give the same results. Note that if the income level falls, the opposite sequence is set into motion and the interest rate declines. In short, it appears that the interest rate is determined by equality between the total demand for and supply of money, not just the demand for and supply of speculative money (as Keynes said).

    f. The Keynesian theory of interest is significant for two basic reasons. First, it emphasizes that equilibrium in the money market is due to forces that are different than those that produce equilibrium in income and employment. Second, by incorporating the asset demand for money into the model, Keynes' theory shows (contra classical theory) that money is not neutral in terms of its effect on income and employment.

    g. Neither the loanable fund theory (which looks at flows) nor the liquidity preference theory(which looks at stocks) is a complete explanation of how interest rates are determined. Both approaches reflect market forces and can be useful. To explain interest rates, however, their conclusions must be tempered and modified to reflect Federal Reserve policy.

A Self-Test

Completion Question

1. flows, stocks, flows
2. surplus, buy, rise, fall
3. lower, higher
4. fall, rise
5. money to hold as an asset, saving, loanable funds
6. saving, net dishoarding and hoarding, newly created money, consumers, businesses, government

True and False

1. False; 2. True; 3. True; 4. False; 5. False; 6. True; 7. False; 8. True;
9. True; 10. True; 11. True; 12. True.

Multiple Choice

1. *b;*   2. *c;*   3. *b;*   4. *a;*   5. *c;*   6. *d;*   7. *d;*   8. *d;*   9. *b;*   10. *a;*   11. *d;*
12. *b;*   13. *d;*   14. *a;*   15. *b;*   16. *b;*   17. *b;*   18. *e;*   19. *c;*   20. *a;*   21. *c;*
22. *c;*   23. *c;*   24. *e;*   25. *d;*   26. *a;*   27. *c;*   28. *a;*   29. *b;*   30. *d;*   31. *b.*

CHAPTER 6   A General Macroeconomic Model

Problems and Essays

1. *b.* The equilibrium rates of interest are 3, 3, 3, 6, and 18 percent for the income
   levels from $200 billion to $1000 billion.

   c. (1) The *LM* curve shows all combinations of the rate of interest and income at
        which the total demand for money—both for transactions and speculative
        purposes—equals the total money supply. At any point on this curve the
        money market is in equilibrium.

     (2) At any point to the right of the *LM* curve, the demand for money exceeds
        the money supply. At any given rate of interest, say 9 percent, the income
        level, say $1,000 billion, exceeds the equilibrium income ($867 billion). As
        the transactions demand for money is a function of the income, a greater
        amount of transactions funds is desired at the $1,000 billion income level
        than at the lower equilibrium income level. Thus *L* must exceed *M.*
        Equilibrium is restored as consumers and businesses attempt to obtain
        more money by selling bonds, reducing consumption and investment, or a
        combination of these actions. If they only sell bonds, bond prices will fall
        and the interest rate increase until equilibrium is restored—since the higher
        interest rate reduces the demand for money—at some higher interest rate
        (18 percent in this case). If consumers and business executives only reduce
        their consumption and investment, income will fall until equilibrium is
        restored—since falling income reduces the demand for money—at some
        lower income level ($867 billion in this case). If consumers and investors
        do both, that is, sell bonds and cut their consumption and investment,
        equilibrium will be restored at a higher interest rate and lower income
        level.

     (3) For any point to the left of the *LM* curve, the demand for money is less
        than the money supply, that is, *L* < *M.* The process of adjustment to
        equilibrium is just the reverse of that given in the answer above.
        Equilibrium will be restored as consumers and investors buy bonds,
        increase consumption and investment, or a combination of these two
        courses of action. Society merely seeks ways of reducing the amount of
        money it holds. Since the money supply is here assumed to be completely
        autonomous, society merely sets into motion forces that cause it to demand
        more money—the money supply remains at its original level.

(4) As the income level advances, more and more money is needed for transactions purposes. Given the money supply, the higher the level of income, the less the money left for speculative purposes and thus the higher the interest rate. At the upper extreme, the *LM* curve becomes completely vertical (often called the classical range), signifying that no further increase in income is possible without an increase in the money supply. The completely vertical part of the *LM* curve does not necessarily correspond with full employment.

d. (1) The increase in the money shifts the M^S curve in part A to the right, causing the equilibrium rates of interest to fall. The new equilibrium interest rates for income levels from $200 billion to $1,000 billion are 3, 3, 3, 4, and 13 percent, respectively. Plotting the new equilibrium rates relative to income in part B gives a new *LM* curve which is farther to the right. Hence increases in the money supply shift the *LM* curve to the right. A reduction in the money supply has the opposite effect and causes the *LM* curve to shift to the left. Note that the *level* of the liquidity trap does not change as the money supply is altered.

  For any given interest rate, say 9 percent, the shift of the *LM* curve—measured in terms of the change in Y_{np} along the horizontal axis—is equal to the change in the money supply ΔM^s divided by the ratio of the transactions demand for money to income *j*; that is, $\Delta Y_{np} = \Delta M^s/j$ where $j = L_t/Y_{np} = \Delta l_t/\Delta Y_{np}$. In this example the *LM* shifts rightward by $\Delta M^s/j = \$20/0.3 = \$67$ billion (approximately) at each interest rate since $j = 0.3$. [Note: The shift in the *LM* curve could also have been measured in terms of the change in the interest rate at any given income level. This exercise is left to the student.]

(2) If the overall increase in the demand for money is for transactions purposes only, the demand curves for money at each income level (in part A) will shift to the right with the liquidity trap remaining at the same interest rate level. If the speculative demand increases as well, the liquidity trap may shift upward as well as shift to the right. In either case the principle is the same. In part A, the demand-for-money curves shift to the right, causing the equilibrium interest rate to be higher at each income level. Plotting the new equilibrium interest rates in part B shows that the *LM* curve is more to the left than it was originally. In short, an increase in the demand for money shifts the *LM* curve to the left in the same manner as a decrease in the money supply. (A reduction in the demand for money has the opposite effect and is analogous to an increase in the money supply.)

e. A reduction in the price level implies that many or all individual prices have fallen. It follows that less money would be required for buying goods and services; that is, less money would be needed for transactions purposes. As the money supply is constant, more money is now available for asset purposes. This would reduce the equilibrium interest rates and cause the *LM* curve to shift to the right. In terms of Figure 6–1, the demand for money curves at each income level would be lower (in part A), causing the equilibrium interest rates to decline and shifting the *LM* curve to the right (in part B). An increase in the price level would have the reverse effect.

f. (1) The equilibrium interest rates are: 3 percent for Y_{np} = \$200; 3 percent for Y_{np} = \$400; 3 percent for Y_{np} = \$600; about 4.35 percent for Y_{np} = \$800; about 9.25 percent for Y_{np} = \$1,000; and 18 percent for Y_{np} = \$1,200.

(2) Yes, except the new *LM* curve specifically recognizes that the money supply is responsive to interest rates; as the interest rate rises, so does the money supply—at least up to a point.

(3) Yes. The new *LM* curve lies to the right of the original one and, in general, has a smaller slope. To see why this is the case, assume that $L = M$. Now let income increase with the corresponding increase in the amount of money needed for transactions. At any given interest rate L now exceeds M^s. This is true regardless of whether M^s is autonomous or interest sensitive. Society may restore equilibrium by cutting consumption and investment, in which case Y_{np} and hence the amount of money needed for transactions purposes will drop back to the original level. On the other hand, society may sell bonds, thereby driving down bond prices and increasing interest rates. As the interest rate increases, it calls forth an increase in the money supply that would not be forthcoming if M^s were autonomous. This induced expansion of the money supply reduces the extent to which L exceeds M and thus results in lower equilibrium interest rates at all income levels beyond the liquidity trap.

(4) Yes. At the extreme the new *LM* curve would also have a segment parallel to the vertical axis, signifying that the money supply prevents a further expansion of Y_{np} beyond that level. As long as M^s is less responsive to the interest rate than the transactions demand for money is to income, the *LM* curve will slope upward. This is because the additional money needed for transactions can only be obtained by drawing it out of idle balances by means of higher interest rates. Once free reserves of the banking system are zero and the money supply no longer responds to increases in interest rates (i.e., M^s becomes parallel to the vertical axis), the *LM* curve also becomes parallel to the vertical axis. [Note: Should the transactions demand for money be sensitive to interest rates, as in Baumol's analysis, the *LM* curve would lie even further to the right. Including this complication in the model would not change the *basic* analysis nor the conclusions of the model.]

(5) The Federal Reserve can increase the money supply by (a) buying government securities and thereby increasing high powered money, (b) reducing the required reserve ratio, or (c) lowering the discount rate. [Further, if it could convince the general public to reduce its currency holdings at a given rate of interest, the money supply could be further increased.] Opposite measures will reduce the money supply.

2. a. (3) For investment rates of 16, 14, 11, 8, 5, and 2 percent, the income levels which make saving equal investment are \$250, \$325, \$400, \$475, \$550, and \$625 billion, respectively.

c. The curve shows all the interest rates and income levels at which saving equals investment; it shows equilibrium in the commodities (or goods) market. The curve must be negatively sloped because the lower the interest rate, the larger the volume of investment, and consequently the higher the income level must be to generate an amount of saving equal to investment.

d. At any point to the right, saving exceeds investment; thus it represents disequilibrium. Inventories will accumulate and profits will decline, causing producers to cut back on production. This will continue until equilibrium is restored (in this case when income has fallen to about $425 billion). There may also be a tendency for the rate of interest to decline slightly. For any point to the left of the IS curve, saving is less than investment and the opposite process of adjustment takes place.

e. (1) As investment is now greater at each interest rate, each equilibrium income level must now be higher to generate the additional saving required to make saving equal investment. Accordingly, the IS curve shifts to the right. The magnitude of shift (i.e., ΔY_{np} at any given rate of interest) is equal to the change in investment (ΔI) times the multiplier (k). As the multiplier in this case is 2.5 (see the saving curve in part B), the IS curve shifts to the right by $25 billion at each interest rate. If the investment function shifts to the left, the opposite occurs, and the IS curve shifts leftward.

   The slope of the IS curve depends on both the slope of the investment function (that is, the interest elasticity of investment) and the slope of the saving function. The steeper the investment and saving functions, the steeper the IS curve (and vice versa). In this case, the slope of the investment function did not change and therefore the slope of the IS curve is unchanged—only its position changed.

   (2) As the original consumption equation must have been $C = \$60$ billion + $0.6Y_{np}$, autonomous consumption has declined to $40 billion, or what is the same thing, autonomous dissaving has declined to dissaving of $40 billion. The saving function will shift to the left (toward the vertical axis) and thus the IS curve will shift to the left as well; more saving is now generated at each income level so the IS curve shifts backward. The IS curve shifts back by the multiplier times the change in autonomous saving; that is, $\Delta Y_{np} = k \times \Delta S_0 = 2.5(-20) = \$50$ billion. A shift to the right in the saving function would cause the IS curve to shift to the right as well; a reduction in society's preference for saving shifts the IS to the right (and vice versa).

   (3) An increase in the marginal propensity to consume is the same as a reduction in the marginal propensity to save and thus the saving curve in part B rotates downward. This causes the IS curve to shift to the right and become less steep—thus a change in the MPS alters the position and slope of the IS curve. An increase in the MPS would shift the IS curve to the left and cause it to become steeper.

3. b. The equilibrium interest rate is about 3 percent and the income level is roughly $600 billion.

c. At this point saving exceeds investment and the money supply exceeds the demand for money. As S exceeds I, inventories accumulate, causing entrepreneurs to reduce production, and consequently the income level tends to fall. As the M^s exceeds L, people are holding more cash than they desire. The attempt to rid themselves of their excess money holdings by purchasing bonds drives up bond prices and causes the interest rate to fall. The decline in income and the interest rate will continue until equilibrium is restored. However, if during the process of adjustment S falls below I, or M^s falls below L, forces will operate in the opposite direction. In any case some forces will continue to operate until equilibrium is restored. (The student should take other points on the diagram and explain the manner in which equilibrium is restored. For example, assume the interest rate is 12 percent with equilibrium in the money market and explain in detail how equilibrium is restored. Remember, of course, that the money market, as well as the goods market, may be in disequilibrium.)

d. Given the situation in Figure 6–4, a decrease in the money supply or an increase in the demand for money will shift the LM curve to the left, increase the interest rate (thereby causing investment to decrease), and lower the income level. An increase in the money supply or decrease in the demand for money would have the opposite consequences if the economy were not in the liquidity trap.

e. The IS curve shifts to the right, and the interest rate and income level increase. The same thing would have occurred had there been an overall reduction in saving; that is, if the saving function had shifted to the right.

f. (1) Yes; note that the income level advances by an even greater amount than it does when investment is not completely interest inelastic. Subsequently we will consider why this is the case.

   (2) The interest rate will still increase. But in this case the higher interest rate will not reduce investment and thus the income level will not fall.

4. a. (1) See Figure 6–5A. $I + G$ is: 285 at 18 percent; 315 at 16 percent; 345 at 14 percent; 375 at 11 percent; 405 at 8 percent; 435 at 5 percent; and 465 at 2 percent. (Billions of dollars.)

   (2) See Figure 6–5A. $I + G + X$ is: 385 at 18 percent; 415 at 16 percent; 445 at 14 percent; 475 at 11 percent; 505 at 8 percent; 535 at 5 percent; and 565 at 2 percent. (Billions of dollars.)

FIGURE 6-5A

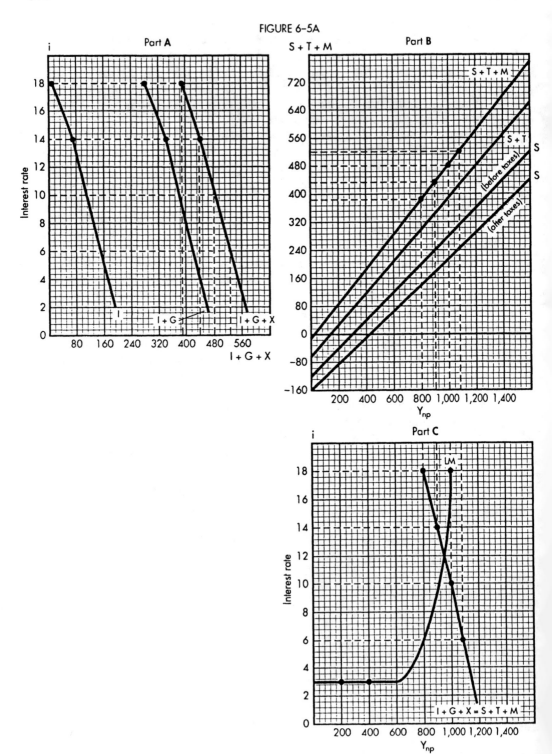

b. (1) $S = -120 + 0.4Y_{np}$.
  (2) T: $80; $100; $120; $140; $160; $180; $200; $220; $240; $260.
  (3) S (after taxes): $-152; $-80; $-8; $64; $136; $208; $280; $352; $424; $496.
  (4) $S + T$: $-72; $20; $112; $194; $296; $388; $480; $572; $664; $756 (all billions), respectively. Note that the $S + T$ curve is not parallel to the saving curve. This is because the marginal rate of taxation is positive instead of zero.
  (5) M: $60; $68; $76; $84; $92; $100; $108; $116; $124; and $132 billion, respectively.
  (6) $S + T + M$: $-12; $88; $188; $288; $388; $488; $588; $688; $788; and $888 billion.

c. Selected points at which $I + G + X = S + T + M$ in part C are $i = 18$ percent and $Y_{np} = \$794$; $i = 14$ percent and $Y_{np} = \$914$; $i = 10$ percent and $Y_{np} = \$994$; $i = 6$ percent and $Y_{np} = \$1074$. The Y_{np} values for the various interest rates can be read off the graph. They can also be found by adding up the saving function, tax function, and import function, which are $S = -120 + 0.4[Y_{np} - (80 + 0.1Y_{np})]$; $T = 80 + 0.1Y_{np}$; and $M = 60 + 0.04Y_{np}$. The sum of these three equations is

$$S + T + M = -12 + 0.5Y_{np}$$

or, since we want to find the level of Y_{np} which will generate an amount of saving/taxes/imports just equal to the amount of investment/government purchases/exports at various income levels,

$$Y_{np} = 2(S + T + M + 12)$$

Thus, for example, when the interest rate is 18 percent, giving the sum of I, G, and X of $385 billion, the level of income which makes $S + T + M$ equal to the $I + G + X$ of $385 is

$$Y_{np} = 2(\$385 + \$12) = 2(\$397)$$
$$= \$794 \text{ billion.}$$

  (1) The equilibrium interest is *approximately* 12 percent and the corresponding equilibrium income level is approximately $954 billion.
  (2) With an increase in I, G, or X the $IGX = STM$ (or IS, for short) curve will shift to the right by the amount of the change in these items times the multiplier. With the LM curve given, the interest rate and income level will both rise. A decrease in any one of these items will shift the IS curve to the left and thus lower the interest rate and income level. [Note: This answer assumes the IS curve is not completely interest inelastic and further that the IS curve does not intersect the LM curve in the liquidity trap. This qualification applies to (3) below as well as here.]
  (3) An increase in S, T, or M at each income level will shift the IS curve to the left, causing both the interest rate and income level to fall. A decrease in either of these items at each income level will shift the IS curve to the right and thereby cause the interest rate and income level to advance.

5. *a.* The interest rate, income, and investment are about 10 percent, $420 billion, and $110 billion, respectively.

   b. (1) The *IS* curve shifts to the right by an amount equal to the change in government purchases times the multiplier. Since the multiplier is 2.5, the *IS* curve shifts rightward by $62.5 billion.

   (2) $i = 11.5$ percent, $Y_{np} = \$445$ billion, and $I = \$95$ billion (all approximate values).

   (3) In the analysis of preceding chapters no allowance was made for changes in the money market—it was assumed that the rate of interest remained constant. It is now apparent that the increase in government purchases requires more money for transactions purposes and hence leaves less cash for speculative purposes. The result is an increase in the interest rate and a consequent reduction in investment. Investment declines by $15 billion, as can be determined from the investment function. Accordingly, the net increase in demand is only about $10 billion ($\Delta G - \Delta I = 25 - 15$), and $10 billion times the multiplier, which is 2.5 in this case, yields an increase in income of $25 billion. Thus we see that the multiplier analysis of preceding chapters must be modified. This assumes that the investment function is not completely interest inelastic.

   (4) In this case the *IS* curve shifts backward toward the vertical axis by $62.5 billion, and the income level falls to about $395 billion, or by $25 billion. Income does not decline by the full $62.5 billion because the interest rate falls (to about 8.5 percent), thereby causing investment to increase (from about $110 billion to about $125 billion) by $15 billion. The net effect is a reduction in aggregate demand of $10 billion. Again the multiplier must be modified. In shift, given the equilibrium situation of Figure 6–6, an increase or decrease in aggregate demand does not have a full multiplier effect. [Note: While here the net effect is $10 billion for both an increase and decrease in *G* of $25 billion, this will not always be the case. The net effect may be more or less for an increase than for a decrease in *G* (or any change in autonomous demand). The shape of the investment function and *LM* curve must be considered.]

   (5) In this case there is no change in the interest rate, thus no change in investment, and consequently the income level increases or decreases by the full multiplier times the change in *G*; for an increase in *G* of $25 billion, the income level rises by $62.5 billion, for a decrease by the same amount, the income level falls by $62.5 billion.

   (6) The income level remains unchanged whether *G* increases or decreases—if we assume the *IS* curve does not move out of the classical range. When *G* increases by $25 billion, it causes the interest rate to advance just enough to reduce investment by $25 billion. The net effect is zero change in aggregate demand. When *G* decreases, the interest rate falls just enough to increase investment by $25 billion. Again the net effect is zero. Accordingly, in this range there is no multiplier effect at all.

   In short, whether the multiplier is modified, or even operates, depends on whether the economy is in the Keynesian range (liquidity trap), intermediate range, or the classical range of the *LM* curve. When the multiplier is modified, it is because the *net* change in aggregate demand is less than in the earlier analysis.

(7) As the interest rate does not increase, there is no decrease in investment and thus the full multiplier applies. Income would increase by $62.5 billion. This is a case where the *IS* and *LM* curves shift rightward at the same time. For the interest rate not to increase, the *LM* curve would have to shift rightward by $62.5 billion which would require an increase in the money supply of $18.75 billion

$$[\Delta Y_{np} = \Delta M^s / j \text{ or } \Delta M^s = \Delta Y_{np} \times j = 62.5(0.3) = 18.75]$$

(8) As the investment function is completely interest inelastic, the *IS* curve will also be completely unresponsive to the interest rate—it will be straight up and down. In this case the full multiplier would operate in both the liquidity trap and the intermediate range. There would still be no multiplier effect in the classical range because the money supply is inadequate to support a net increase in transactions.

Thus there are two qualifications to the general rule that the multiplier will be less when the money market is taken into consideration. The first, as demonstrated in (5), is when the economy is in the liquidity trap. The second, as indicated here, is when the investment function is completely interest inelastic.

6. The answers to this problem are incorporated into the questions.

7. *a.* (1) They are 3 percent and $400 billion, respectively.
   (2) The *LM* curve shifts gradually upward, if we assume the money supply is held constant, from LM_3 to LM_2 to LM_1, and so on until the inflation stops. If we assume that the *IS* curve remains constant, the interest rate increases, thereby reducing investment and the level of output and employment decline.
   (3) In effect the money supply declines because the purchasing power of money continually falls with inflation. As prices increase, a greater portion of the existing stock of money is required to facilitate transactions of goods and services. Given the money supply, less money is available for speculative purposes. The result is a higher interest rate at each output level except those associated with the liquidity trap.
   (4) Yes.
   b. (1) No. Keynes doubted that deflation would have a direct favorable effect on *C, I,* or *G.* He did point out that the trade balance would improve but thought that this effect would be relatively small for the United States (but perhaps relatively large for the United Kingdom). Let us assume that the improvement in the trade balance, which would tend to shift the *IS* curve to the right, is negligible so that the *IS* curve is unchanged.
   (2) Yes. As the price level falls, the purchasing power of money rises; this amounts to the same thing as saying there has been an increase in the money supply. The reduction in prices (and, of course, wages) reduces the amount of money needed for transactions at all income levels and thus increases the amount of money for speculative purposes. As the asset money supply now exceeds the asset demand for money, the excess money

balances are used to purchase bonds. Bond prices increase and reduce the interest rate. In short, the increase in the real money supply shifts the *LM* curve gradually to the right from LM_1 to LM_2 to, say, LM_3.

(3) Yes. As the *LM* curve shifts gradually to the right, the interest rate declines, causing investment to increase and the income level, as well as employment, to advance.

(4) No, not in this case which is probably close to the general rule according to Keynes and most economists. The maximum output level from deflation is $400 billion; at this level IS_1 cuts the *LM* curve in the liquidity trap. Any further fall in the price level, say a fall that causes the *LM* curve to shift from LM_3 to LM_4, may release transactions funds, but the freed money goes into idle balances and is not used to purchase securities. Consequently, the interest rate cannot fall any further and thereby increase investment.

(5) The modern view is that to increase employment, money wage cuts must increase aggregate demand; and it is unlikely that money wage cuts will increase total demand. Even though the Keynes effect is one possible way that wage cuts could increase aggregate demand and thus employment, this effect is an exception and, furthermore, would be relatively small. Even if the Keynes effect were relatively large, however, there is the possibility that full employment would require an interest rate below the liquidity trap. Accordingly, since it is doubtful that aggregate demand would be increased significantly, Keynes and most economists are skeptical of wage reductions as a means to increase employment. But even if wage cuts are effective, why use such a painful process when the monetary authorities could achieve the same thing by increasing the money supply? (Note also that if the investment function is highly interest inelastic, as Keynes believed, the Keynes effect would be even smaller.)

c. (1) The Pigou effect (also called the "real balances effect") will shift the *IS* curve to the right as the price level falls. The rationale is that a falling price level increases the real value of currency and government bonds. As individuals' net worth has increased, the necessity to save out of the current income is less, and a larger fraction of income goes into consumption. This causes the saving function to shift downward and shifts the *IS* curve to the right. The curve will continue to shift rightward, say from IS_1 to IS_2 and so on, as long as the price level falls.

(2) The Pigou effect alters only the *IS* curve. However, as the price level falls, the *LM* curve shifts to the right (for the reason given above). Thus the analysis should consider the *IS* and *LM* curves both shifting to the right.

(3) Yes. As the *IS* curve shifts to the right, even if we assume the *LM* curve remains constant, the income level expands. With the *LM* curve shifting at the same time, there is a much greater increase in income and employment.

(4) Yes. Even if the *LM* curve were to remain at LM_1, full employment would be achieved when the price level declines enough to shift the *IS* curve to IS_3. However, as the *LM* curve also shifts, full employment is attained at the intersection of IS_2 and LM_2. If the full-employment output level is

higher, say 650, it can still be attained by reducing prices; IS_4 and LM_4 intersect at this level.

(5) As the strength of the Pigou effect is related to the degree of fall in the price level, it follows that there must be some price level that will produce full employment. Pigou proved that *theoretically* it may be possible to attain full employment if only wages and prices are reduced enough.

(6) The Pigou effect is probably not very important. Many qualifications and limitations have to be recognized. From a practical point of view it would have to be demonstrated that the price and wage level that would insure full employment is not very far from the present level. Otherwise any attempt to attain full employment by this means would cause hopeless social and economic disruption. On theoretical grounds there is room for doubt as well. Some of the more important considerations are the effect of a falling price level—a once-and-for-all decline is not possible—on expectations, the importance of net worth as a determinant of consumption, and the effect of the redistribution of income on consumption.

8. a. When $p = 2.5$, $AD = \$400$ billion. See Figure 6–10A.
   b. For $p = 2.0$, $AD = \$515$ billion. See Figure 6–10A.
   c. For $p = 1.5$, $AD = \$625$ billion.
   d. At $p = 1.0$, $AD = \$725$ billion and at $p = 0.5$, $AD = \$820$ billion.
   e. There are several factors other than the Keynes effect and Pigou effect that may cause the quantity demanded to expand as the price level falls, although it is doubtful that they should be given much weight under normal conditions. Some of the more important ones are (1) Tax effect—as prices fall, so does money income and thus people move into lower tax brackets, the result being that they have to pay less taxes and have more money to spend for consumption. Hence the *IS* curve shifts outward and increases *AD*. (2) Balance of trade effect— falling prices tend to increase exports and reduce imports, thereby shifting the *IS* curve rightward and increasing the quantity of *AD*.
   (3) Redistribution of income effect—as prices fall, profits may be squeezed relative to wages, thereby shifting the *IS* curve outward and increasing the quantity of *AD*.
   f. An autonomous (with respect to the price level) increase in consumption, investment, government purchases and/or exports and a reduction of autonomous imports. The opposite changes cause the *AD* curve to shift inward toward the origin.
   g. Although responsive to price changes, the extent of responsiveness is probably less than that implied in part B of Figure 6–10.
   h. $AD = \$550$ billion.
   i. Yes. Conceptually the *AD* curve is the summation of the individual demand curves.

9. a. See Figure 6–11A.
   b. Expressed in constant dollars (starting with the change from 0 to 10 million workers), we have $18,000, $16,000, $14,000, $12,000, $10,000, $8000, $6000, and $4000. See Figure 6–13A.

FIGURE 6-10A
Part **A**

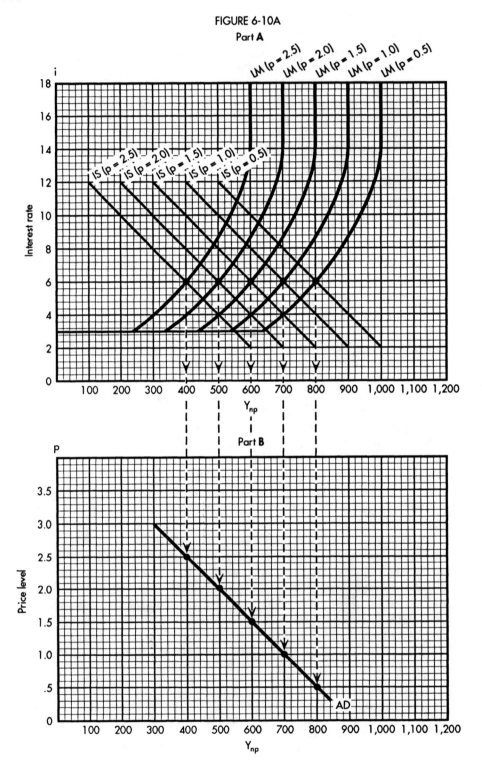

FIGURE 6–11A

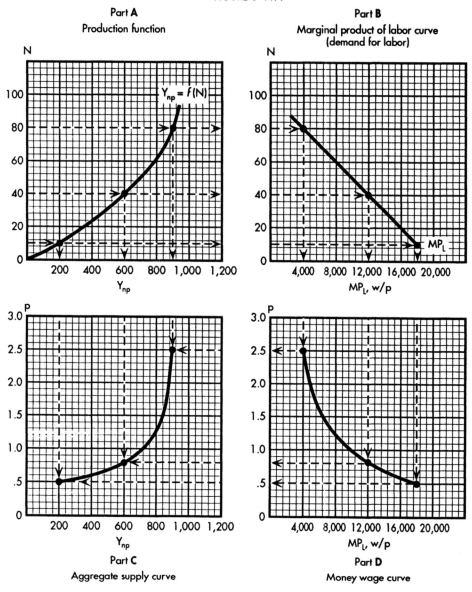

Part **A**
Production function

Part **B**
Marginal product of labor curve
(demand for labor)

Part **C**
Aggregate supply curve

Part **D**
Money wage curve

c. If we start with Y_{np} = \$180 billion (so that MP_L = \$18,000), the values of p are 0.556, 0.625, 0.714, 0.833, 1.00, 1.25, 1.67, and 2.50.

d. (1) This answer is provided in the question for guidance purposes.

   (2) Y_{np} = \$600 billion; MP_L = \$12,000; p = 0.833. We now have a second point on the AS curve at p = 0.833 and Y_{np} = \$600 billion.

   (3) When N = 80 million, Y_{np} = \$880 billion; MP_L = \$4000, and p = 2.5. Thus a third point on the AS curve is at Y_{np} = \$880 and p = 2.5.

f. (1) In a recession with prices inflexible downward.

   (2) Yes, at the full-employment level of output. At this point output cannot be increased and attempts to do so will cause pure inflation.

g. (1) The AS curve will shift outward and downward. For the opposite shift of the production function the AS curve shifts inward and upward.

   (2) The money wage curve in part D will shift to the right, causing the AS curve in part C to shift upward. The opposite occurs for a reduction of the money wage.

10. a. (1) The aggregate supply cure is basically a summation of the industry supply curves. It shows the price level associated with various levels of output up to the maximum output that the existing stock of land, labor, capital, and technology can produce. It is a short-run concept because all factors are assumed given except labor. (Note: Each industry supply curve is equal to the sum of the supply curves of all the firms in the industry; or, in pure competition, the sum of the marginal cost curves above the average variable cost curves.)

     The basic explanation for the rising price level as output expands—for the upward climb of the curve—is the diminishing marginal product of labor as employment increases. Given the money wage, the shape of the aggregate curve is a reflection of diminishing returns to labor. When all labor is fully employed, the aggregate supply curve becomes vertical, signifying that no further increase in output is possible; at this point any increase in demand will merely raise the price level by a proportionate amount.

     Although the basic shape of the supply curve is given by the diminishing productivity of labor, many economists, including Keynes, have pointed out other considerations that may cause the price level to rise as output expands. The more important factors are the nonhomogeneity of variable resources, bottlenecks that arise because not all industries are capable of expanding at the same rate, and increased pressure by organized labor for higher wage rates. However, as we shall see shortly, the latter consideration may cause shifts in the supply curve.

   (2) As the aggregate supply curve is derived from the production function, it follows that anything causing the production function to shift will also shift the aggregate supply curve. Thus an increase in capital or technological advance will, *ceteris paribus*, cause the curve to shift downward and probably also shift the full-employment output level to the right. A deterioration of technology or the capital stock would have the opposite effect, if one could imagine such occurring. Second, a change in the money wage will cause shifts in the supply curve; if the money wage rate

increases, the supply curve will shift upward and vice versa. Third, an improvement in the quality of labor through education, retraining, and so forth may, *ceteris paribus,* cause the supply curve to shift downward. It should also be noted that an increase in the labor force will tend to shift the vertical section of the supply curve to the right so that a higher output is possible. Fourth, the imposition of (or an increase in) excise taxes, or any other consideration which raises the firms' marginal cost curves, will shift the aggregate supply curve upward (and vice versa).

b. (1) The aggregate demand curve implies that there is a relationship between the price level and aggregate demand. It shows the output level that will be demanded at various price levels during the period under consideration. The student should note that the relationship between output demand and the price level, if it does exist in any systematic manner, is probably much less than that implied by the graph. Conceptually, the aggregate demand curve related to the price level is the "summation" of the demand curves for each individual product, the quantity demanded of the individual product being expressed as a function of the price of the product.

(2) The negative slope of the aggregate demand curve implies that as the price level falls, there is a change in either consumption, government purchases, investment, or net exports, which causes the income level to advance. There are two basic reasons why the aggregate demand curve may be downward sloping; they are the Keynes effect and the Pigou effect. [See answer to 8*e* above.]

Keynes effect. Keynes doubted that a decline in the price level would have any *direct* effect on aggregate demand by increasing *C, I,* or *G*. (Keynes did point out that a price reduction relative to other countries would tend to improve the trade balance, but he thought this effect would be insignificant for the U.S.) However, he felt that a falling price level might cause an indirect increase in aggregate demand—up to a point—by increasing the "real" value of money. If the money supply is initially $150 billion and the price level falls by one-half, the purchasing power of this amount of money becomes $300 billion. Thus as the price level falls, less money is needed for transactions balances. But this means that more is now available for speculative purposes, and consequently the interest rate declines, causing investment to increase—if we assume investment is not completely interest inelastic. If so, the level of output demanded increases as the price level declines due to the rise in investment. The student should note that, although not illustrated by the demand curve in Figure 6–12, Keynes' aggregate demand curve would become completely vertical once the price level falls enough to lower the interest rate to the liquidity trap— the aggregate demand curve would be ⌐-shaped. (The student is advised to see Keynes, *op. cit.,* Ch. 19, pp. 260–69.)

Pigou effect. A. C. Pigou argued, contra Keynes, that changes in the price level alter consumption. Pigou recognized that a decline in the price level would cause a corresponding reduction in the prices of most business assets and consumer durables. However, it will not reduce the "price" of currency or government bonds. Hence those people holding currency and government bonds realize an increase in their net worth, and this increase in their net worth causes them to increase their consumption; people have to save less to have a certain amount of purchasing power in the future. Thus the Pigou effect also leads to a negatively-sloped demand curve. Note that, as the classical economist denied the existence of a liquidity trap, there is always some price level low enough to generate a level of aggregate demand that will insure full employment.

Most economists believe that, while theoretically possible, the Pigou effect would be relatively insignificant. It requires many qualifications. [The interested student should read A. C. Pigou, "The Classical Stationary State," *Economic Journal*, December 1943, pp. 345–51 and "Economic Progress in a Stable Environment," *Economica*, August 1947, pp. 180–88, reprinted in AEA, *Readings in Monetary Theory* (Homewood, Ill.: Richard D. Irwin, Inc., 1951).]

The Keynes effect, Pigou effect, net exports effect, tax effect, and redistribution effect (see the answer to problem 10*a* above for the latter two effects) should all be combined to explain why the aggregate demand curve is negatively sloped.

  (3) An autonomous change in any of the components of aggregate demand— consumption, investment, government purchases, exports and imports— will shift the aggregate demand curve.

c. The approximate equilibrium values are $p = 1.1$ and $Y_{np} = \$720$ billion.

  (1) At $p = 1.5$ the quantity of aggregate demand is less than that of aggregate supply and hence producers cannot sell all their output. Prices will fall— if we assume fully flexible prices—until this imbalance is removed. As prices fall, consumers increase their purchases and producers cut back on production.

  (2) At $p = 0.75$ the quantity of aggregate demand exceeds that of aggregate supply. Consumers will bid up prices until the excess demand is eliminated. As prices increase, production will be expanded and the quantity demanded will drop.

  (3) There is no way of knowing this until the full-employment level is specified.

  (4) No, equilibrium may be at less than full employment—there is nothing in the model to guarantee full employment will generally prevail.

d. The aggregate demand curve shifts outward and, in this case, increases the price level, output, and (via the production function) employment. Note that had the *AD* curve intersected *AS* in the portion that is (almost) parallel to the horizontal axis, p would not have changed while Y_{np} and N would have increased. Had *AD* intersected *AS* in the portion of the *AS* curve that is completely vertical—which would be the case beyond the point $p = 2.5$, $Y_{np} = \$880$—$p$ would increase while Y_{np} and N would not change. Thus your answer depends on where the *AD* curve intersects the *AS* curve.

e. The *AS* curve will shift upward, thereby increasing the price level and reducing output. Note that the extent of reduction in output depends on how sensitive *AD* is to the price level.

f. An increase in the money supply should indirectly increase aggregate demand and thereby increase prices and output.

A Self-Test

Completion Questions

1. left, right, reducing, a decrease, an increase
2. interest rate, income, saving, investment
3. left, right, a decrease
4. will, less, increase, reducing, less
5. saving, investment, investment and government purchases, saving and taxes, investment, government purchases, exports, saving, taxes, imports
6. liquidity trap, does not, increase, likely, higher, liquidity trap
7. an increase, increases, freed from, increase, fall, advance, increasing, doubled
8. $2000 - 50i$, $40 - 0.02Y_{np}$
9. $0.2Y_{np} + 200 - 20i$, $500 + 100i$, $-5 + 0.01Y_{np}$
10. $1500, 10 percent
11. increase, expand, rise

True and False

1. False; 2. True; 3. False; 4. False; 5. False; 6. True; 7. False; 8. True;
9. False; 10. True; 11. True; 12. False; 13. True; 14. True; 15. True;
16. True; 17. False.

Multiple Choice

1. *c*; 2. *a*; 3. *d*; 4. *a*; 5. *c*; 6. *e*; 7. *b*; 8. *c*; 9. *a*; 10. *f*; 11. *b*; 12. *d*;
13. *b*; 14. *b*; 15. *d*; 16. *c*; 17. *b*; 18. *c*; 19. *e*; 20. *a*; 21. *c*; 22. *b*; 23. *d*;
24. *b*; 25. *a*; 26. *b*; 27. *c*; 28. *c*; 29. *c*; 30. *b*; 31. *a*.

CHAPTER 7   Consumption, Saving, and the Multiplier

Problems and Essays

2. *a. C*, dependent variable; Y_d, independent variable; *a*, slope $= MPC$; C_0, autonomous consumption.
   c. C: 400, 300, 600, and 350, respectively. (If Figure 7–1 yields different values, the equations have been plotted incorrectly.)
3. *a.* (3) $Y_d = C_0 + aY_d + S.$
   (4) $Y_d - aYd = C_0 + S.$
   (5) $Y_d(1 - a) = C_0 + S.$
   (6) $Y_d(1 - a) - C_0 = S.$
   b. (1) $S = -C_0 + sY_d.$ (Saving function)
   (2) $S + \Delta S = -C_0 + s(Y_d + \Delta Y_d).$
   (3) $S + \Delta S = -C_0 + sY_d + s\Delta Y_d.$
   (4) $S + \Delta S - S = -C_0 + sY_d + s\Delta Y_d - (-C_0 + sY_d).$

    (5) $\Delta S = s\Delta Y_d$.
    (6) $s = \Delta S/\Delta Y_d$.
  c. $s = 0.25Y_d$.
    $s = -50 + 0.10Y_d$.

4. a. MPS is constant.
  b. MPS is the slope of the saving function.
  c. APS increases (while APC decreases).
  d. The saving function shifts upward parallel to itself.
  e. The MPS will decline.
  f. The sum of the slopes equals unity; that is, MPC + MPS = 1. This is always
    the case in the simplified model currently being discussed. It can be proven
    algebraically as follows:
    (1) $Y_d = C + S$.   (Disposition of income in simple model)
        Should there be a change in income, it equals the change in C and/or S:
    (2) $\Delta Y_d = \Delta C + \Delta S$.
        Divide both sides of equation (2) by ΔY_d. This gives:
    (3) $\dfrac{\Delta Y_d}{Y_d} = \dfrac{\Delta C}{\Delta Y_d} + \dfrac{\Delta S}{\Delta Y_d}$
        or:
    (4) $1 = $ MPC + MPS.
  g. The APC + APS = 1. That this is true for the simple model can be proven
    algebraically as follows:
    (1) $Y_d = C + S$.
        Divide both sides of equation (1) by Y_d. This gives:
    (2) $\dfrac{Y_d}{Y_d} = \dfrac{C}{Y_d} + \dfrac{S}{Y_d}$
        or:
    (3) $1 = $ APC + APS.

5. a. C: 75; 225; 375; 525; 675; 825; 975; 1125; 1275; and 1425 (all billions of
    dollars). $C + I$: 275; 425; 575; 725; 875; 1025; 1175; 1325; 1475; and 1625
    (billions of dollars).
  b. $Y_d = \$1100$ billion; $S = \$200$ billion; $I = \$200$ billion; $C = \$900$ billion.
  c. Yes, this must always be the case. Equilibrium can be determined by using
    either approach.
  d. (1) The consumption function shifts upward by $25 billion, and the saving
        function shifts downward by $25 billion at each level of income. At the
        new equilibrium, $Y_d = \$1200$ billion, $C = \$1000$ billion, and $I = \$200$
        billion.
    (2) Yes.
    (3) Yes. Y_d is still $1200 but now $C = \$975$ billion and $I = \$225$ billion.
    (4) The results are just the opposite. Both approaches give the same
        equilibrium values.
  e. Yes.

6. a. (5) $\Delta Y_d = a\Delta Y_d + \Delta I$.
    (6) $\Delta Y_d - a\Delta Y_d = \Delta I$.

(7) $\Delta Y_d(1 - a) = \Delta I.$

(8) $\Delta Y_d = \dfrac{\Delta I}{1-a} = \dfrac{1}{1-a}\Delta I.$

(9) $\dfrac{\Delta Y_d}{\Delta I} = \dfrac{1}{1-a} = \dfrac{1}{1-MPC}.$

b. $k = 5.$

$\Delta Y_d = k\Delta I = 5\,(\$8\text{ billion}) = \$40\text{ billion}.$
Increase (positive)
$\Delta C = a\Delta Y_d = 0.8\,(\$40\text{ billion}) = \$32\text{ billion}.$

7. a. (4) $Y_d = C_0 + aY_d + I_0.$
   (5) $Y_d - aY_d = C_0 + I_0.$
   (6) $Y_d(1 - a) = C_0 + I_0.$
   (7) $\Delta Y_d = \dfrac{1}{1-a}(C_0 + I_0).$

   b. $k = 5;\ Y_d = \$1100\text{ billion};\ C = \$920\text{ billion}.$

8. a. MPC: 0.85 at all disposable income levels.
      APC: ∞; 1.55; 1.20; 1.08; 1.03; 0.99; 0.97; 0.95; 0.94.
   b. If the consumption function is a straight line going through the origin.
   c. MPS: 0.15 at all income levels.
      APS: –∞; -0.55; -0.20; -0.08; -0.03; 0.01; 0.03; 0.05; 0.06.
   d. Equation (4), which is $APC = C_0/Y_d + MPC$, shows that for all positive income levels the APC always is larger than the MPC since the APC includes C_0/Y_d plus the MPC. It further shows, since the term C_0/Y_d gets smaller—C_0 remains constant while Y_d increases—that the APC falls gradually as the income level rises, becoming closer and closer in magnitude to the MPC.

9. a. See Figure 7–4A. The APC declines.
   b. See Figure 7–4A.
   c. See Figure 7–4A.
   d. For the short run a variant of C_2 is most realistic; for the long run C_3 is probably most realistic.

10. a. See Figure 7–5A.
    b. See Figure 7–5A.
    c. See Figure 7–5A.
    d. S_2 in the short run and S_3 in the long run.

11. a. $Y_d = \$800\text{ billion};\ C = \$650\text{ billion};\ S = \$150\text{ billion};\ I = \$150\text{ billion}.$
    b. There will be unintended investment in inventories that will ultimately cause producers to cut back on production, both to reduce inventories to the desired level and to produce for the lower level of demand. This will continue until equilibrium is restored.
    c. In this case there will be unintended depletion of inventories that will cause producers to increase production until equilibrium is achieved.
    d. $Y_d = \$900\text{ billion};\ C = \$725\text{ billion};\ S = \$175\text{ billion}.$ The equilibrium income level will decline to its initial level.

FIGURE 7–4A

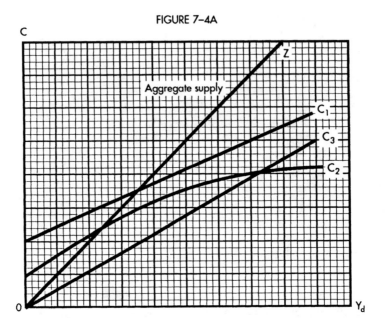

FIGURE 7–5A

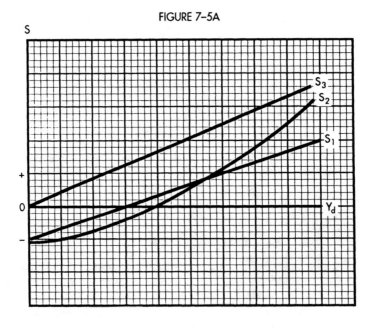

e. $k = 4$. It can be determined by using the reciprocal of $(1 - MPC)$ or by dividing the change in income by the change in investment.

f. The multiplier will increase if the consumption function becomes steeper and decrease if the slope of the function becomes less.

g. No.

13. $k = \dfrac{Y_1 Y_2}{bc}$

14. a. If we start with the third period, the approximate values are:
Y_d: 425; 455; 461; 473.8; 484; 493; . . . 525.
C: 370; 386; 398.8; 409; 417.2; 423.8; . . . 450.

b. If we start with the third period, the approximate values are:
Y_d: 425; 420; 416; 412.8; 410; 408.2; . . . 400.
C: 370; 366; 362.8; 360.2; 358.2; 356.6; . . . 350.

c. Lesson: The change in income will be permanent only when the change in investment is permanent. If the increase or decrease of investment is temporary, the level of income will ultimately return to its initial equilibrium. All of this applies *ceteris paribus*. Note that if investment is reduced, the results are just the opposite.

d. No, the results would be the same.

A Self-Test

Completion Questions

1. a. attitudes toward thrift
   b. assets of the consumer
   c. distribution of income
   d. rate of interest
   e. price changes and consumer expectations
   f. consumer credit
   g. taxes and transfer payments
   h. tariffs and quotas (etc.)
   i. advertising?
   j. population
   k. other
2. a. They are related in a systematic and dependable way, and
   b. Whenever income increases, consumption will also increase but by less than the increase in income and vice versa
3. a schedule showing the amounts consumers intend to spend at various levels of income during a specific time period.
4. Y_4
5. HY_4, HI, $HI = CB$, and so forth
6. increasing, decreasing
7. 100 percent, greater, less
8. $500 billion, $100 billion, $400 billion
9. 0.5, 0.5, 2
10. $300 billion

11. remains constant, decreases
12. $300 billion
13. dissaving, saving
14. increases, remains unchanged
15. $300 billion
16. $20 billion, $10 billion, $10 billion
17. induced, induced
18. 1, infinity

True and False

1. True; 2. False; 3. True; 4. False; 5. True; 6. False; 7. True; 8. True;
9. True; 10. False; 11. True; 12. True; 13. False; 14. True; 15. True;
16. True; 17. True; 18. True; 19. True; 20. True; 21. True; 22. True.

Multiple Choice

1. *c*; 2. *c*; 3. *a*; 4. *b*; 5. *c*; 6. *a*; 7. *c*; 8. *a*; 9. *d*; 10. *c*; 11. *b*; 12. *e*; 13. *b*;
14. *d*; 15. *d*; 16. *b*; 17. *b*; 18. *f*; 19. *c*; 20. *a*; 21. *c*; 22. *a*; 23. *c*; 24. *d*;
25. *b*; 26. *a*; 27. *c*; 28. *a*; 29. *a*; 30. *d*; 31. *d*.

CHAPTER 8   Investment and Finance

Problems and Essays

1. *a*. (1) Yes; $V_p = \dfrac{R_1}{1+i} = \dfrac{\$5,450}{1.07} =$ $\$5,093.45$. Net profit is $V_p - K_s = \$5,093.45$
$- \$5,000 = \$93.45$ (R_1, R_2, and so forth representing the expected income stream).

(2) (*a*) Yes; $V_p = \dfrac{R_1}{1+i} + \dfrac{R_2}{(1+i)^2} + \dfrac{R_3}{(1+i)^3} + \dfrac{R_4}{(1+i)^4}$

$= \dfrac{\$1,600}{(1.07)} + \dfrac{\$1,600}{(1.07)^2} + \dfrac{\$1,600}{(1.07)^3} + \dfrac{\$1,600}{(1.07)^4}$

$= \$1,495.33 + \$1,397.50 + \$1,306.12 + \$1,220.45$

$= \$5,419.40$

Net profit is $\$5,419.40 - \$5,000 = \$419.40$.

(*b*) The investment is still profitable as the following shows:

$V_p = \dfrac{\$1,550}{(1.07)} + \dfrac{\$1,500}{(1.07)^2} + \dfrac{\$1,450}{(1.07)^3} + \dfrac{\$1,400}{(1.07)^4}$

$= \$1,448.60 + \$1,310.16 + \$1,183.63 + \$1,068.05 = \$5,010.44$

Net profit is $\$5,010.44 - \$5,000 = \$10.44$.

b. (1) Yes. The *MEC* or $r = \dfrac{R_1}{K_s} - 1 = \dfrac{\$5,450}{\$5,000} - 1 = 1.09 - 1 = 9$ percent, which

exceeds the interest rate. The net profit rate is $r - i = 9$ percent $- 7$ percent $= 2$ percent. (Note: This formula applies only if the machine lasts one year—as postulated in this case.)

(2) Yes. Plugging the supply price and expected income stream data into the MEC formula gives the following:

$$K_s = \frac{R_1}{(1+r)} + \frac{R_2}{(1+r)^2} + \frac{R_3}{(1+r)^3} + \frac{R_4}{(1+r)^4}$$

$$\$5,000 = \frac{\$1,600}{(1+r)} + \frac{\$1,600}{(1+r)^2} + \frac{\$1,600}{(1+r)^3} + \frac{\$1,600}{(1+r)^4}$$

The MEC is approximately 10.6 percent. As the MEC exceeds the current interest rate (7 percent), this investment is profitable. The net profit rate is about 3.6 percent.

c. Yes, both approaches must give the same results. If the present value exceeds the supply price, then the MEC must exceed the interest rate (and vice versa). When the present value equals the supply price, the MEC equals the interest rate. Either approach can be used. (Note: This is the simplified answer. There are situations where the two approaches will not give the same results.)

2. *a.* See Figure 8–1A.
   b. $20,000.
   c. $57,500.

FIGURE 8–1A

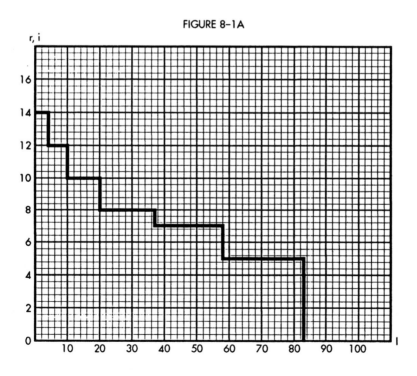

3. *a.* (6) $\Delta Y_{np} = a\Delta Y_{np} + b\Delta Y_{np} + \Delta I_0$.

   (7) $\Delta Y_{np} - a\Delta Y_{np} - b\Delta Y_{np} = \Delta I_0$.

   (8) $\Delta Y_{np}(1 - a - b) = \Delta I_0$.

   (9) $\Delta y_{np} = \dfrac{\Delta I_0}{1-a-b} = \Delta I_0 \times \dfrac{1}{1-a-b}$.

   (10) $\dfrac{\Delta Y_{np}}{\Delta I_0} = \dfrac{1}{1-a-b}$.

b. (1) $k = 1/1 - 0.75 = 4$.

   (2) $k_i = 1/1 - 0.75 - 0.15 = 10$.

   (3) Without induced investment, the change in income is $16 billion; with induced investment, it is $40 billion.

4. *a.* (4) $Y_{np} = C_0 + aY_{np} + I_0 + bY_{np}$.

   (5) $Y_{np} - aY_{np} - bY_{np} = C_0 + I_0$.

   (6) $Y_{np}(1 - a - b) = C_0 + I_0$.

   (7) $Y_{np} = \dfrac{C_0 + I_0}{1-a-b} = \dfrac{1}{1-a-b}(C_0 + I_0)$

b. $k_i = 4$; $Y_{np} = 4(45 + 95) = 560$.

5. *a.* (1) $k = \dfrac{1}{1-0.6} = 2.5$.

   (2) $\Delta Y_{np} = \$62.5$ billion.

   (3) $Y_{np} = 2.5 \times (60 + 90) = \$375$ billion.

b. (1) $k_i = \dfrac{1}{1-0.6-.02} = 5$.

   (2) $\Delta Y_{np} = \$125$ billion.

   (3) $Y_{np} = 5 \times (60 + 90) = \$750$ billion.

c. Induced investment increases the multiplier, causes changes in investment to have a greater effect on income, and increases the equilibrium level of income.

d. (1) $375 billion.

   (2) $750 billion.

   (3) $875 billion with induced investment; $437.50 billion without induced investment.

6. *a.* Capital stock: 600; 660; 780; 900; 960; 960; 900; 780; 660; 600; 600; 630.
   Replacement investment: 60; 60; 66; 78; 90; 96; 96; 90; 78; 66; 60; 60.
   Required new capital: 0; 60; 120; 120; 60; 0; -60; -120; -120; -60; 0; 30.
   Total investment: 60; 120; 186; 198; 150; 96; 36; 0(-30); 0(-72); 0(-66); 0(-6); 84. (Note: Without the accumulating excess capacity the total investment figures for Periods 9–12 would be –42, 6, 60, and 90. However, additional investments are not needed until the unused capacity is eliminated. Total investment (I_g) can be determined from the equation, $I_g = I_r + A(Y_t - Y_{t-1}) - E_t$, where A is the accelerator, t refers to the time period, and E_t is excess capacity. Negative *gross* investment is not possible.)

b. (1) When output increases by an increasing amount, net investment increases.
   (2) When output increases by constant amounts, net investment is constant.
   (3) When output increases by decreasing amounts, net investment decreases.
   (4) When output decreases by increasing amounts, net disinvestment increases.
c. The accelerator makes investment more volatile.
d. Fluctuations in total investment are less than fluctuations in net investment. This implies that the more durable the capital goods, the greater will be the fluctuations in investment; the less durable, the less the fluctuations in investment.
e. No. See periods 4 and 5. Output *increased* from $300 billion to $320 billion but total investment dropped from $198 billion to $150 billion. On the other hand, in periods 9 and 10 output *decreased* from $220 billion to $200 billion, while investment increased from "disinvestment of $42 billion" (actually $0) to investment of $6 billion.
f. The basic limitations are: (1) the accelerator concept is too mechanical in the sense that it has no motivation content; (2) it operates only at full employment, that is, when there is no excess capacity; (3) it applies when there is an increase in demand only if entrepreneurs believe the change in demand is permanent and not temporary. (See your text.)
g. Yes, the accelerator and multiplier can be combined. Such an approach can be used to explain, among other things, cyclical fluctuations and economic growth.

7. The flexible accelerator makes net investment a function of the difference between the desired stock of capital and the capital stock of the prior income period, $I_n = a(K^* - K_{t-1})$ where K^* is desired K and a is the proportion of the gap which can be closed in the present income period. It differs, in brief, from the simple accelerator in that it does not imply that the gap will be removed in a single income period, is not mechanical, and does not relate net I directly to the rate of change of output. I_n responds to output but with a lag.

A Self-Test

Completion Questions

1. increases
2. remains constant
3. decreases
4. depreciation allowances, retained earnings, borrowing or the sale of new equities
5. present value of the net expected income stream, supply price
6. income stream, rate of interest
7. investment induced from changes in income
8. plant and equipment, residential construction, net changes in business inventories
9. net investment, replacement investment
10. stream of net expected returns on capital, supply curve of capital goods

True and False

1. True;   2. True;   3. False;   4. True;   5. True;   6. True;   7. False;   8. False;
9. True;   10. False;   11. True;   12. True;   13. True;   14. False;   15. False;
16. False;   17. True;   18. False;   19. False;   20. True;   21. True.

Multiple Choice

1. *b*;   2. *b*;   3. *e*;   4. *c*;   5. *c*;   6. *b*;   7. *e*;   8. *b*;   9. *a*;   10. *c*;   11. *d*;   12. *e*;
13. *c*;   14. *a*;   15. *c*;   16. *b*;   17. *b*;   18. *d*;   19. *c*;   20. *d*;   21. *a*;   22. *b*;   23. *b*;
24. *c*;   25. *a*;   26. *a*;   27. *c*;   28. *b*;   29. *a*;   30. *c*;   31. *d*;   32. *c*;   33. *a*;   34. *b*;
35. *b*.

CHAPTER 9   Public Expenditures, Taxes, and Finance

Problems and Essays

1. *a.* (3) $Y - C = I + G$
      (4) $Y - C = S + TX - TR$
   b. $I =$ \$60 billion. No, there is a deficit of \$20 billion.

2. *a.* (1) $C = 95 + 0.4(Y_{np} - 60 + 10)$ [Algebraically it is: $C = C_0 + a(Y_{np} - TX + TR)$ as $MPT = 0$], $I = 25 + 0.2Y_{np}$.
      (2) $Y_{np} =$ \$1,250 billion, $C =$ \$575 billion, $I =$ \$275 billion.
      (3) \$250 billion.
      (4) 2.5. No.
      (5) \$1,312.5 billion.
      (6) The aggregate demand curve would drop by \$10 billion ($MPC \times \Delta TX$) at all levels of income, causing equilibrium income to decline to \$1,225 billion.
      (7) The aggregate demand schedule would shift upward by \$10 billion at all income levels, causing the equilibrium income to increase to \$1,275 billion.
      (8) Taxes and transfer payments alter disposable income and, as consumption is a function of disposable income, cause the consumption function to shift up or down by the marginal propensity to consume times the change in taxes or transfers.
   b. (1) $S + TX - TR$: –75; 0; 75; 150; 225; 300; 375; 450; 525; 600; 675; 750; 825.
            $I + G$: 425; 450; 475; 500; 525; 550; 575; 600; 625; 650; 675; 700; 725.
      (2) Equilibrium income is \$1,250 billion; $C =$ \$575 billion; $I =$ \$275 billion.
      (3) The new equilibrium is \$1,187.5 billion.
      (4) The equilibrium income level will decline.
      (5) The $S + TX$ curve would shift upward by \$10 billion (S decreases \$15 billion and TX increases \$25 billion), causing the equilibrium income to fall to \$1,225 billion.

    (6) The $S + TX$ curve shifts downward by \$10 billion (in effect government saving declined \$25 billion but private saving increased \$15 billion), causing the new equilibrium income level to be \$1,275 billion.

  c. Yes. Both approaches must always yield the same results.

3.*a.* (3) $\Delta Y_{np} = \Delta C + \Delta G$

    (4) $\Delta C = a(\Delta Y_{np})$

    (5) $\Delta Y_{np} = a(\Delta Y_{np}) + \Delta G$

    (6) $\Delta Y_{np} - a(\Delta Y_{np}) = \Delta G$

    (7) $\Delta Y_{np}(1 - a) = \Delta G$

    (8) $\Delta Y_{np} = \dfrac{\Delta G}{1-a} = \Delta G \times \dfrac{1}{1-a}$

    (9) $\dfrac{\Delta Y_{np}}{\Delta G} = \dfrac{1}{1-a} = \dfrac{1}{1-\text{MPC}} = k_g$

  b. (4) $\Delta C_o = a(\Delta TR)$

    (5) $\Delta C_i = a(\Delta Y_{np})$

    (6) $\Delta Y_{np} = a\Delta TR + a\Delta Y_{np}$

    (7) $\Delta Y_{np} - a\Delta Y_{np} = a\Delta TR$

    (8) $\Delta Y_{np}(1 - a) = a\Delta TR$

    (9) $\Delta Y_{np} = \dfrac{a\Delta TR}{1-a} = \dfrac{a}{1-a} \times \Delta TR$

    (10) $\dfrac{\Delta Y_{np}}{\Delta Tr} = \dfrac{a}{1-a} = \dfrac{\text{MPC}}{1-\text{MPC}} = k_{tr}$

  c. (3) $\Delta Y_{np} = \Delta C_o + \Delta C_i$

    (4) $\Delta C_o = a(\Delta TX)$

    (5) $\Delta C_i = a(\Delta Y_{np})$

    (6) $\Delta Y_{np} = -a\Delta TX + a\Delta Y_{np}$

    (7) $\Delta Y_{np} - aY_{np} = -a\Delta TX$

    (8) $\Delta Y_{np}(1 - a) = a\Delta TX$

    (9) $\Delta Y_{np} = \dfrac{a\Delta TX}{1-a} = \dfrac{a}{1-a} \times \Delta TX$

    (10) $\dfrac{\Delta Y_{np}}{\Delta TX} = \dfrac{a}{1-a} = \dfrac{\text{MPC}}{1-\text{MPC}} = k_{tx}$

  d. (1) $k_{tx} = -4$. Income declines by \$60 billion.

    (2) $k_{tr} = 4$. Income increases by \$60 billion.

    (3) Both alter disposable income by the same amount and the effect of each on consumption depends on the marginal propensity to consume. However, an increase in transfer payments expands disposable income and thus consumption, whereas an increase in taxes reduces disposable income and thus consumption.

4.*a.* (3) $\Delta Y_{np} = \Delta C + \Delta I + \Delta G$

    (4) $\Delta C = a\Delta Y_{np}$

    (5) $\Delta I = b\Delta Y_{np}$

    (6) $\Delta Y_{np} = a\Delta Y_{np} + b\Delta Y_{np} + \Delta G$

    (7) $\Delta Y_{np} - a\Delta Y_{np} - b\Delta Y_{np} = \Delta G$

    (8) $\Delta Y_{np}(1 - a - b) = \Delta G$

(9) $\Delta Y_{np} = \Delta G \times \dfrac{1}{1-a-b}$

(10) $\dfrac{\Delta Y_{np}}{\Delta G} = \dfrac{1}{1-a-b} = \dfrac{1}{1-MPC-MPI} = k_g$

   b. Yes, whether induced investment is included or excluded.

5. *a.* (4) $C = C_0 + a(Y_{np} - T)$
     (5) $T = T_0 + tY_{np}$
     (6) $C = C_0 + a[Y_{np} - (T_0 + tY_{np})]$
     (7) $C = C_0 + aY_{np} - aT_0 - atY_{np}$
     (8) $C = C_0 - aT_0 + Y_{np}(a - at)$

   b. $C = 461$

   c. The slope of the consumption function is now $(a - at)$, which equals $[0.8 - 0.8(0.2)] = 0.64$ for the data provided in part *b* above. The slope of the consumption function is no longer equal to the MPC.

6. *a.* (5) $\Delta I = b\Delta Y_{np}$
     (6) $\Delta Y_{np} = a\Delta Y_{np} - at\Delta Y_{np} + b\Delta Y_{np} + \Delta G$
     (7) $\Delta Y_{np} - a\Delta Y_{np} + at\Delta Y_{np} - b\Delta Y_{np} = \Delta G$
     (8) $\Delta Y_{np}(1 - a + at - b) = \Delta\Delta G$
     (9) $\Delta Y_{np} = \Delta G \times \dfrac{1}{1-a+at-b}$
     (10) $\dfrac{\Delta Y_{np}}{\Delta G} = \dfrac{1}{1-a+at-b}$
     (11) $\dfrac{\Delta Y_{np}}{\Delta DD} = \dfrac{1}{1-a+at-b} = \dfrac{1}{1-MPC+MPC(MPT)-MPI}$

   b. $k = 2.5$

7. *a.* (4) $Y_{np} = C_0 - aT_0 + Y_{np}(a - at) + I_0 + bY_{np} + G$
     (5) $Y_{np} = C_0 - aT_0 + aY_{np} - atY_{np} + I_0 + bY_{np} + G$
     (6) $Y_{np} - aY_{np} + atY_{np} - bY_{np} = C_0 - aT_0 + I_0 + G$
     (7) $Y_{np}(1 - a + at - b) = C_0 - aT_0 + I_0 + G$
     (8) $Y_{np} = \dfrac{1}{1-a+at-b}(C_0 - aT_0 + I_0 + G)$

   b. $Y_{np} = 660$

8. *a.* The change in income from the increase in $G = 4 \times 20 = \$80$ billion. The change in income from the increase in $TX = -3 \times 20 = -\$60$ billion. Thus income will increase by $20 billion. This example demonstrates that an equal increase (or decrease) in government taxes and expenditures is not neutral with respect to its impact on the economy. Be sure you understand why this is the case. (Note: The balanced budget multiplier may be less than unity depending on the assumptions utilized.)

   b. If k_g is 5, then k_{tr} is -4. In absolute terms the tax (and transfer) multiplier is equal to the government expenditures multiplier minus 1. (Note: As implied above, this is a simplification.)

A Self-Test

Completion Questions

1. disposable income
2. MPC/1 – MPC
3. fall, $45 billion
4. rise, $44 billion
5. remain unchanged, rise, $12 billion
6. tax
7. 4
8. amount by which taxes change from a change in income
9. a straight line, concave from above. convex from above
10. 550, 25, 33 1/3, 33 1/3

True and False

1. True;   2. False;   3. False;   4. True;   5. True;   6. True;   7. True;   8. False;
9. True;   10. False;   11. True;   12. True;   13. False.

Multiple Choice

1. e;   2. a;   3. c;   4. b;   5. c;   6. a;   7. c;   8. c;   9. b;   10. c;   11. c;   12. a;
13. c;   14. b;   15. d;   16. b;   17. d;   18. b;   19. b;   20. a;   21. d;   22. a;   23. c;
24. b;   25. a;   26. b;   27. a;   28. a;   29. c;   30. b;   31. d;   32. b.

CHAPTER 10   The International Economy

Problems and Essays

2. *a.* (3) $Y_{np} - C = I + G + X - M$
   (4) $Y_{np} - C = S + TX - TR$
   (5) $I + G + X - M = S + TX - TR$
   (6) $I + G + X = S + TX - TR + M$

   b. No. Saving does not have to equal investment, government purchases do not have to equal net taxes, and exports do not have to equal imports. All that is required is that the sum of I, G, and X equal the sum of S, $TX - TR$, and M.

3. *a.* (1) $60; 65; 70; 75; 80; 85; 90; 95; 100; 105; 110; 115; 120; 125; 130; 135; 140 (billions).

   (2) $k = \dfrac{1}{1 - a - b + m} = \dfrac{1}{1 - 0.4 - 0.2 + 0.04} = 2.273.$

   (3) $Y_{np} = \dfrac{1}{1 - a - b + m}(C_0 - aT_0 + I_0 + G + X - M_0)$

$$= \frac{1}{1 - 0.4 - 0.2 + 0.04}[95 - 0.4(50) + 25 + 400 + 120 - 60]$$

$= 2.273(560) = 1,272.9$ billions approximately.

$C = C_0 + a(Y_{np} - T_0) = C_0 - aT_0 + aY_{np} = 95 - 0.4(50) + 0.4(1272.9) =$ $584.16 billions

$I = I_0 + bY_{np} = 25 + 0.2(1,272.9) = 279.58 billions

$M = M_0 + mY_{np} = 60 + 0.04(1,272.9) = 110.92 billions

(4) An increase in the MPM will cause the aggregate demand curve to rotate downward; autonomous aggregate demand will be unchanged. The lower demand curve will reduce the equilibrium income level. A reduction in the MPM would have the opposite results.

(5) An increase in autonomous imports will cause the aggregate demand curve to shift downward parallel to itself. Consequently, the income level will decline. A reduction in autonomous imports would have the opposite effect.

(6) If exports increase, the aggregate demand curve will shift upward parallel to itself, and consequently income will rise. The reverse will occur with a decline in exports.

b. (1) $S + TX - TR + M$: -15; 65; 145; 225; 305; 385; 465; 545; 625; 705; 785; 856; 945; 1,025; 1,105; 1,185; 1,265 (billions).
$I + G + X$: $545; 570; 595; 620; 645; 670; 695; 720; 745; 770; 795; 820; 845; 870; 895; 920; 945 (billions).

(2) Yes.

(3) If the MPM increases, the $S + TX - TR + M$ schedule will rotate upward and cause the equilibrium income level to decline. A reduction in the MPM will have the opposite result.

(4) An increase in autonomous imports will shift the $S + TX - TR + M$ curve upward parallel to itself and thus lower the income level.

(5) The equilibrium value of income will remain unchanged. However, the $S + TX - TR + M$ and $I + G + X$ curves will intersect at a higher vertical level.

4. a. MPM $= \dfrac{CD}{BD} = \dfrac{CD}{Y_2Y_3}$

b. $M = A + = \dfrac{CD}{BD}Y_{np}$

c. Deficit = passive

d. Surplus = active

e. $k = \dfrac{Y_2Y_3}{CD}$

f. Yes, a change by the same amount in either will alter income by the same amount. However, an increase in exports will cause an increase in income by a multiple of the change in exports, whereas an increase in imports causes a *decrease* in income by a multiple of the change in imports.

g. There could be either a reduction in autonomous imports or a reduction in the MPM. An increase in either or both of these would cause income to contract.

5. a. (3) $\Delta Y_{np} = \Delta C + \Delta X - \Delta M$
   (4) $\Delta C = a\Delta Y_{np}$
   (5) $\Delta M = m\Delta Y_{np}$
   (6) $\Delta Y_{np} = a\Delta Y_{np} + \Delta X - m\Delta Y_{np}$
   (7) $\Delta Y_{np} - a\Delta Y_{np} + m\Delta Y_{np} = \Delta X$
   (8) $\Delta Y_{np}(1 - a + m) = \Delta X$
   (9) $\Delta Y_{np} = \Delta X \times \dfrac{1}{1 - a + m}$
   (10) $\dfrac{\Delta Y_{np}}{\Delta X} = \Delta X \times \dfrac{1}{1 - a + m} = \dfrac{1}{\text{MPS} + \text{MPM}}$

   b. $k_f = \dfrac{1}{MPM}$
   c. It reduces the multiplier effect.
   d. $k_f = \dfrac{1}{1 - a - b + m} = \dfrac{1}{1 - \text{MPC} - \text{MPI} + \text{MPM}}$
   e. $k_f = 2.5$. Income will fall by \$20 billion.

6. a. (3) $\Delta Y_{np} = \Delta C + \Delta I + \Delta X - \Delta M$
   (4) $\Delta C = a\Delta Y_{np} - at\Delta Y_{np}$
   (5) $\Delta I = b\Delta Y_{np}$
   (6) $\Delta M = m\Delta Y_{np}$
   (7) $\Delta Y_{np} = a\Delta Y_{np} - at\Delta Y_{np} + b\Delta Y_{np} + \Delta X - m\Delta Y_{np}$
   (8) $\Delta Y_{np} = a\Delta Y_{np} - at\Delta Y_{np} + b\Delta Y_{np} + m\Delta Y_{np} = \Delta X$
   (9) $\Delta Y_{np}(1 - a + at - b + m) = \Delta X$
   (10) $\Delta Y_{np} = \Delta X \dfrac{1}{1 - a + at - b + m}$
   (11) $\dfrac{\Delta Y_{np}}{\Delta X} = \dfrac{1}{1 - a + at - b + m}$
   (12) $\dfrac{\Delta Y_{np}}{\Delta DD} = \dfrac{1}{1 - a + at - b + m}$

   b. $k' = 4$
   c. It is smaller because imports are a leakage from the income stream; thus m in the denominator is positive.
   d. Yes, they both make the multiplier smaller.
   e. (1) $\dfrac{1}{1 - a + m} = \dfrac{1}{\text{MPS} + \text{MPM}}$
      (2) $\dfrac{1}{1 - a - b + m} = \dfrac{1}{\text{MPS} - \text{MPI} + \text{MPM}}$
   f. The multiplier becomes larger.

7. a. (5) $Y_{np} = C_0 + aY_{np} - aT_0 - atY_{np} + I_0 + bY_{np} + G + X - (M_0 + mY_{np})$
   (6) $Y_{np} = C_0 + aY_{np} - aT_0 - atY_{np} + I_0 + bY_{np} + G + X - M_0 - mY_{np}$
   (7) $Y_{np} - aY_{np} + atY_{np} - bY_{np} + mY_{np} = C_0 + aT_0 + I_0 + G + X - M_0$
   (8) $Y_{np}(1 - a + at - b + m) = C_0 - aT_0 + I_0 + G + X - M_0$

(9) $Y_{np} = \dfrac{1}{1-a+at-b+m}(C_0 - aT_0 + I_0 + G + X - M_0)$

b. $Y_{np} = \dfrac{1}{1-0.85+0.85(0.2)-0.12+0.05}[30 - 0.85(40) + 84 + 200 + 100 - 60]$

$= 4(320) = \$1,280$ billion

$C = C_0 - aT_0 + aY_{np} - atY_{np} = 30 - 0.85(40) + 0.85(1,280) - 0.85(0.2)(1,280)$
$= \$866.4$ billion

$I = I_0 + bY_{np} = 84 + 0.12(1,280) = \$237.6$ billion

$M = M_0 + mY_{np} = 60 + 0.05(1,280) = \$124$ billion

$BOT = X - (M_0 + mY_{np}) = 100 - 60 + 0.05(1,280) = 100 - 124 = \$-24$ billion

9. a. $S - I$: –50; –40; –30; –20; –10; 0; 10; 20; 30; 40; 50.
    $X - M$: 40; 32; 24; 16; 8; 0; –8; –016; –24; –32; –40.

b. $500 billion.

c. (1) The slope of the $X - M$ curve is the MPM except that it is negative. It slopes downward to the right because as income increases, a continuously growing volume of imports is deducted form a constant volume of exports.

   (2) The higher the MPM, the greater the slope (and vice versa).

   (3) The slope of the $S - I$ curve is equal to the MPS minus the MPI. It is positively sloped because saving increases at a faster rate than investment.

   (4) It would equal the MPS.

   (5) No.

   (6) The balance of trade continually declines, becoming negative (deficit) for all income levels above $500 billion.

   (7) Saving is less than investment up to $500 billion. At higher income levels saving exceeds investment.

   (8) Yes. To have a deficit in the balance of trade, the X-M curve must intersect the S-I curve at income levels below $500 billion. At all income levels below $500 billion, saving is less than investment.

d. (1) The S-I curve shifts downward parallel to itself, income increases, and the trade balance deteriorates into a deficit. A decrease in autonomous investment has the opposite effect.

   (2) The curve shifts upward, income declines, and the trade balance improves—would be in surplus. A reduction in the desire to save results in the opposite movements.

e. (1) The X-M curve shifts upward parallel to itself, income rises, the trade balance improves—but not by the full amount of the expansion in X as M increases as well—and saving moves above investment. The reverse follows for a decrease in X.

   (2) The curve shifts downward, income falls, the trade balance deteriorates into a deficit, and saving declines. Note that the trade balance would not deteriorate by the full amount of the increase in imports.

f. Suppose domestic income advances due to an increase in autonomous investment. The S-I curve shifts downward and the income level expands. But the advance in income would increase imports as well. Because imports are exports from the viewpoint of foreign countries, their incomes would increase and cause their imports to expand. If we assume part of the augmented imports of foreign countries derives from the country under consideration, the $X - M$ curve would shift upward by a small amount. Thus income would not fall as much, and the trade balance would not deteriorate as much, as would be the case without the foreign-repercussion effect. A decline in domestic income would cause the foreign-repercussion effect to work in the opposite direction.

g. Yes. An increase in domestic income will tend to deteriorate, and a decrease in domestic income to improve, the balance of trade.

10. a. (1) $13,000, $12,000, $11,000, $10,000, and $9,000.

(2) The lower the exchange rate, the less dollars an American has to pay for the VW. Since a falling exchange rate lowers the price of German goods relative to what they were prior to the drop in the exchange rate (and relative to prices of goods produced in other countries), U.S. demand for German exports would increase.

(3) The higher the rate of exchange, the more costly the VW in dollars. Accordingly, as the exchange rate rises—the dollar price of DMs increases—the U.S. demand for German goods and services would fall.

b. (1) DM16,923, DM18,333, DM20,000, DM22,000, and DM24,444.

(2) The DM price increases as the rate of exchange falls. The German demand for U.S. goods and services will decline since American products are now relatively more expensive than before (and relatively more expensive than similar products of other nations).

(3) The Ford Escort becomes cheaper in terms of DMs as the rate of exchange rises. Thus the German demand for imports would expand.

12. b. (1) When $Y_{np} = 600$, $X - M = 12$, so $i = 8.8$ percent. When $Y_{np} = 1,000$, $X - M = -20$, so $i = 12$ percent

c. As we have derived it, the BP curve shows all those i, Y_{np} combinations at which net exports equals the net capital flow (and hence the BP is in equilibrium with a zero balance). $BP = 0$ would necessarily be the case in theory with a freely fluctuating exchange rate system, but under a pegged exchange rate system, the balance could be positive or negative depending on the policy of the country concerned. With pegged exchange rates the amount of the imbalance would be financed (deficit) from or added to (surplus) the nation's international reserves. Actually, one could visualize a family of BP curves. Those to the *right* of the $BP = 0$ curve would signify BP *deficits* (with the deficit getting larger the further the BP curve lies out from the $BP = 0$ curve); those to the *left* would signify BP *surpluses* (the surplus getting larger the further the BP curve lies inward from the $BP = 0$ curve).

d. (1) The BP curve is positively sloped because the interest rate must increase to reduce the net capital outflow, or entice a larger net capital inflow, to offset the deterioration in net exports that occurs as rising income generates additional imports of goods and services.

(2) The slope of the $X - M$ curve would become more negative and hence the slope of the BP curve would increase.

(3) The slope of the net capital flow curve in Part A would decrease (K_n would become flatter) and so would the slope of the BP curve.

e. (1) The $X - M$ curve shifts up and causes the BP curve to shift outward to the right.

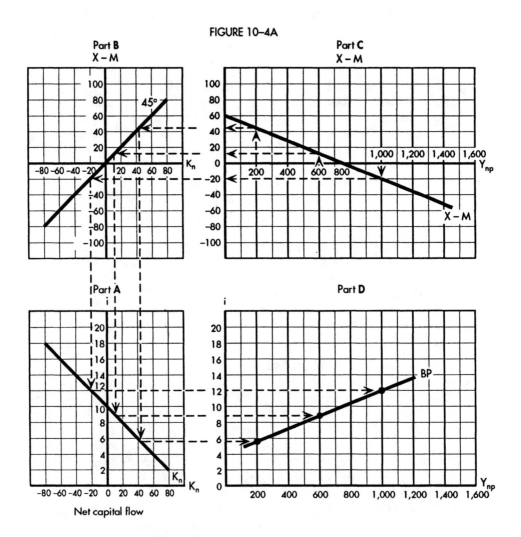

FIGURE 10–4A

(2) Because of the overall increase in the capital inflow to the United States, the net capital flow curve will shift left at all interest rates and thereby cause the *BP* curve to shift inward toward the origin.

(3) The *X – M* curve will shift up and the *BP* curve will shift out.

(4) Because the net capital flow curve is constructed assuming foreign interest rates are constant at some given level, the net capital flow curve will shift upward (due to the larger capital outflow at each interest rate) and cause the *BP* curve to shift upward (or inward toward the origin). Higher relative returns abroad would encourage a greater capital outflow or smaller capital inflow at each interest rate.

(5) U.S. exports become less competitive, the *X – M* curve shifts down, and the *BP* curve shifts in. [Note: If the exchange rate were freely floating, the dollar would depreciate, neutralizing the difference in the inflation rates and thereby keeping exports from dropping and imports from increasing. In this case, theory says the *X – M* curve would not shift and therefore the *BP* curve also would not shift. In practice, things are not this simple.]

13. *a.* (2) If not neutralized by the Fed and assuming no inflation, a *BP* surplus would shift the *LM* curve outward to the right; a *BP* deficit would shift it inward to the left.

(3) Since a *BP* surplus increases the money supply and creates excess demand it may cause inflation. If prices increase, the real money supply will not increase as much as otherwise and thus the *LM* curve will not shift outward as much as in the absence of inflation. In addition, the inflation will shift the *IS* curve inward because (1) the reduced purchasing power of certain assets will reduce consumption, and (2) the inflation will have a negative effect on real net exports.

(4) Exchange rates are set in the foreign exchange market. With a freely fluctuating exchange rate system in effect, changes in supply and demand cause the exchange rate to adjust rapidly by whatever amount is necessary to maintain *BP* equilibrium.

A Self-Test

Completion Questions

1. $M = 10 + 0.2Y_{np}$
2. $95 billion
3. government purchases, investment, consumption, exports, consumption, saving, taxes, imports
4. Exports, imports
5. deteriorate, improve
6. smaller
7. smaller
8. current
9. 1/MPM. 1/MPS + MPM, 1/MPS + MPC(MPT) + MPM. 1/MPS + MPC(MPT) – MPI + MPM

10. 5, 2, 1.75, 2.13
11. MPM, MPT, MPI, MPS, larger

True and False

1. True;   2. True;   3. True;   4. False;   5. True;   6. False;   7. False;   8. False;
9. True;   10. False;   11. False;   12. False;   13. True;   14. True;   15. False;
16. True;   17. True;   18. True.

Multiple Choice

1. *d*;   2. *d*;   3. *a*;   4. *d*;   5. *b*;   6. *a*;   7. *b*;   8. *d*;   9. *c*;   10. *b*;   11. *d*;   12. *d*;
13. *b*;   14. *c*;   15. *c*;   16. *b*;   17. *e*;   18. *a*;   19. *a*;   20. *e*;   21. *a*;   22. *d*;   23. *c*;
24. *e*;   25. *a*;   26. *b*;   27. *c*;   28, *c*;   29. *b*;   30. *a*;   31. *d*;   32. *b*;   33. *d*.

CHAPTER 11   Monetary Theory

Problems and Essays

2. *a.* The higher the income level, the more money is desired for transaction
   purposes; that is, the more money is desired to facilitate the exchange of goods
   and services.
   b. The medium-of-exchange function of money.
   c. 3.10. Yes.
   d. The straight line function implies that the transactions velocity is constant. It
   would be more realistic to recognize that velocity tends to increase in cyclical
   expansions and decrease in cyclical contractions. To represent this on the
   graph, the transactions demand curve would have to increase at a slightly
   decreasing rate. However, the change in velocity is normally relatively small. It
   would not alter the analytical technique nor the conclusions derived from the
   analysis. For this reason the assumption of a constant velocity of money is an
   adequate approximation for purposes of simplification. The transactions
   velocity is 3 1/3 in this case; it is the reciprocal of the L_t/Y ratio.
   e. The slope is determined by such institutional and structural conditions in the
   economy as the stage of development of credit institutions, the frequency with
   which people are paid, the rapidity with which money can be transported from
   one place to another, degree of vertical integration, and other minor factors. It
   is even possible that the interest rate may affect the curve (as we shall see
   subsequently). The more developed are the credit institutions, the greater is the
   frequency with which people are paid; and the more rapidly money can be
   transported, the smaller will be the ratio of transactions demand for money to
   income—the steeper is the curve in Figure 11–2.

f. (1) The L_t curves for the various income levels may become responsive to the interest rate (especially above some critical level) and, if so, bend toward the vertical axis (which is the same as saying the velocity of transactions money increases). As the reward for lending is now relatively high, both consumers and businesses may economize in the use of money. More specifically, business firms which hold a relatively large amount of money—such as the giant corporations—for transaction in the future (say a month hence) would normally convert this money into assets earning a rate of interest for the month or less as long as they could make a profit by doing so. The interest rate would not have to be very high before they would take this action. Consumers are generally less interest conscious because they can make only a very small profit due to their small balances. Thus for consumers the interest rate would probably have to be well above the normal level before their demand for transactions balances would become interest responsive to even the slightest degree.

3. *a.* There is an inverse relationship between the interest rate and the price of bonds; a decrease in the interest rate increases bond prices and vice versa. This relationship is evident from the simple present value formula, $V_p = R/(1 + i)$, where V_p is the present value of a bond and R the sum of money to be received when the bond matures. Note what happens to V_p when there is a change in i.

 b. (1) Simply stated, the opportunity cost explanation of the negative slope is as follows: The higher the rate of interest, the greater is the amount of interest income that must be sacrificed when people choose to hold money instead of other earning assets (such as bonds)—the higher the rate of interest, the greater the opportunity cost of holding money. It follows thus that the higher the interest rate, the smaller the amount of cash balances individuals and businesses will hold. On the other hand, the lower the opportunity cost of holding idle money balances, the larger the amount of cash balances that society will hold.

  (2) The crux of Keynes' explanation is as follows: Individuals want asset money balances because of *uncertainty* with respect to future changes in the interest rate. Should they hold bonds, rather than cash, they will earn an interest income. But they will also realize a capital gain or suffer a capital loss if bond prices increase or decrease, respectively. As bond prices and the interest rate move inversely, a fall in the interest rate results in a capital gain, and a rise in the interest rate results in a capital loss for those holding bonds.

   Keynes argues that individuals have a "safe" or "normal" level to which they think the current interest rate will return should there be a divergence between the normal and current rate. If the current rate exceeds the normal rate, individuals expect the former to fall and, consequently, that they will realize a capital gain from holding bonds (plus an interest income); if the current rate is less than the normal rate, they expect the former to rise, causing a capital loss on bonds. If the capital loss exceeds the interest income, the net amount will be a loss. If we assume the interest return is relatively small, people will hold all bonds when the current rate exceeds the normal rate (as they expect to realize a capital gain), and they will hold all cash when the current rate is below the normal level (for in this case they would sustain a capital loss on bonds). Thus, an increase in the interest rate reduces the demand for cash and vice versa. Note that there is a spread of normal rates of interest so that some people hold all bonds and others hold all cash. If this were not the case, the speculative demand for money curve would have to be a straight line parallel to the horizontal axis at the normal interest rate.

(3) Keynes' explanation seems reasonable. At any one time, the total stock of assets will be divided between cash and bonds because not all individuals have the same normal rate; and thus the current rate would be above the normal rate for some, while below for others. Yet Keynes' explanation implies that any one individual will hold either all bonds or all cash; and this is not normally the case. Individuals hold both bonds and cash; they diversify their assets between cash and other assets.

(4) In brief, Tobin's explanation is as follows: Most people are risk averters (as opposed to risk lovers) and bear *risk* only if compensated by an interest income. Individuals realize that there is a chance of both a capital gain and a capital loss from holding bonds. Assume they think the most probable outcome is zero capital gain or loss. Yet there is still some risk associated with holding bonds; the more bonds they hold, the greater the risk. The larger the risk involved in holding bonds, the higher must be the interest rate to entice asset owners to hold a larger proportion of their assets in bonds. In short, the greater the compensation in the form of interest income, the more risk people will accept and thus more bonds they will hold. This gives an inverse relationship between the interest rate and speculative demand for money. (If people are risk lovers, they will always hold bonds and no cash.)

c. The liquidity trap is the horizontal portion of the speculative demand for money curve—in this case at an interest rate of 3 percent and after the demand for money reaches $100 billion. Within this range the demand for asset money is infinitely elastic. The liquidity trap indicates that the interest rate cannot fall below 3 percent. Any increase or decrease in the money supply will be put into or taken out of money holding of consumers and business firms with no impact on the interest rate. Therefore, monetary policy working through the rate of interest is completely ineffective (in this range).

d. The most important determinant causing shifts in the L_a curve is the state of opinion as to what constitutes the normal rate of interest. If the consensus, or climate, of opinion is that the normal rate has increased, the curve will shift upward; if the consensus is that the normal rate has fallen, the curve will shift downward. Changes in the economy's wealth may also cause shifts in this curve; an increase in the total wealth causing the curve to move gradually upward and a decline in the total wealth causing it to shift downward. Changes in the liquidity, safety, and so forth of other assets will also cause shifts in the speculative demand curve.

4. a. $Y = 200$: 60; 80; 100; 120; 140; 160 or more (plus).
   $Y = 400$: 120; 140; 160; 180; 200; 220 or more (plus).
   $Y = 600$: 180; 200; 220; 240; 260; 280 or more (plus).

$Y = 800$: 240; 260; 280; 300; 320; 340 or more (plus).
$Y = 1,000$: 300; 320; 340; 360; 380; 400 or more (plus).
$Y = 1,200$: 360; 380; 400; 420; 440; 460 or more (plus).
$Y = 1,400$: 420; 440; 460; 480; 500; 520 or more (plus).
$Y = 1,600$: 480; 500; 520; 540; 560; 580 or more (plus).

b. Assuming as we are that the transactions demand for money is completely unresponsive to the interest rate, the curvature of the total demand for money curve is given by the speculative demand for money curve.

6. a. (1) 6 percent. Equilibrium is where the asset demand for money equals the amount of money available to hold as an asset.

(2) At 9 percent the money supply available to hold ($60 billion) exceeds the asset demand for money ($40 billion). If we assume no change in consumption the full amount of the excessive supply of asset money will be used to purchase securities. The increased demand for bonds will force up the price of bonds and reduce the rate of interest. This continues until equilibrium is restored.

(3) In this case the demand for cash ($80 billion) exceeds the money supply available to hold as an asset ($60 billion). Consumers and business firms want to hold more money than they are currently holding. Again if we assume no change in consumption, people try to obtain the additional cash by selling bonds. This reduces bond prices and increases the interest rate until equilibrium is restored.

(4) Probably not. The money supply curve should be tipped slightly away from the vertical axis, indicating that at most rates of interest the money supply is slightly interest elastic. However, at a relatively high interest rate the curve would probably become completely interest inelastic. The commercial bank, due to the fractional reserve requirement, can increase the money supply by creating demand deposits and will do so as long as they can make loans, and so forth. It is only when the banking system becomes "loaned up," that most of the changes in the money supply become autonomous in that it requires action by the Federal Reserve authorities before the money supply can increase further. However, the zero interest elasticity assumption is a useful approximation for analytical purposes since the recognition of some elasticity in the money supply does not alter the conclusions of the analysis.

b. (1) Before the full adjustment has taken place, the supply of money to hold as an asset exceeds the asset demand for money. The demand for bonds will increase, causing bond prices to rise and the interest rate to fall until the new equilibrium is attained. The new equilibrium interest rate is 4 percent. For a reduction in the asset money supply, the process is just the opposite.

(2) Before the full adjustment has occurred, the L_a exceeds M^o_a. To obtain more cash, bonds are sold. Bond prices decrease and the interest rate increases until equilibrium is restored at a higher level of the interest rate.

Yes, shifts in the speculative demand for money curve are realistic. The curve, in reality, is never still and shifts up or down as the climate of opinion, wealth of the economy, and so forth change.

  c. It depends on the interest elasticity of the asset demand curve. The more interest inelastic the L_a curve, the more a given change in the asset money supply will alter the interest rate; the more elastic the L_a curve, the less a change in M^o_a will alter the rate of interest. In the liquidity trap, there is no change in the interest rate whatsoever.

  d. There is a great deal of controversy over whether the liquidity trap is theoretically possible. Most economists, however, accept the theoretical existence of the liquidity trap although questioning its practical relevance. In the last 50 years, the only time when the United States *may* have been in the liquidity trap was during the 1930s, excluding periods when the interest rate was controlled.

  e. This can be answered with two different analytical techniques, both of which amount to exactly the same thing. First, think in terms of Figure 11–5. As the income level rises, more money is needed for transactions purposes. If we assume the total money supply is constant, the additional transactions money must come from the asset balances. As this occurs, there is less money left for speculative purposes, and the interest rate advances. The other approach is to use Figure 11–4 in problem 6 above. In this case the transactions and speculative demands for money are combined and related to the total money supply. As the income level advances, the total demand for money curve rotates to the right—from 100 to 200 to 300, and so forth—because more money is desired for transactions. As this occurs, the interest rate rises.

  Either approach can be used and both give the same results. Note that if the income level falls, the opposite sequence is set into motion and the interest rate declines. In short, it appears that the interest rate is determined by equality between the total demand for and supply of money, not just the demand for and supply of speculative money (as Keynes said). (In subsequent chapters, more will be said about interest rate determination.)

A Self-Test

Completion Questions

1. an inverse, lower
2. demand for money, supply of money
3. $25 billion
4. interest rate, income level
5. right, the increase in transactions demand for money, left
6. $105 billion
7. classical, Keynesian
8. medium of exchange, store of value
9. transactions, precautionary, speculative, transactions, speculative
10. speculative, transactions
11. money, money, speculative
12. current, downward, capital gain, buy, money, rate of interest, rise, capital loss, cash
13. all, all, is not
14. risk, greater, more, interest rate

True and False

1. True; 2. True; 3. True; 4. False; 5. True; 6. True; 7. True; 8. True;
9. True; 10. True; 11. True; 12. True; 13. True; 14. False; 15. False;
16. True; 17. False; 18. True; 19. False; 20. False; 21. False; 22. True;
23. True; 24. False; 25. True; 26. False; 27. True; 28. False; 29. False;
30. True; 31. True; 32. False; 33. True; 34. True; 35. True; 36. False;
37. False; 38. True; 39. True; 40. False; 41. True; 42. True.

Multiple Choice

1. b; 2. b; 3. c; 4. b; 5. b; 6. c; 7. a; 8. b; 9. d; 10. b; 11. a;
12. c; 13. a; 14. c; 15. b; 16. c; 17. c; 18. a; 19. a; 20. c; 21. b;
22. d; 23. a; 24. e; 25. d; 26. d; 27. a; 28. c; 29. d; 30. c; 31. a; 32. a;
33. b; 34. c; 35. b; 36. d; 37. a; 38. c; 39. a; 40. a; 41. d; 42. a; 43. b;
44. a; 45. b; 46. e; 47. c.

CHAPTER 12   Output, Employment, and Inflation

Problems and Essays

1. *a.* The price level remains at its initial position. This situation may illustrate what happens in the early part of a cyclical expansion.

   b. The economy experiences a larger and larger degree of inflation as the aggregate demand curve shifts successively to the right. Inflation within the range from DD_2 to DD_5 is sometimes referred to as bottleneck inflation; if aggregate demand shifts beyond DD_5, the economy is experiencing Keynes' "true inflation." Note that a given increase in aggregate demand calls forth a greater increase in output the lower the level of output (or aggregate demand).

   c. The term *demand-pull* implies that there is excess demand for goods and services; demand exceeds supply and the excess demand pulls up prices. Note that costs also rise, as indicated by the movement along the aggregate supply curve, due to diminishing returns, bottlenecks, and so forth. But costs are pulled up by rising prices; costs do not push prices upward. The supply curve, as we shall see subsequently, may shift as aggregate demand increases.

   d. The price level would fall but not all the way back to 1.05, while output would fall to a level below $750 billion. Why? The answer is predicated on the downward inflexibility of costs and prices. When aggregate demand expanded before the recession, it pulled up prices and costs along the supply curve. With the recession these costs and prices declined somewhat but not to the same extent as their earlier rise because of downward rigidity. This implies that as aggregate demand expanded, the supply curve shifted gradually upward as well. With the aggregate supply curve at a higher level, prices would not fall as much as, and output would fall more than, otherwise should aggregate demand decline due to a recession. Of course, a deep and prolonged recession would probably push the price-cost structure downward; a relatively mild recession would not. Thus aggregate demand and aggregate supply are not completely independent under these conditions.

e. The implication is that inflation and employment move together. The higher the level of employment, the greater the inflation (up to full employment). It implies that *growing* unemployment and inflation are inconsistent.

f. Yes.

g. Classical economists viewed the cause of inflation as "too much money chasing too few goods." The price level, as is apparent from the simple quantity theory, is a direct function of the money supply. Any increase in the supply of money is automatically translated into a proportionate increase in aggregate demand, and if the economy is at full employment, $775 billion in Figure 12–1, the increase in aggregate demand causes a proportionate increase in the price level. This implies that the monetary authorities are endowed with control over aggregate demand, the price level, and thus inflation. To stop inflation, stop the money supply from expanding.

h. This version drops the full-employment conclusion and recognizes that the velocity of money does fluctuate. As used by these economists, it is really a theory of income rather than a theory of the price level. However, money is still assigned a very important role: it is argued that there is a direct relationship between changes in the money supply and changes in income, although not necessarily a proportional relationship. In short, while allowing for other factors, this version alleges that increases in the money supply are still the basic cause of inflation.

i. Money is not the major cause of inflation in Keynesian theory, although it is one factor to consider. Inflation is explained in terms of an expansion of aggregate demand, whatever the reason for the expansion of demand. The emphasis is on autonomous changes in C, I, G, and net exports, combined with the multiplier. An increase in these factors, if the economy is approaching full employment (or at full employment), will cause inflation. Of course changes in the money supply may increase aggregate demand by reducing the interest rate and increasing investment. But investment depends on many other factors besides the interest rate. Thus money is only one of the factors that causes inflation in Keynesian theory.

2. a. The equilibrium price level and output are approximately 1.06 and 750. Full employment is at the output level of 775 and hence the economy is experiencing some unemployment.

b. The price level advances with the upward shift of the supply curve, from its initial level of about 1.06 to about 1.09, 1.13, and 1.17, respectively; this is cost-push inflation. Both output and employment, the latter being directly related to output, decline; output falls from $750 billion to about $740, $729, and $717 billion, respectively. This model implies that cost-push inflation, which pushes the aggregate supply curve upward, will reduce employment even though the aggregate demand curve remains constant.

c. It implies that it is possible to have both inflation and growing unemployment simultaneously. In the case of demand-pull inflation this is not possible; under conditions of demand-pull, an increase in unemployment will tend to reduce inflation.

d. If the inflation is to be controlled by altering aggregate demand, the latter must be reduced. It is evident from the diagram that such a reduction will have only a small effect on the degree of inflation; the degree of inflation would decline only slightly. But while a reduction in aggregate demand would only lessen inflation by a small degree, it would tend to increase unemployment significantly as the output level would fall. Thus measures other than general monetary and fiscal policies must be used to control cost-push inflation. The control of cost-push inflation may call for such measures as direct wage and price controls, wage and price guideposts, strengthening the antitrust laws, and enacting legislation to curb the power of big unions.

e. Yes. Unemployment could be kept from increasing by using monetary and fiscal policies to expand aggregate demand just enough to offset each increase in costs; demand would have to shift to the right with each upward shift of the aggregate supply curve. This is illustrated in Figure 12-2A below. If the government is committed to a full-employment policy, it may be forced to use this approach. If so, the government is put in the awkward position of "justifying" the inflation. Note that while the expansionary monetary and fiscal policies may prevent a decline in employment, they make inflation more severe.

f. There are two major explanations of cost-push inflation, each having many versions. These two basic causes may be classified as wage-push and profit-push inflation. With respect to the wage-push type, the basic idea is that wage increases in excess of productivity increases push up unit costs and consequently the aggregate supply function. This kind of inflation is associated with strong labor unions and imperfect market structures. The higher unit costs force businesses to raise their prices. Profit-push inflation is a situation where businesses raise prices more than is necessary to offset increases in their costs. This also requires imperfect market structures and is associated with administered prices. In terms of the relative importance of these two types, it is usually thought that the wage push by labor unions is the more important cause. It can be argued that wage-push inflation requires administered prices. (The student is urged to consider this question in more depth and to emphasize the qualifications that are necessary for any version of cost-push inflation.)

3. a. The structural inflation hypothesis is based on three conditions: (1) wages and prices inflexible in the downward direction, (2) a high degree of immobility of resources—resources do not move rapidly from declining to expanding industries, and (3) substantial shifts in demand from one group of industries to another occurring in a relatively short period of time. In addition, rising wages and prices in expanding industries may cause cost-push pressures in declining industries.

b. Prices increased in Industry A but did not fall in Industry B, despite the fact that the change in demand for both is the same. Consequently, the net effect is an increase in the price level (that is, inflation) even though aggregate demand has remained constant.

FIGURE 12–2A

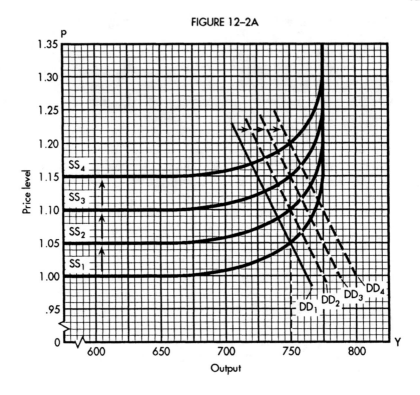

c. Output fell by more in Industry B than it increased in Industry A; the net effect, given the conditions in the diagram, is a reduction in output and thus in employment.

d. Output in B falls even farther and, accordingly, so does employment. The net effect would be an even greater reduction in output and employment. Structural inflation as analyzed for the two industries can be applied to the entire economy. Note that this type of inflation is really a combination of demand-pull and cost-push; there is demand-pull in the expanding sectors and cost-push in the declining sectors. However, the cost-push aspect is not absolutely necessary in order to have structural inflation. What is required is that prices and wages do not fall in the declining industries.

e. The use of general monetary and fiscal policies is not desirable for controlling this type of inflation because it will tend to decrease employment. If it is not important how much unemployment results, general monetary and fiscal policies could prevent structural inflation. But as employment is important, more selective monetary and fiscal controls must be utilized.

5. a. Briefly, it is a negatively-sloped curve showing the percentage change in money wages associated with various levels of unemployment (during a given time period) when other factors affecting money wages are held constant. The

curve shows—and this is important—the possibility of simultaneous inflation and unemployment.

b. Money wages increase at a faster rate. In this example the increase in money wages rises from 5 percent (at 5 percent unemployment) to 7 percent (at 4 percent unemployment). As this Phillips curve is constructed—which makes some sense—the increase in money wages for each 1 percent drop in the unemployment rate becomes greater as unemployment declines. (The slope of the PC curve is greater at lower levels of unemployment.)

c. An increase in aggregate demand would reduce unemployment and thereby increase the percentage increase in money wages—it is a movement *along* the PC curve as opposed to a shift of the curve.

d. The inflation rate would be about 1.5 percent. It is roughly equal to the percentage increase in money wages *less* the rise in labor productivity (5.0 percent – 3.5 percent).

e. At 5 percent unemployment inflation is 1.5 percent, at 4 percent unemployment it is 3.5 percent, so the additional inflation is 2 percent per year. Hence, the cost of reducing unemployment from 5 to 4 percent is an additional 2 percent inflation.

f. 6 percent. It is the unemployment rate at which the increase in money wages is just equal to (offset by) the gain in labor productivity.

g. 3.5 percent.

h. The rate of inflation drops from 3.5 to 3.0 percent. Hence, an increase in labor productivity is anti-inflationary.

i. At each unemployment rate the increase in money wages (and hence inflation) is less.

j. PC_1.

k. No. Monetary policy and fiscal policy could be used to reduce aggregate demand and thereby cut inflation. However, in doing so it would increase the rate of unemployment. Since full employment is also a goal—and one given priority over price-level stability by some people—governments may not want to pay this price. Hence, monetary and fiscal policy could not be relied on in this case—although they might be part of the solution when other policies are also adopted.

l. Wage-price controls; manpower programs to train, retrain, and increase the mobility of workers; policies to increase competition; and most important, increase productivity.

A Self-Test

Completion Questions

1. suppressed
2. inverse, rate of change of money wages (or inflation)
3. cost-push
4. demand-pull, cost-push
5. voluntary, mandatory
6. 3
7. may

8. *a.* a large shift in the composition of aggregate demand
   b. immobility of resources
   c. downward wage and price inflexibility
9. movement along, shift of

True and False

1. True; 2. False; 3. False; 4. True; 5. True; 6. False; 7. True; 8. False;
9. True; 10. True; 11. False; 12. True; 13. False; 14. True; 15. False;
16. True; 17. True; 18. True; 19. True; 20. True; 21. False; 22. True;
23. True; 24. False; 25. False; 26. True; 27. True; 28. False; 29. True;
30. True; 31. False; 32. True; 33. True.

Multiple Choice

1. *c*; 2. *c*; 3. *c*; 4. *a*; 5. *c*; 6. *a*; 7. *a*; 8. *c*; 9. *a*; 10. *a*; 11. *c*; 12. *a*;
13. *b*; 14. *d*; 15. *b*; 16. *a*; 17. *b*; 18. *d*; 19. *c*; 20. *c*; 21. *a*; 22. *d*; 23. *d*;
24. *d*; 25. *b*; 26. *a*; 27. *e*; 28. *d*; 29. *d*; 30. *d*; 31. *d*; 32. *a*; 33. *b*; 34. *d*;
35. *b*.

CHAPTER 13   Productivity and Growth

Problems and Essays

5. *a.* (1) $\Delta Y_c = I\sigma$

   (2) $\Delta Y_d = \Delta I \times \dfrac{1}{\alpha}$

   (3) $I\sigma = \Delta I \times \dfrac{1}{\alpha}$

   (4) $\Delta I = \alpha \sigma I$

   (5) $\dfrac{\Delta I}{I} = \alpha \sigma$

   b. (2) $\Delta Y_c = \sigma I$
   (3) $\Delta Y_d = \sigma I$
   (4) $I = \alpha Y$
   (5) $\Delta Y_d = \sigma \alpha Y$

   (6) $\dfrac{\Delta Y}{Y} = \alpha \sigma$

   c. See equation (3) in part *a*; the equilibrium rate is $I\sigma = \Delta I \times 1/\alpha$. Net investment
   is included on both sides of this equation. However, the capacity-creating effect
   is not the same as the demand-creating effect. All net investment increases
   productive capacity (the left side), whereas only the increment to net investment

times the multiplier increases aggregate demand. The paradox is that if net investment remains constant over time, productive capacity will continually increase, but actual output will remain at its initial level. If this year's net investment is to be justified, net investment next year must be greater than net investment this year. As long as there is net investment, net investment must grow in each succeeding period to justify the increase in capacity that occurs from net investment. Only in a stationary economy is this not the case.

d. 5.25 percent per year.

6. a. (1) K: 882.00; 926.10; and 972.41.
   Y_c: 220.50; 231.53; and 243.10.
   Y_d: 220.50; 231.53; and 243.10.
   C: 176.40; 185.22; and 194.48.
   I: 44.10; 46.31; and 48.62.
   ΔI: 2.10; 2.21; and 2.32.

   (2) Yes.

   (3) When net investment increases at the required rate, aggregate demand grows at a rate just sufficient to absorb added capacity into use. Producers have no incentive to increase or decrease the rate of investment, and consequently the system remains in equilibrium.

b. (1) Starting with the second year, the figures are as follows:
   K: 840.00; 882.40; 927.34; and 974.98.
   Y_c: 210.00; 220.60; 231.83; and 243.74.
   Y_d: 212.00; 224.70; 238.20; and 252.50.
   C: 169.60; 179.76; 190.56; and 202.00.
   I: 42.40; 44.94; 47.64; and 50.50.
   ΔI: 2.40; 2.54; 2.70; and 2.86.

   (2) Aggregate demand is growing at a faster rate than productive capacity.

   (3) If actual investment exceeds the required rate, the increase in aggregate demand exceeds the increase in productive capacity. Producers will try to expand capacity, which is inadequate to satisfy demand, more and more in each period. But as producers continually accelerate investment, aggregate demand will exceed productive capacity by continually greater amounts in each successive period; the gap will become larger. The capital shortage will cause chronic inflation until something occurs to break the spiral. The system will move farther and farther from equilibrium.

c. (1) Starting with year 2, the data are as follows:
   K: 840.00; 881.20; 923.64; and 967.35.
   Y_c: 210.00; 220.30; 230.91; and 241.84.
   Y_d: 206.00; 212.20; 218.55; and 225.10.
   C: 164.80; 169.76; 174.84; and 180.08.
   I: 41.20; 42.44; 43.71; and 45.02.
   ΔI: 1.20; 1.24; 1.27; and 1.31.

   (2) No. Aggregate demand is increasing, but productive capacity is increasing even faster. Productive capacity is moving farther and farther above aggregate demand.

   (3) Aggregate demand does not increase at a rate fast enough to absorb the increased capacity into use. There is excess capacity; a capital surplus.

Producers will reduce investment more and more each period but this will only cause aggregate demand to fall farther and farther below capacity; the result is chronic deflation. As in the preceding case, the system does not return to, but moves continually away from, equilibrium.

7. *a.* The increase in productive capacity depends on net investment, I_1, and the productivity of capital, σ. Once net investment is known, which can be determined from the level of the I function, it is necessary to find out how much this net investment increases capacity. The increase in productive capacity can be determined by finding the amount of net investment ($I = \Delta K$) on the vertical axis, moving horizontally over to the K/Y curve, and then dropping a vertical line to the horizontal axis; the increase in capacity is then represented by the movement from Y_1 to Y_2. To understand why the increase in capacity can be determined in this manner, it is necessary to recognize that the slope of the K/Y curve is the marginal capital-output ratio, $\Delta K/\Delta Y$. which by assumption equals the average capital-output ratio. Because the K/Y ratio is the reciprocal of the average productivity of investment (or capital), it follows that the slope of the K/Y curve equals the reciprocal of σ.

b. An increase in the productivity of capital, σ, will cause the K/Y curve to rotate downward to the right; the slope of the function becomes less. If the productivity of capital declines, the curve will become steeper.

c. Y_1Y_2.

d. Y_1Y_2.

e. There is no automatic mechanism to insure that investment expands enough to increase aggregate demand by the required amount (via the multiplier process). To have full-capacity equilibrium in year 2, investment must increase to I_2, or by I_1I_2.

f. For year 3, capacity expands by Y_2Y_3 as a result of the net investment of I_2 in year 2. Aggregate demand must increase by the same amount (Y_2Y_3) and thus requires that investment increase to I_3 (a change of I_2I_3). The procedure is the same for subsequent years.

g. The absolute increase in investment from one period to the next must become larger and larger. This is necessary because the absolute increase in productive capacity also becomes greater from one period to the next and, as the multiplier is constant, requires a greater and greater amount of investment in each successive period to increase aggregate demand by the same amount as the increase in capacity.

h. It is apparent from Figure 16-1 that excess capacity will build up under these circumstances. The result will be a fall in investment and a decline in actual output. There will be chronic recession.

i. Under these conditions, aggregate demand would continually exceed capacity by larger and larger amounts. Producers would increase investment to satisfy the greater aggregate demand but in so doing would cause aggregate demand to increase at an even faster pace. Secular inflation would result.

j. No. This would be a situation in which the saving curve rotates downward to the right over time. There would still be an increase in capacity and an increase in aggregate demand; but now the increase in aggregate demand would spring from an expansion of consumption rather than investment. This is not realistic.

Empirical studies indicate that the average propensity to save has remained relatively constant over the long run.

k. The K/Y curve would rotate to the right, causing the required rate of growth to increase. Thus investment would have to grow at an even higher rate in each successive period. In short, the greater the productivity of capital, *ceteris paribus*, the greater the increase in investment needed to absorb the increase in capacity.

8. *a.* (1) $G_wC_r = s.$
   (2) $GC = s.$
   (3) $G_nC_r = s \neq s.$

   b. The warranted rate of growth is that rate which leaves business executives satisfied with changes in business activity and therefore with the rate of past investment. It is the rate of growth which keeps *ex ante* investment equal to *ex ante* saving over time. The actual rate of growth is, of course, the rate of advance which is actually achieved; it is *ex post.* And the natural growth rate is the maximum rate allowed by the increase in population and technological change. It is the ceiling rate of growth that cannot be exceeded in the long run, although the economy may grow at a faster rate for short periods of time. Whereas the warranted rate is the full-capacity growth rate, the natural rate is the one which insures full employment of labor.

   c. C_r represents the *ex ante* (or desired) capital requirement or accelerator; C is the *ex post* (or actual) capital requirement or accelerator. C_r refers to the desired increase in capital, whereas C relates to the actual increase in capital, both relative to the change in output. Both equal $\Delta K/\Delta Y$, or $I/\Delta Y$, but the former is intended, whereas the latter is actual.

   d. $G_wC_r = s$

   $$G_w = \frac{\Delta Y}{Y}$$

   $$C_r = \frac{I}{\Delta Y}$$

   $$s = \frac{\Delta S}{\Delta Y} = \frac{S}{Y}$$

   Substituting the expressions into the equation gives:

   $$\frac{\Delta Y}{Y} \times \frac{I}{\Delta Y} = \frac{S}{Y}$$

   Canceling out the ΔYs on the left side gives:

   $$\frac{I}{Y} = \frac{S}{Y}$$

   Using this same approach for the actual rate will yield the same results. The difference is that in the G_w formula the saving-investment equality is *ex ante*, whereas the saving-investment equality for the G formula is *ex post.*

   e. (1) $G_w = \dfrac{s}{C_r} = 4$ percent per year

   (2) $s = G_wC_r = 0.06(3) = 0.18$

(3) $C = \dfrac{s}{G} = \dfrac{0.12}{4} = 3$

f. (1) When G exceeds G_w, C is less than C_r; thus the actual increase in investment is less than the desired increase. Aggregate demand exceeds aggregate supply with the consequent shortage of capital. Business executives will increase investment in order to satisfy the excess demand, but his will only make the disequilibrium worse as the expansion of investment increases G and causes it to exceed G_w more and more in each successive period. Accordingly, the economy experiences secular inflation until something happens, if it does, to alter the situation. (Note: Both $G_w C_r$ and GC equal s, and therefore, $G_w C_r = GC$. If $G > G_w$, then $C < C_r$.)

(2) This is the reverse of the preceding case. Now the actual increase in investment is more than the desired amount. Aggregate demand falls short of the capacity to produce. There is a capital surplus which induces business executives to cut back on investment in each successive period. But this only causes G to diverge more from G_w. In each successive period the divergence becomes greater and greater; the result is secular deflation.

g. (1) Harrod argues that if G_n exceeds G_w, then G will exceed G_w most of the time, and the economy will experience continual inflation (as indicated in the above answer).

(2) If G_n is less than G_w, it follows that G must also be less than G_w because G_n is the maximum rate of growth in the long run. With G less than G_w, the actual increase in the capital stock is too rapid, as indicated above, and this will induce entrepreneurs to cut back on investment. Investment will be reduced more and more in each period and continual stagnation results. Note that G may exceed G_w for short periods of time, such as when the economy is moving out of a recession, but not in the long run.

h. There will be a growing volume of unemployed labor.

9. a. (1) $\dfrac{\Delta I}{I} = \alpha \sigma$

(2) $G_w = \dfrac{s}{C_r}$

(3) $G_w = \dfrac{\alpha}{C_r}$

(4) $G_w = \dfrac{\alpha}{1}$

(5) $G_w = \dfrac{\sigma}{\alpha \sigma}$

A Self-Test

Completion Questions

1. the same as

2. exceeds, increase, increase, shortage, increase, exceed, shortage, inflation, does not, more and more
3. is less than, reduce, deflation
4. 4.8
5. 4
6. 0.28
7. 5
8. marginal (average) propensity to save, the average productivity of investment, the marginal (average) propensity to save, the K/Y ratio, is
9. is
10. 0.20
11. will not, increase, must grow
12. *ex ante,* equal, differently, forward, increase, equal, increase, present, backward, increased, past, investment, present
13. induced, autonomous
14. the same, is, equal
15. $G_w \times C_r$, $G \times C$, is less than, exceeds
16. less than, greater, increased, faster, shortage, *ex post, ex ante,* increase, does not, increases, exceeds, inflationary, opposite
17. less than, ceiling, cannot
18. capital, labor, did not
19. 2.6, 2.4, 1.2; 1.1.

True and False

1. True; 2. True; 3. False; 4. True; 5. False; 6. False; 7. False; 8. True; 9. False; 10. True; 11. False; 12. True; 13. True; 14. True; 15. True; 16. True; 17. False; 18. False; 19. True.

Multiple Choice

1. *a*; 2. *c*; 3. *d*; 4. *a*; 5. *b*; 6. *d*; 7. *a*; 8. *d*; 9. *e*; 10. *c*; 11. *d*; 12. *b*; 13. *c*; 14. *c*; 15. *a*; 16. *d*; 17. *c*; 18. *b*; 19. *d*; 20. *e*; 21. *d*; 22. *b*; 23. *b*; 24. *d*; 25. *f*; 26. *b*; 27. *a*; 28. *b*; 29. *c*; 30. *c*; 31. *d*; 32. *d*; 33. *b*; 34. *d.*

CHAPTER 14   Business Cycles and Forecasting

A Self-Test

Completion Questions

1. 30, 33, 18
2. 9-10, 50-60, 3, 40
3. money-using, profit, cumulative, repetitive

4. *a.* As a cyclical expansion progresses, costs of production ultimately rise faster than prices of finished products and thereby adversely affect profits.

  b. Financial conditions become tighter as the demand for funds increases faster than the supply of funds. This decrease in availability of funds and increase in interest rates reduces the actual and expected profitability of investment and thereby causes investment to decline.

  increasing, liquidation, recession

5. Exogenous, Endogenous, profit-oriented

6. *a.* underconsumption theories.

  b. overinvestment theories

7. MEC, increases, fall, low, impede, could, increase

True and False

1. True; 2. False; 3. False; 4. True; 5. True; 6. True; 7. False; 8. True; 9. False; 10. False; 11. True; 12. True; 13. False; 14. True; 15. True; 16. True; 17. True; 18. True; 19. True.

Multiple Choice

1. *b*; 2. *a*; 3. *a*; 4. *b*; 5. *a*; 6. *b*; 7. *f*; 8. *h*; 9. *f*; 10. *b*; 11. *a*; 12. *d*; 13. *a*; 14. *b*; 15. *b*; 16. *c*; 17. *a*; 18. *b*; 19. *a*; 20. *d*; 21. *a*; 22. *a*; 23. *e*.

CHAPTER 15   Managing the Macroeconomy in a Global Setting

Problems and Essays

1. *a.* An economic indicator is an economic variable used by the government to assist in determining when to make policy changes. It may relate to monetary policy, fiscal policy, or any other policy instrument. Moreover, the policy change called for may be a general reversal or a change in the intensity of current policies.

  b. Although there is room for debate, most economists would accept the following: (1) Changes in the indicator should lead to changes in aggregate spending—and hence output, employment, and the price level. (2) The indicator should be something over which the Fed has control.

  c. See your text and outside readings for the relative merits of the money supply and interest rates. There is much disagreement. In general, monetarists prefer some variant of the money supply and Keynesians prefer interest rates (credit conditions)

  d. There are various lags involved in the application of monetary policy. Although these lags can be defined in various ways, they relate in general to the length of time between when a change in policy is needed and the effect the policy change has on the economy. Unfortunately, empirical data indicate the lags may be highly variable, ranging from a few months to a couple of years. The *inside lag* is the length of time between the need for action and when the action is actually taken by the Fed. The *outside lag* is the interval that passes between the time the Fed takes action and the time that the action affects economic activity.

e. This question is controversial. In general, small businesses are hit harder by tight money policy than large businesses, as the former rely more heavily on external, than internal, financing. Moreover, investment in housing and plants is more sensitive to monetary policy than investment in inventories and equipment. See your text for other considerations.

2. b. The full-employment budget is an important concept. Yet is has shortcomings and for this reason should not be used alone. The Reagan administration did not, at least up to 1984, utilize this budget concept. A readable treatment of the full-employment budget concept is contained in the *1962 Economic Report of the President*, pp. 78–81. See your text and outside readings for further clarifications and shortcomings.

c. Like monetary policy, fiscal policy has many problems and limitations. Some of the more important ones are as follows: (1) The need for deliberate fiscal policy changes in taxes and expenditures may conflict with long-term government programs designed to provide basic social goods and services. (2) Even with the Budget Reform Act of 1974, the political process for changing taxes and expenditures may be a very long drawn out one with the end result being tax and expenditure changes that do not adequately accomplish the fiscal policy objective. Hence, like monetary policy, the lags—although different— may be long and variable. (3) Like monetary policy, fiscal policy may have a greater impact on some segments of the economy than others. It thus also poses questions of equity.

d. Many economists feel this change would be desirable in order to give fiscal policy the same speed and flexibility that is true of monetary policy.

3. a. (1) Both the interest rate and income level are unchanged. This is the liquidity trap (or the Keynesian range) and as the interest rate cannot fall and thereby increase investment, monetary policy is completely ineffective.

(2) Yes, monetary policy is effective within this range. The larger money supply reduces the interest rate, increases investment, and causes the income level to expand. In a.(1) above, the interest rate did not decline.

(3) Monetary policy is highly effective. The income level increases by a much greater amount than when the *IS* curve is in the intermediate range (at IS_2). The change in income is such as to absorb all the new money into transactions.

b. (1) Fiscal policy is fully effective. There is no increase in the rate of interest which would tend to reduce private investment expenditures, and thus the income level increases by the full amount of the change in aggregate demand times the multiplier.

(2) Fiscal policy is effective but not to the same degree as in the preceding case. The reason is that in this intermediate range the need for more transactions balances forces the interest rate upward, thereby reducing

investment. The income level does not rise by the full extent of the increase in government demand times the multiplier.

(3) Fiscal policy is completely *ineffective* in this range (which some call the classical range). All money is being used for transactions purposes, and there is not enough money to allow a further increase in the level of income. Consequently, although government demand rises, the net increase in aggregate demand is zero as the interest rate increases and reduces private demand by an amount equal to the increase in government demand.

Thus we see that in the liquidity trap (Keynesian range) fiscal policy is fully effective, and monetary policy is completely ineffective. In the intermediate range both monetary and fiscal policy are effective to some degree. And when the *LM* curve is completely vertical (the classical range), monetary policy is effective and fiscal policy ineffective. (The student should consider which of these ranges is most realistic.)

c. (1) The *IS* curve will also tend to be highly interest inelastic; thus the *IS* curves in Figure 15-1 will be almost vertical.

(2) The conclusion concerning the effectiveness of fiscal policy is still valid. Fiscal policy is just as effective in the liquidity trap and is still completely ineffective in the classical range. Note, however, that fiscal policy would now be more effective in the intermediate range and would be almost as effective as when the economy is in the liquidity trap. The greater effectiveness springs from the fact that the increase in the rate of interest does not reduce investment as much as before. If the *IS* curve is completely interest inelastic, fiscal policy would be just as effective in the intermediate range as in the liquidity trap.

(3) While fiscal policy becomes more effective, monetary policy becomes virtually useless from the viewpoint of stimulating the economy through interest rate changes. If the *IS* curve is completely interest inelastic, monetary policy, even though it causes changes in the interest rate, cannot stimulate investment and therefore income. No matter how much the money supply is increased, the income level will not rise. [The student should beware of generalizing this conclusion to the effect that monetary policy is completely useless in all cases. Monetary policy may be effective, even with an interest-inelastic investment function by limiting the availability of funds—the availability thesis. In addition, even if monetary policy were completely ineffective domestically, it could still have important policy effects in the international arena.]

d. Yes. If only government purchases are increased, the income level will advance. But if the money supply is increased, so that the interest rate does not rise, at the same time the income level will expand by approximately twice as much as otherwise (in this case). Accordingly, the question is not whether fiscal policy *or* monetary policy should be used for controlling the business cycle, but rather what is the appropriate combination of the two types of policies. In this case, the degree of effectiveness of fiscal policy depends on the appropriate monetary policy being utilized.

4. *a.* (1) In brief, the answer is as follows: The increase in the money supply (and hence outward shift of the *LM* curve) lowers the rate of interest and thereby stimulates increased business demand for investment purposes. This raises aggregate demand to Y_1. Since initially aggregate demand equaled aggregate supply, aggregate demand now exceeds aggregate supply, the amount of excess demand being the distance Y_fY_1. The excess demand pulls up prices, thereby increasing the demand for money (or alternatively, reducing the real money supply) and causes the *LM* curve to rotate upward and inward. This backward movement of the *LM* curve continues until the *LM* curve is back at LM_1. As the *LM* curve rotates inward, the interest rate increases, choking off some investment, and curtails aggregate demand until aggregate demand is again equal to aggregate supply at Y_f. The expansion of the money supply caused inflation but did not result in different *equilibrium* real interest rate and real income levels. [Caution: Inflation will be reflected in the nominal, as opposed to real, rate of interest by an amount representing the inflation premium.]

(2) Yes. There is a difference, however. In the above case, the money supply remains at the higher level and equilibrium of L and M^s results from an increase in the demand for money. In this case the money supply remains constant. The demand for money increases and offsets the initial decrease in the demand for money.

b. (1) The outward shift of the *IS* curve represents an increase in aggregate demand. Since aggregate demand and aggregate supply were equal at the initial full-employment level Y_f, it now follows that there is excess demand. Before the interest rate starts to rise, this excess demand equals the distance Y_fY_2; if we compare "equilibrium" positions, it is equal to Y_fY_1. The excess demand causes inflation. If we assume for now that the *IS* curve is not significantly affected by changes in the price level, the inflation increases the demand for money (or alternatively, reduces the real money supply), thereby causing the *LM* curve to rotate upward and inward. The *LM* curve continues to rotate inward until the excess demand is eliminated. This requires that the *LM* curve continue shifting upward until it intersects the *IS* curve at the interest rate i_2. Hence, at the new equilibrium the *LM* curve intersects the *IS* curve at the full-employment income level Y_f and the interest rate i_2. [At this new equilibrium, investment is less. It is the reduction in investment that offsets the initial increase in I, G, or X (or the decrease in S, T, or M^i).]

5. *"Crowding-Out" Effect.*
a. Crowding out relates to the effect that an increase in government demand has on private demand. If an increase in government demand, financed by the sale of bonds to the public or by increased taxes, does not stimulate economic activity, the private sector is crowded out by the government sector. In short, the increase in government demand is offset by a decrease in private demand. In such a case, fiscal policy has no lasting effect on real income and employment. If a $1 increase in government demand displaces $1 of private demand, the crowding-out effect is complete; if it displaces less than $1 of private demand, the effect is partial crowding out; if it displaces more than $1 of private

FIGURE 15-3A

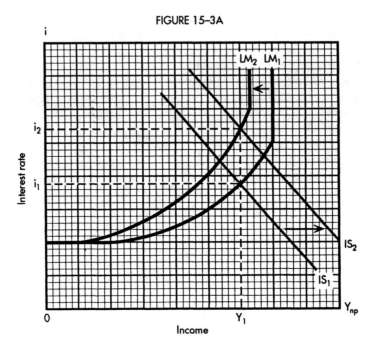

FIGURE 15-4A

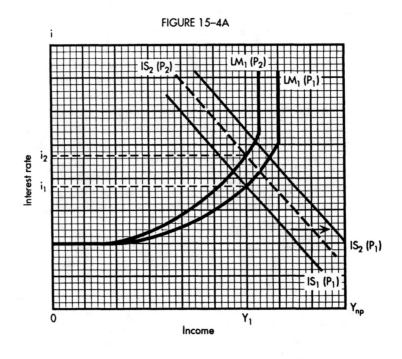

demand, the effect is over-crowding out. Note that the money supply is held constant so that the increase in government demand is due to fiscal and not monetary policy.

b. Monetarists, such as Milton Friedman, generally believe the crowding-out effect will be largely complete over the relevant time period. Accordingly, fiscal policy is viewed as a weak tool compared to monetary policy. Keynesians typically believe the crowding-out effect will be partial.

c. The crowding-out effect will be complete if the *IS* curve initially intersects the *LM* curve in the classical range; partial if the *IS* and *LM* intersection is in the intermediate range, and zero if the *IS* intersects the *LM* in the Keynesian range. In the classical range the increase in government demand results in an increase in interest rates that chokes off (i.e., crowds out) an equal amount of private demand. In the intermediate range private demand also falls, but by less than the increase in government demand.

d. Graphically, the expansionary fiscal policy shifts the *IS* curve from *IS* to IS_2 (see Figure 15–3A). If we use Friedman's demand for money function, the sale of bonds to the public, which increases the public's wealth, increases the demand for money. This causes the *LM* curve to rotate upward from LM_1 to LM_2. If the crowding-out effect is complete, as illustrated here, the equilibrium *Y* is unchanged while the interest rate increases to i_2.

e. As in the above case, expansionary fiscal policy shifts the *IS* curve outward to $IS_{2(p1)}$. See Figure 15–4A. This increased government demand results in an increase in the price level. The higher price level has a negative Pigou effect which shifts the *IS* curves back to $IS_{2(p2)}$—it is assumed (which seems quite realistic) that the Pigou effect does not swamp the original increase in government demand. It also reduces the real money supply and thereby causes the *LM* curve to rotate upward to $LM_{2(p2)}$. If the crowding out effect of all these changes is zero, then the income level does not change while the interest rate moves up to i_2.

6. a. (1) (a) The *IS* curve will shift outward, thereby increasing income and interest rates. The higher interest rates will induce a net capital inflow which will increase in the money supply and thereby cause the *LM* curve to shift outward. The final equilibrium of *IS* and *LM* will be on the *BP* curve at a high income level and interest rate. Foreign income will have increased via the multiplier process because of the higher level of domestic imports.

   (b) The increased money supply shifts the *LM* curve outward, thereby lowering interest rates and increasing domestic income. The lower interest rates results in a net capital outflow. To keep the exchange rate pegged, the central bank must use its international reserves to buy up the excessive amount of domestic currency on the foreign exchange market and thereby reduce the money supply. This causes the *LM* curve to shift back to its original position. Hence, with fixed exchange rates and high capital mobility, monetary policy is impotent—it has no lasting effect on domestic income. This relationship is called the *Mundell-Fleming condition.* [Note: Once the central bank runs out of reserves it can no longer keep its currency from depreciating unless it relies upon exchange controls and other restrictions.]

b. (1) (a) The *IS* shifts outward, thereby increasing the interest rate and domestic income. The higher interest rate induces a greater capital inflow which increases the demand for domestic currency and causes it to appreciate. The stronger domestic currency makes domestic exports more expensive to foreigners and imports less expensive to domestic residents—the result is a drop in net exports. Hence, the *IS* curve shifts back toward its original position, but not all the way, and the *BP* curve shifts upward. The net result at the new equilibrium where all the curves intersect is a higher interest rate and domestic income level. Since net exports were crowded out it follows that the expansionary fiscal policy has also increased foreign income.

(b) The increased money supply shifts the *LM* curve outward, lowers interest rates, and increases domestic income. The lower interest rate causes a capital outflow, and hence a balance-of-payments deficit which causes a depreciation of the domestic currency. As a result, net exports increase, shifting the *IS* curve outward and the *BP* curve downward. The end result is an equilibrium with all three curves intersecting at a lower interest rate and higher domestic income level. Note that foreign income has fallen in this case.

A Self-Test

Completion Questions

1. ineffective, right, will not, remains constant, the interest rate, investment
2. will not, transactions, increases, less, speculative, an increase, a reduction, will, reducing, increasing, effective
3. cannot, advance, chokes off, zero, effective, reducing, increasing, advances, is not, monetary, fiscal
4. vertical, fiscal, monetary, regardless of

True and False

1. True; 2. True; 3. True; 4. False; 5. True; 6. False; 7. True; 8. True;
9. True; 10. True; 11. False; 12. True; 13. False; 14. False; 15. True;
16. False; 17. True; 18. True; 19. True; 20. True; 21. False; 22. True;
23. True; 24. False; 25. True; 26. True; 27. False; 28. True; 29. False;
30. True; 31. True; 32. False; 33. True; 34. True.

Multiple Choice

1. c; 2. c; 3. d; 4. c; 5. a; 6. c; 7. d; 8. a; 9. b; 10. c; 11. e; 12. c;
13. c; 14. a; 15. d; 16. a; 17. b; 18. c; 19. b; 20. c; 21. a; 22. a; 23. e;
24. d; 25. c 26. d; 27. a; 28. c; 29. a; 30. b; 31. d; 32. d; 33. b; 34. b.

CHAPTER 16   The Rebirth of Classical Economics

A Self-Test

True and False

1. True; 2. True; 3. False; 4. True; 5. True; 6. True; 7. True.

Multiple Choice

1. *c*; 2. *a*; 3. *e*; 4. *b*; 5. *d*; 6. *g*; 7. *e*; 8. *a*; 9. *b*; 10. *e*; 11. *b*; 12. *d*;
13. *b*; 14. *c*.

CHAPTER 17   The New Keynesian Macroeconomics

Problems and Essays

1. *a.* The assumption of rational expectations is accepted by both schools of thought.
   b. New classical economics accepts and relies heavily on this assumption. New Keynesian economics denies the validity of this assumption because of a variety of institutional and microeconomic factors that make nominal wages and prices sticky. New Keynesian economists say the assumption of continuous market clearing amount to the same thing as assuming pure competition.
   c. New classical economics says macroeconomic policy will typically be ineffective, while new Keynesian economics denies this and says it *can* be effective.

2. Excess demand drives the price level up from p_1 to p_2. In new Keynesian economics, labor contracts, contracts between suppliers and producers, and other microeconomic factors preclude the price level and nominal wages from being bid downward. Hence, the labor market and product market do not clear at the natural rate. Since contract negotiations are staggered, the labor market imbalance could get even worse. Those workers still employed and currently entering into contract negotiations, having seen the increase in prices cut their real wage, may negotiate for even higher nominal wages to catch up to the real wage they expected to earn and to get real wage increases equal to what other workers might be getting. In addition, if labor negotiators expect higher future prices, they may demand even larger nominal wage increases. Hence, the economy may produce at less than the natural rate of income for an extended period of time.

3. The new classical school says a *credible* disinflationary policy will lower inflation with only a small temporary reduction in employment. Its view is based on the assumptions of rational expectations and continuously clearing markets. The new Keynesian school says overlapping contracts and other microeconomic factors make it difficult for disinflationary policy not to cause a substantial reduction in

output and employment for a significant period of time even with rational expectations and a disinflationary policy that is fully credible. Markets will not clear fast enough to maintain full employment.

A Self-Test

Completion Questions

1. classical, Keynesian, not
2. unanticipated, differ from, are, temporary

True and False

1. True; 2. False; 3. False; 4. True; 5. False; 6. False; 7. False; 8. True; 9. True; 10. False; 11. True.

Multiple Choice

1. *d;* 2. *b;* 3. *d;* 4. *d;* 5. *f;* 6. *e;* 7. *d;* 8. *b;* 9. *a;* 10. *e.*

CHAPTER 18   Post Keynesian Economics

A Self-Test

Completion Questions

1. unstable, does not, inconsistent, leaves out
2. relies on
3. Walrasian
4. are not
5. are not, different
6. *I* (investment), *I*, Keynes, financial, financial, capital
7. complexity and sophistication, greater, investment
8. demand price for capital goods, exceed, stimulate, generate, high, demand price, *I*, an increase, increase, speculative, financial

True and False

1. True; 2. False; 3. True; 4. False; 5. False; 6. True; 7. False; 8. True; 9. True; 10. True; 11. False; 12. True; 13. True.

Multiple Choice

1. *d;* 2. *e;* 3. *a;* 4. *c;* 5. *b;* 6. *a;* 7. *c;* 8. *c;* 9. *d;* 10. *e;* 11. *a;* 12. *b;* 13. *a;* 14. *a;* 15. *a;* 16. *d;* 17. *b;* 18. *c.*

APPENDIX

Selected Tables of Aggregate Economic Data

TABLE 1
Gross domestic product, 1959–94 [billions of dollars]

Year or quarter	Gross domestic product	Personal consumption expenditures				Gross private domestic investment						Change in business inventories
							Fixed investment					
								Nonresidential				
		Total	Durable goods	Non-durable goods	Services	Total	Total	Total	Structures	Producers' durable equipment	Residential	
1959	494.2	318.1	42.8	148.5	126.8	78.8	74.6	46.5	18.1	28.3	28.1	4.2
1960	513.3	332.4	43.5	153.1	135.9	78.7	75.5	49.2	19.6	29.7	26.3	3.2
1961	531.8	343.5	41.9	157.4	144.1	77.9	75.0	48.6	19.7	28.9	26.4	2.9
1962	571.6	364.4	47.0	163.8	153.6	87.9	81.8	52.8	20.8	32.1	29.0	6.1
1963	603.1	384.2	51.8	169.4	163.1	93.4	87.7	55.6	21.2	34.4	32.1	5.7
1964	648.0	412.5	56.8	179.1	175.9	101.7	96.7	62.4	23.7	38.7	34.3	5.0
1965	702.7	444.6	63.5	191.9	189.2	118.0	108.3	74.1	28.3	45.8	34.2	9.7
1966	769.8	481.6	68.5	208.5	204.6	130.4	116.7	84.4	31.3	53.0	32.3	13.8
1967	814.3	509.3	70.6	216.9	221.7	128.0	117.6	85.2	31.5	53.7	32.4	10.5
1968	889.3	559.1	81.0	235.0	243.1	139.9	130.8	92.1	33.6	58.5	38.7	9.1
1969	959.5	603.7	86.2	252.0	265.3	155.2	145.5	102.9	37.7	65.2	42.6	9.7
1970	1,010.7	646.5	85.3	270.4	290.8	150.3	148.1	106.7	40.3	66.4	41.4	2.3
1971	1,097.2	700.3	97.2	283.3	319.8	175.5	167.5	111.7	42.7	69.1	55.8	8.0
1972	1,207.0	767.8	110.7	305.2	351.9	205.6	195.7	126.1	47.2	78.9	69.7	9.9
1973	1,349.6	848.1	124.1	339.6	384.5	243.1	225.4	150.0	55.0	95.1	75.3	17.7
1974	1,458.6	927.7	123.0	380.8	423.9	245.8	231.5	165.6	61.2	104.3	66.0	14.3
1975	1,585.9	1,024.9	134.3	416.0	474.5	226.0	231.7	169.0	61.4	107.6	62.7	-5.7
1976	1,768.4	1,143.1	160.0	451.8	531.2	286.4	269.6	187.2	65.9	121.2	82.5	16.7
1977	1,974.1	1,271.5	182.6	490.4	598.4	358.3	333.5	223.2	74.6	148.7	110.3	24.7
1978	2,232.7	1,421.2	202.3	541.5	677.4	434.0	406.1	274.5	93.9	180.6	131.6	27.9
1979	2,488.6	1,583.7	214.2	613.3	756.2	480.2	467.5	326.4	118.4	208.1	141.0	12.8
1980	2,708.0	1,748.1	212.5	682.9	852.7	467.6	477.1	353.8	137.5	216.4	123.3	-9.5
1981	3,030.6	1,926.2	228.5	744.2	953.5	558.0	532.5	410.0	160.1	240.9	122.5	25.4
1982	3,149.6	2,059.2	236.5	772.3	1,050.4	503.4	519.3	413.7	178.8	234.9	105.7	-15.9
1983	3,405.0	2,257.5	275.0	817.8	1,164.7	546.7	552.2	400.2	153.1	247.1	152.0	-5.5
1984	3,777.2	2,460.3	317.9	873.0	1,269.4	718.9	647.8	468.9	175.6	293.3	178.9	71.1
1985	4,038.7	2,667.4	352.9	919.4	1,395.1	714.5	689.9	504.0	193.4	310.6	185.9	24.6
1986	4,268.6	2,850.6	389.6	952.2	1,508.8	717.6	709.0	492.4	174.0	318.4	216.6	8.6
1987	4,539.9	3,052.2	403.7	1,011.1	1,637.4	749.3	723.0	497.8	171.3	326.5	225.2	26.3
1988	4,900.4	3,296.1	437.1	1,073.8	1,785.2	793.6	777.4	545.4	182.0	363.4	232.0	16.2
1989	5,250.8	3,523.1	459.4	1,149.5	1,914.2	832.3	798.9	568.1	193.3	374.8	230.9	33.3
1990	5,546.1	3,761.2	468.2	1,229.2	2,063.8	808.9	802.0	586.7	201.6	385.1	215.3	6.9
1991	5,724.8	3,902.4	456.6	1,257.8	2,188.1	744.8	746.6	557.0	182.9	374.1	189.6	-1.8
1992	6,020.2	4,136.9	492.7	1,295.5	2,348.7	788.3	785.2	561.4	171.1	390.3	223.8	3.0
1993	6,343.3	4,378.2	538.0	1,339.2	2,501.0	882.0	866.7	616.1	173.4	442.7	250.6	15.4
1994	6,736.9	4,627.0	590.9	1,393.8	2,642.2	1,037.5	979.8	697.5	182.6	514.9	282.3	57.7

Source: *Economic Report of the President* (Washington, D.C.: U.S. Government Printing Office, 1995), Table B-1.

TABLE 1 (Continued)

Gross domestic product, 1959–94 [billions of dollars]

| Year | Net exports of goods and services | | | Government purchases of goods and services | Federal | | | State and local | Final sale of domestic product | Gross domestic purchases | Addendum: gross national rpoduct | Percent change from preceding period | |
	Net exports	Exports	Imports	Total	Total	National defense	Non-defense					Gross domestic product	Gross domestic purchase
1959	-1.7	20.6	22.3	99.0	57.1	46.4	10.8	41.8	490.0	495.8	497.0	6.7	9.1
1960	2.4	25.3	22.8	99.8	55.3	45.3	10.0	44.5	510.1	510.9	516.6	3.9	3.0
1961	3.4	26.0	22.7	107.0	58.6	47.9	10.6	48.4	528.9	528.4	535.4	3.6	3.4
1962	2.4	27.4	25.0	116.8	65.4	52.1	13.3	51.4	565.5	569.1	575.8	7.5	7.7
1963	3.3	29.4	26.1	122.3	66.4	51.5	14.9	55.8	597.5	599.8	607.7	5.5	5.4
1964	5.5	33.6	28.1	128.3	67.5	50.4	17.0	60.9	643.0	642.5	653.0	7.4	7.1
1965	3.9	35.4	31.5	136.3	69.5	51.0	18.5	66.8	693.0	698.8	708.1	8.4	8.8
1966	1.9	38.9	37.1	155.9	81.3	62.0	19.3	74.6	756.0	767.9	774.9	9.5	9.9
1967	1.4	41.4	39.9	175.6	92.8	73.4	19.4	82.7	803.8	812.9	819.8	5.8	5.9
1968	-1.3	45.3	46.6	191.5	99.2	79.1	20.0	92.3	880.2	890.6	895.5	9.2	9.6
1969	-1.2	49.3	50.5	201.8	100.5	78.9	21.6	101.3	949.8	960.7	965.6	7.9	7.9
1970	1.2	57.0	55.8	212.7	100.1	76.8	23.3	112.6	1,008.4	1,009.5	1,017.1	5.3	5.1
1971	-3.0	59.3	62.3	224.3	100.0	74.1	25.9	124.3	1,089.2	1,100.2	1,104.9	8.6	9.0
1972	-8.0	66.2	74.2	241.5	106.9	77.4	29.4	134.7	1,197.1	1,215.0	1,215.7	10.0	10.4
1973	.6	91.8	91.2	257.7	108.5	77.5	31.1	149.2	1,331.9	1,349.0	1,362.3	11.8	11.0
1974	-3.1	124.3	127.5	288.3	117.6	82.6	35.0	170.7	1,444.4	1,461.8	1,474.3	8.1	8.4
1975	13.6	136.3	122.7	321.4	129.4	89.6	39.8	192.0	1,591.5	1,572.3	1,599.1	8.7	7.6
1976	-2.3	148.9	151.1	341.3	135.8	93.4	42.4	205.5	1,751.7	1,770.7	1,785.5	11.5	12.6
1977	-23.7	158.8	182.4	368.0	147.9	100.9	47.0	220.1	1,949.4	1,997.8	1,994.6	11.6	12.8
1978	-26.1	186.1	212.3	403.6	162.2	108.9	53.3	241.4	2,204.8	2,258.8	2,254.5	13.1	13.1
1979	-23.8	228.9	252.7	448.5	179.3	121.9	57.5	269.2	2,475.9	2,512.5	2,520.8	11.5	11.2
1980	-14.7	279.2	293.9	507.1	209.1	142.7	66.4	298.0	2,717.5	2,722.8	2,742.1	8.8	8.4
1981	-14.7	303.0	317.7	561.1	240.8	167.5	73.3	320.3	3,005.2	3,045.3	3,063.8	11.9	11.8
1982	-20.6	282.6	303.2	607.6	266.6	193.8	72.7	341.1	3,165.5	3,1770.2	3,179.8	3.9	4.1
1983	-51.4	276.7	328.1	652.3	292.0	214.4	77.5	360.3	3,410.6	3,456.5	3,434.4	8.1	9.0
1984	-102.7	302.4	405.1	700.8	310.9	233.1	77.8	389.9	3,706.1	3,879.9	3,801.5	10.9	12.2
1985	-115.6	302.1	417.6	772.3	344.3	258.6	85.7	428.1	4,014.1	4,154.3	4,053.6	6.9	7.1
1986	-132.5	319.2	451.7	833.0	367.8	276.7	91.1	465.3	4,260.0	4,401.2	4,277.7	5.7	5.9
1987	-143.1	364.0	507.1	881.5	384.9	292.1	92.9	496.6	4,513.7	4,683.0	4,544.5	6.4	6.4
1988	-108.0	444.2	552.2	918.7	387.0	295.6	91.4	531.7	4,884.2	5,008.4	4,908.2	7.9	6.9
1989	-79.7	508.0	587.7	975.2	401.6	299.9	101.7	573.6	5,217.5	5,330.5	5,266.8	7.2	6.4
1990	-71.4	557.1	628.5	1,047.4	426.5	314.0	112.5	620.9	5,539.3	5,617.5	5,567.8	5.6	5.4
1991	-19.9	601.1	620.9	1,097.4	445.8	322.8	123.1	651.6	5,726.6	5,744.7	5,740.8	3.2	3.2
1992	-30.3	638.1	688.4	1,125.3	449.0	314.2	134.8	676.3	6,017.2	6,050.5	6,025.8	5.2	5.3
1993	-65.3	659.1	724.3	1,148.4	443.6	302.7	140.9	704.7	6,327.9	6,408.6	6,347.8	5.4	5.9
1994	-102.1	716.1	818.2	1,174.5	436.6	292.1	144.5	737.9	6,679.1	6,838.9	—	6.2	6.7

Source: *Economic Report of the President* (Washington, D.C.: U.S. Government Printing Office, 1995), Table B-1.

TABLE 2
Gross domestic product in 1987 dollars, 1959–94 [billions of 1987 dollars]

Year or quarter	Gross domestic product	Personal consumption expenditures				Gross private domestic investment						Change in business inventories
							Fixed investment					
								Nonresidential				
		Total	Durable goods	Non-durable goods	Services	Total	Total	Total	Structures	Producers' durable equipment	Residential	
1959	1,928.8	1,178.9	114.4	518.5	546.0	296.4	282.8	165.2	74.4	90.8	117.6	13.6
1960	1,970.8	1,210.8	115.4	526.9	568.5	290.8	282.7	173.3	80.8	92.5	109.4	8.1
1961	2,023.8	1,238.4	109.4	537.7	591.3	289.4	282.2	172.1	82.3	89.8	110.1	7.2
1962	2,128.1	1,293.3	120.2	553.0	620.0	321.2	305.6	185.0	86.1	98.9	120.6	15.6
1963	2,215.6	1,341.9	130.3	563.6	648.0	343.3	327.3	192.3	86.9	105.4	135.0	16.0
1964	2,340.6	1,417.2	140.7	588.2	688.3	371.8	356.2	214.0	95.9	118.1	142.1	15.7
1965	2,470.5	1,497.0	156.2	616.7	724.1	413.0	387.9	250.6	111.5	139.1	137.3	25.1
1966	2,616.2	1,573.8	166.0	647.6	760.2	438.0	401.3	276.7	119.1	157.6	124.5	36.7
1967	2,685.2	1,622.4	167.2	659.0	796.2	418.6	391.0	270.8	116.0	154.8	120.2	27.6
1968	2,796.9	1,707.5	184.5	686.0	837.0	440.1	416.5	280.1	117.4	162.7	136.4	23.6
1969	2,873.0	1,771.2	190.8	703.2	877.2	461.3	436.5	296.4	123.5	172.9	140.1	24.8
1970	2,873.9	1,813.5	183.7	717.2	912.5	429.7	423.8	292.0	123.3	168.7	131.8	5.9
1971	2,955.9	1,873.7	201.4	725.6	946.7	475.7	454.9	286.8	121.2	165.6	168.1	20.8
1972	3,107.1	1,978.4	225.2	755.8	997.4	532.2	509.6	311.6	124.8	186.8	198.0	22.5
1973	3,268.6	2,066.7	246.6	777.9	1,042.2	591.7	554.0	357.4	134.9	222.4	196.6	37.7
1974	3,248.1	2,053.8	227.2	759.8	1,066.8	543.0	512.0	356.5	132.3	224.2	155.6	30.9
1975	3,221.7	2,097.5	226.8	767.1	1,103.6	437.6	451.5	316.8	118.0	198.8	134.7	−13.9
1976	3,380.8	2,207.3	256.4	801.3	1,149.5	520.6	495.1	328.7	120.5	208.2	166.4	25.5
1977	3,533.3	2,296.6	280.0	819.8	1,196.8	600.4	566.2	364.3	126.1	238.2	201.9	34.3
1978	3,703.5	2,391.8	292.9	844.8	1,254.1	664.6	627.4	412.9	144.1	268.8	214.5	37.2
1979	3,796.8	2,448.4	289.0	862.8	1,296.5	669.7	656.1	448.8	163.3	285.5	207.4	13.6
1980	3,776.3	2,447.1	262.7	860.5	1,323.9	594.4	602.7	437.8	170.2	267.6	164.8	−8.3
1981	3,843.1	2,476.9	264.6	867.9	1,344.4	631.1	606.5	455.0	182.9	272.0	151.6	24.6
1982	3,760.3	2,503.7	262.5	872.2	1,368.9	540.5	558.0	433.9	181.3	252.6	124.1	−17.5
1983	3,906.6	2,619.4	297.7	900.3	1,421.4	599.5	595.1	420.8	160.3	260.5	174.2	4.4
1984	4,148.5	2,746.1	338.5	934.6	1,473.0	757.5	689.6	490.2	182.8	307.4	199.3	67.9
1985	4,279.8	2,865.8	370.1	958.7	1,537.0	745.9	723.8	521.8	197.4	324.4	202.0	22.1
1986	4,404.5	2,969.1	402.0	991.0	1,576.1	735.1	726.5	500.3	176.6	323.7	226.2	8.5
1987	4,539.9	3,052.2	403.7	1,011.1	1,637.4	749.3	723.0	497.8	171.3	326.5	225.2	26.3
1988	4,718.6	3,162.4	428.7	1,035.1	1,698.5	773.4	753.4	530.8	174.0	356.8	222.7	19.9
1989	4,838.0	3,223.3	440.7	1,051.6	1,731.0	784.0	754.2	540.0	177.6	362.5	214.2	29.8
1990	4,897.3	3,272.6	443.1	1,060.7	1,768.8	746.8	741.1	546.5	179.5	367.0	194.5	5.7
1991	4,867.6	3,259.4	425.3	1,047.7	1,786.3	683.8	684.9	515.4	160.6	354.9	169.5	−1.1
1992	4,979.3	3,349.5	452.6	1,057.1	1,839.1	725.3	722.9	525.9	149.8	376.2	196.9	2.5
1993	5,134.5	3,458.7	489.9	1,078.5	1,890.3	819.9	804.6	591.6	147.7	443.9	213.0	15.3
1994	5,342.3	3,578.5	531.5	1,109.3	1,937.8	955.5	903.1	672.4	150.4	522.0	230.6	52.4

Source: *Economic Report of the President* (Washington, D.C.: U.S. Government Printing Office, 1995), Table B-2.

TABLE 2 (Continued)
Gross domestic product in 1987 dollars, 1959–94 [billions of 1987 dollars]

Year or quarter	Net exports of goods and services			Government purchases					State and local	Final sales of domestic product	Gross domestic purchases	Addendum: Gross national product	Percent change from preceding period	
	Net exports	Exports	Imports	Total	Federal Total	Federal National defense	Federal Non-defense						Gross domestic product	Gross domestic purchases
1959	−21.8	73.8	95.6	475.3	265.7	—	—	209.6	1,915.2	1,950.6	1,939.6	5.5	5.8
1960	−7.6	88.4	96.1	476.9	259.0	—	—	217.9	1,962.7	1,978.5	1,982.8	2.2	1.4
1961	−5.5	89.9	95.3	501.5	270.1	—	—	231.4	2,016.6	2,029.3	2,037.1	2.7	2.6
1962	−10.5	95.0	105.5	524.2	287.3	—	—	236.9	2,112.5	2,138.6	2,143.3	5.2	5.4
1963	−5.8	101.8	107.7	536.3	285.7	—	—	250.6	2,199.6	2,221.4	2,231.8	4.1	3.9
1964	2.5	115.4	112.9	549.1	281.8	—	—	267.3	2,324.9	2,338.1	2,358.1	5.6	5.3
1965	−6.4	118.1	124.5	566.9	282.1	—	—	284.8	2,445.4	2,476.9	2,488.9	5.5	5.9
1966	−18.0	125.7	143.7	622.4	319.3	—	—	303.1	2,579.5	2,634.2	2,633.2	5.9	6.4
1967	−23.7	130.0	153.7	667.9	350.9	—	—	317.0	2,657.5	2,708.9	2,702.6	2.6	2.8
1968	−37.5	140.2	177.7	686.8	353.1	—	—	333.7	2,773.2	2,834.4	2,815.6	4.2	4.6
1969	−41.5	147.8	189.2	682.0	340.1	—	—	341.9	2,848.2	2,914.5	2,890.9	2.7	2.8
1970	−35.2	161.3	196.4	665.8	315.0	—	—	350.9	2,868.0	2,909.1	2,891.5	.0	−.2
1971	−45.9	161.9	207.8	652.4	290.8	—	—	361.6	2,935.2	3,001.8	2,975.9	2.9	3.2
1972	−56.5	173.7	230.2	653.0	284.4	209.6	74.8	368.6	3,084.5	3,163.6	3,128.8	5.1	5.4
1973	−34.1	210.3	244.4	644.2	265.3	191.3	74.1	378.9	3,230.9	3,302.7	3,298.6	5.2	4.4
1974	−4.1	234.4	238.4	655.4	262.6	185.8	76.8	392.9	3,217.2	3,252.2	3,282.4	−.6	−1.5
1975	23.1	232.9	209.8	663.5	262.7	184.9	77.8	400.8	3,235.6	3,198.6	3,247.6	−.8	−1.6
1976	−6.4	243.4	249.7	659.2	258.2	179.9	78.3	401.1	3,355.3	3,387.1	3,412.2	4.9	5.9
1977	−27.8	246.9	274.7	664.1	263.1	181.6	81.4	401.0	3,499.0	3,561.1	3,569.0	4.5	5.1
1978	−29.9	270.2	300.1	677.0	268.6	182.1	86.5	408.4	3,666.3	3,733.3	3,739.0	4.8	4.8
1979	−10.6	293.5	304.1	689.3	271.7	185.1	86.6	417.6	3,783.2	3,807.4	3,845.3	2.5	2.0
1980	30.7	320.5	289.9	704.2	284.8	194.2	90.6	419.4	3,784.6	3,745.7	3,823.4	−.5	−1.6
1981	22.0	326.1	304.1	713.2	295.8	206.4	89.4	417.4	3,818.6	3,821.2	3,884.4	1.8	2.0
1982	−7.4	296.7	304.1	723.6	306.0	221.4	84.7	417.6	3,777.8	3,767.7	3,796.1	−2.2	−1.4
1983	−56.1	285.9	342.1	743.8	320.8	234.2	86.6	423.0	3,902.2	3,962.8	3,939.6	3.9	5.2
1984	−122.0	305.7	427.7	766.9	331.0	245.8	85.1	436.0	4,080.6	4,270.5	4,174.5	6.2	7.8
1985	−145.3	309.2	454.6	813.4	355.2	265.6	89.5	458.2	4,257.6	4,425.1	4,295.0	3.2	3.6
1986	−155.1	329.6	484.7	855.4	373.0	280.6	92.4	482.4	4,395.9	4,559.6	4,413.5	2.9	3.0
1987	−143.1	364.0	507.1	881.5	384.9	292.1	92.9	496.6	4,513.7	4,683.0	4,544.5	3.1	2.7
1988	−104.0	421.6	525.7	886.8	377.3	287.0	90.2	509.6	4,698.6	4,822.5	4,726.3	3.9	3.0
1989	−73.7	471.8	545.4	904.4	376.1	281.4	94.8	528.3	4,808.3	4,911.7	4,852.7	2.5	1.8
1990	−54.7	510.5	565.1	932.6	384.1	283.6	100.4	548.5	4,891.6	4,951.9	4,916.5	1.2	.8
1991	−19.5	542.6	562.1	944.0	386.7	281.4	105.3	557.2	4,868.7	4,887.2	4,882.3	−.6	−1.3
1992	−32.3	578.8	611.2	936.9	373.5	261.4	112.2	563.3	4,976.9	5,011.6	4,985.7	2.3	2.5
1993	−73.9	602.5	676.3	929.8	356.6	243.7	113.0	573.1	5,119.3	5,208.4	5,140.3	3.1	3.9
1994	−114.2	654.8	769.0	922.5	337.3	226.5	110.7	585.2	5,289.8	5,456.5	—	4.0	4.8

Source: *Economic Report of the President* (Washington, D.C.: U.S. Government Printing Office, 1995), Table B-2.

TABLE 3
Changes in fixed-weighted and alternative quantity, and price indexes for total GDP, 1959–94 [percent change from preceding period]

Year or quarter	Current dollars	Quantity indexes			Price indexes			Implicit price deflator
		Fixed 1987 weights	Chain-type annual weights	Benchmark years weights	Fixed 1987 weights	Chain-type annual weights	Benchmark years weights	
1959	8.7	5.5	—	—	—	—	—	2.8
1960	3.9	2.2	2.3	2.3	—	1.5	1.4	1.6
1961	3.6	2.7	2.4	2.3	—	1.2	1.1	1.2
1962	7.5	5.2	6.1	6.2	—	1.3	1.3	2.3
1963	5.5	4.1	4.3	4.4	—	1.2	1.2	1.1
1964	7.4	5.6	5.9	5.9	—	1.4	1.3	1.8
1965	8.4	5.5	6.4	6.3	—	1.9	1.9	2.5
1966	9.5	5.9	6.5	6.5	—	2.8	2.9	3.5
1967	5.8	2.6	2.6	2.7	—	3.2	3.2	3.1
1968	9.2	4.2	4.6	4.5	—	4.4	4.3	5.0
1969	7.9	2.7	3.1	3.0	—	4.7	4.7	5.0
1970	5.3	0	-.1	0	—	5.3	5.3	5.4
1971	8.6	2.9	3.4	3.4	—	5.0	5.0	5.4
1972	10.0	5.1	5.5	5.7	—	4.3	4.5	4.6
1973	11.8	5.2	5.9	5.8	—	5.6	5.5	6.4
1974	8.1	-.6	-.6	-.6	—	8.8	8.6	8.7
1975	8.7	-.8	-.7	-.9	—	9.4	9.4	9.6
1976	11.5	4.9	5.3	5.5	—	5.8	5.9	6.3
1977	11.6	4.5	4.9	5.2	—	6.4	6.5	6.9
1978	13.1	4.8	5.2	5.2	—	7.5	6.6	7.9
1979	11.5	2.5	2.8	2.9	—	8.4	8.4	8.6
1980	8.8	-.5	-.2	0	—	9.0	9.2	9.5
1981	11.9	1.8	2.5	2.7	—	9.2	9.1	10.0
1982	3.9	-2.2	-2.2	-1.9	—	6.3	6.4	6.2
1983	8.1	3.9	3.8	3.9	3.9	4.1	4.1	4.1
1984	10.9	6.2	7.0	6.7	3.4	3.6	3.6	4.4
1985	6.9	3.2	3.2	3.3	3.5	3.6	3.6	3.7
1986	5.7	2.9	2.9	2.9	2.8	2.7	2.9	2.6
1987	6.4	3.1	3.1	3.2	3.1	3.1	3.2	3.2
1988	7.9	3.9	3.9	3.8	4.0	3.9	3.9	3.9
1989	7.2	2.5	2.6	2.5	4.5	4.4	4.4	4.4
1990	5.6	1.2	1.2	1.2	4.6	4.4	4.4	4.4
1991	3.2	-.6	-.7	-.7	4.0	3.9	4.0	3.8
1992	5.2	2.3	2.1	2.2	3.2	3.0	3.1	2.8
1993	5.4	3.1	2.5	2.5	3.0	2.8	2.8	2.2
1994	6.2	4.0	3.5	3.5	2.7	2.7	2.7	2.1

Source: *Economic Report of the President* (Washington, D.C.: U.S. Government Printing Office, 1995), Table B-5

TABLE 4

Selected per capita product and income series in current and 1987 dollars, 1959–94

Year or quarter	Current dollars							Constant (1987) dollars						Population (thousands)
	Gross domestic product	Personal income	Disposable personal income	Personal consumption expenditures				Gross domestic product	Disposable personal income	Personal consumption expenditures				
				Total	Durable goods	Non-durable goods	Services			Total	Durable goods	Non-durable goods	Services	
1959	2,791	2,209	1,958	1,796	242	838	716	10,892	7,256	6,658	646	2,928	3,083	177,073
1960	2,840	2,264	1,994	1,839	240	847	752	10,903	7,264	6,698	638	2,915	3,145	180,760
1961	2,894	2,321	2,048	1,869	228	857	784	11,014	7,382	6,740	595	2,926	3,218	183,742
1962	3,063	2,430	2,137	1,953	252	878	823	11,405	7,583	6,931	644	2,964	3,323	186,590
1963	3,186	2,516	2,210	2,030	273	895	861	11,704	7,718	7,089	688	2,977	3,423	189,300
1964	3,376	2,661	2,369	2,149	296	936	917	12,195	8,140	7,384	733	3,065	3,586	191,927
1965	3,616	2,845	2,527	2,287	327	987	974	12,712	8,508	7,703	803	3,173	3,726	194,347
1966	3,915	3,061	2,699	2,450	348	1,060	1,041	13,307	8,822	8,005	844	3,294	3,867	196,599
1967	4,097	3,253	2,861	2,562	355	1,091	1,116	13,510	9,114	8,163	841	3,316	4,006	198,752
1968	4,430	3,536	3,077	2,785	404	1,171	1,211	13,932	9,399	8,506	919	3,417	4,169	200,745
1969	4,733	3,816	3,274	2,978	425	1,244	1,308	14,171	9,696	8,737	941	3,469	4,327	202,736
1970	4,928	4,052	3,521	3,152	416	1,318	1,418	14,013	9,875	8,842	896	3,497	4,449	205,089
1971	5,283	4,302	3,779	3,372	468	1,364	1,540	14,232	10,111	9,022	970	3,494	4,558	207,692
1972	5,750	4,671	4,042	3,658	528	1,454	1,676	14,801	10,414	9,425	1,073	3,601	4,751	209,924
1973	6,368	5,184	4,521	4,002	585	1,602	1,814	15,422	11,013	9,752	1,164	3,670	4,917	211,939
1974	6,819	5,637	4,893	4,337	575	1,780	1,982	15,185	10,832	9,602	1,062	3,552	4,988	213,898
1975	7,343	6,053	5,329	4,745	622	1,926	2,197	14,917	10,906	9,711	1,050	3,552	5,110	215,981
1976	8,109	6,632	5,796	5,241	734	2,072	2,436	15,502	11,192	10,121	1,176	3,674	5,271	218,086
1977	8,961	7,269	6,316	5,772	829	2,226	2,717	16,039	11,406	10,425	1,271	3,722	5,433	220,289
1978	10,029	8,121	7,042	6,384	909	2,432	3,043	16,635	11,851	10,744	1,316	3,795	5,633	222,629
1979	11,055	9,032	7,787	7,035	952	2,725	3,359	16,867	12,039	10,876	1,284	3,833	5,760	225,106
1980	11,892	9,948	8,576	7,677	933	2,999	3,745	16,584	12,005	10,746	1,154	3,779	5,814	227,715
1981	13,177	11,021	9,455	8,375	994	3,236	4,146	16,710	12,156	10,770	1,150	3,774	5,845	229,989
1982	13,564	11,589	9,989	8,868	1,018	3,326	4,523	16,194	12,146	10,782	1,131	3,756	5,895	232,201
1983	14,531	12,216	10,642	9,634	1,173	3,490	4,971	16,672	12,349	11,179	1,270	3,842	6,066	234,326
1984	15,978	13,345	11,673	10,408	1,345	3,693	5,370	17,549	13,029	11,617	1,432	3,953	6,231	236,393
1985	16,933	14,170	12,339	11,184	1,480	3,855	5,849	17,944	13,258	12,015	1,552	4,019	6,444	238,510
1986	17,735	14,917	13,010	11,843	1,619	3,956	6,269	18,299	13,552	12,336	1,670	4,118	6,548	240,691
1987	18,694	15,655	13,545	12,568	1,662	4,163	6,742	18,694	13,545	12,568	1,662	4,163	6,742	242,860
1988	19,994	16,630	14,477	13,448	1,783	4,381	7,284	19,252	13,890	12,903	1,749	4,223	6,930	245,093
1989	21,224	17,706	15,307	14,241	1,857	4,647	7,737	19,556	14,005	13,029	1,781	4,251	6,997	247,397
1990	22,189	18,699	16,205	15,048	1,873	4,918	8,257	19,593	14,101	13,093	1,773	4,244	7,077	249,951
1991	22,656	19,234	16,766	15,444	1,807	4,978	8,659	19,263	14,003	12,899	1,683	4,146	7,069	252,688
1992	23,564	20,175	17,636	16,192	1,928	5,071	9,193	19,490	14,279	13,110	1,772	4,140	7,199	255,484
1993	24,559	20,810	18,153	16,951	2,083	5,185	9,683	19,879	14,341	13,391	1,897	4,176	7,318	258,290
1994	25,813	21,847	19,002	17,728	2,264	5,340	10,124	20,469	14,696	13,711	2,036	4,250	7,425	260,991

Source: Economic Report of the President (Washington, D.C.: U.S. Government Printing Office, 1995), Table B-6.

TABLE 5
Foreign transactions in the national income and product accounts, 1959–94 [billions of dollars]

Year or quarter	Receipts from rest of the world					Payments to rest of the world									
		Exports of goods and services			Receipts of factor income		Imports of goods and services			Payments of factor income	Transfer payments (net)				Net foreign investment
	Total	Total	Merchandise	Services		Total	Total	Merchandise	Services		Total	From persons (net)	From government (net)	From business	
1959	25.0	20.6	16.5	4.2	4.3	25.0	22.3	15.3	7.0	1.5	2.4	0.4	1.8	0.1	-1.2
1960	30.3	25.3	20.5	4.8	5.0	30.2	22.8	15.2	7.6	1.8	2.4	.5	1.9	.1	3.2
1961	31.4	26.0	20.9	5.1	5.4	31.4	22.7	15.1	7.6	1.8	2.7	.5	2.1	.1	4.3
1962	33.5	27.4	21.7	5.7	6.1	33.5	25.0	16.9	8.1	1.8	2.8	.5	2.1	.1	3.9
1963	36.1	29.4	23.3	6.1	6.6	36.1	26.1	17.7	8.4	2.1	2.8	.6	2.1	.2	5.0
1964	41.0	33.6	26.7	6.9	7.4	41.0	28.1	19.4	8.7	2.4	3.0	.7	2.1	.2	7.5
1965	43.5	35.4	27.8	7.6	8.1	43.5	31.5	22.2	9.3	2.7	3.0	.8	2.1	.2	6.2
1966	47.2	38.9	30.7	8.2	8.3	47.2	37.1	26.3	10.7	3.1	3.2	.8	2.2	.2	3.9
1967	50.2	41.4	32.2	9.2	8.9	50.2	39.9	27.8	12.2	3.4	3.4	1.0	2.1	.3	3.5
1968	55.6	45.3	35.3	10.0	10.3	55.6	46.6	33.9	12.6	4.1	3.2	1.0	1.9	.3	1.7
1969	61.2	49.3	38.3	11.0	11.9	61.2	50.5	36.8	13.7	5.8	3.2	1.1	1.8	.4	1.8
1970	70.8	57.0	44.5	12.4	13.0	70.8	55.8	40.9	14.9	6.6	3.6	1.2	2.0	.4	4.9
1971	74.2	59.3	45.6	13.8	14.1	74.2	62.3	46.6	15.8	6.4	4.1	1.3	2.4	.5	1.3
1972	83.4	66.2	51.8	14.4	16.4	83.4	74.2	56.9	17.3	7.7	4.3	1.3	2.5	.7	-2.9
1973	115.6	91.8	73.9	17.8	23.8	115.6	91.2	71.8	19.3	11.1	4.6	1.4	2.5	1.0	8.7
1974	152.6	124.3	101.0	23.3	30.3	152.6	127.5	104.4	22.9	14.6	5.4	1.2	3.2	.7	5.1
1975	164.4	136.3	109.6	26.7	28.2	164.4	122.7	99.0	23.7	14.9	5.4	1.2	3.5	1.1	21.4
1976	181.6	148.9	117.8	31.1	32.8	181.6	151.1	124.6	26.5	15.7	6.0	1.2	3.7	1.1	8.8
1977	196.5	158.8	123.7	35.1	37.7	195.5	182.4	152.6	29.8	17.2	6.0	1.2	3.4	1.4	-9.2
1978	233.3	186.1	145.4	40.7	47.1	233.3	212.3	177.4	34.8	25.3	6.4	1.3	3.8	1.4	-10.7
1979	299.7	228.9	184.2	44.7	69.7	299.7	252.7	212.8	39.9	37.5	7.5	1.4	4.1	2.0	2.0
1980	360.9	279.2	226.0	53.2	80.6	360.9	293.9	248.6	45.3	46.5	9.0	1.6	5.0	2.4	11.5
1981	398.2	303.0	239.3	63.7	94.1	398.2	317.7	267.7	49.9	60.9	10.0	1.8	5.0	3.2	9.5
1982	379.9	282.6	215.2	67.4	97.3	379.9	303.2	250.6	52.6	67.1	12.1	2.1	6.4	3.6	-2.5
1983	372.5	276.7	207.5	69.2	95.8	372.5	328.1	272.7	55.4	66.5	12.9	1.8	7.3	3.8	-35.0
1984	410.5	302.4	225.8	76.6	108.1	410.5	405.1	336.3	68.8	83.8	15.6	2.3	9.4	3.9	-94.0
1985	399.3	302.1	222.4	79.7	97.3	399.3	417.6	343.3	74.3	82.4	17.4	2.7	11.4	3.2	-118.1
1986	415.2	319.2	226.2	93.0	96.0	415.2	451.7	370.0	81.7	86.9	18.3	2.5	12.3	3.5	-141.7
1987	469.0	364.0	257.7	106.2	105.1	469.0	507.1	414.8	92.3	100.5	16.6	3.0	10.4	3.2	-155.1
1988	572.9	444.2	325.8	118.4	128.7	572.9	552.2	452.1	100.1	120.8	17.8	2.7	10.4	4.8	-118.0
1989	665.5	508.0	371.6	136.4	157.5	665.5	587.7	485.1	102.6	141.5	25.6	8.9	11.3	5.4	-89.3
1990	725.7	557.1	398.7	158.4	168.6	725.7	628.5	509.0	119.5	146.9	28.8	10.1	13.2	5.5	-78.5
1991	756.8	601.1	427.1	173.9	155.7	756.8	620.9	501.4	119.6	139.7	-12.0	10.4	-27.8	5.4	8.1
1992	771.6	638.1	449.7	188.5	133.5	771.6	668.4	544.6	123.8	127.9	31.8	9.5	16.5	5.8	-56.6
1993	795.6	659.1	461.0	198.1	136.6	795.6	724.3	592.1	132.2	132.1	31.5	9.9	15.7	5.9	-92.3
1994	—	716.1	509.8	206.3	—	—	818.2	678.2	139.9	—	33.3	10.5	15.7	7.1	—

Source: Economic Report of the President (Washington, D.C.: U.S. Government Printing Office, 1995), Table B-21.

TABLE 6

Exports and imports of goods and services and receipts and payments of factor income in 1987 dollars, 1959–94 [billions of 1987 dollars]

Year or quarter	Exports of goods and services					Receipts of factor income	Imports of goods and services					Payments of factor income
		Merchandise						Merchandise				
	Total	Total	Durable goods	Non-durable goods	Services		Total	Total	Durable goods	Non-durable goods	Services	
1959	73.8	58.0	31.5	26.5	15.8	17.0	95.6	60.2	26.0	34.2	35.4	6.2
1960	88.4	71.2	39.2	32.0	17.2	19.1	96.1	59.1	24.7	34.4	37.0	7.2
1961	89.9	71.5	39.4	32.1	18.4	20.6	95.3	59.2	23.7	35.5	36.1	7.2
1962	95.0	74.8	41.2	33.5	20.3	22.5	105.5	68.0	28.0	40.0	37.5	7.3
1963	101.8	80.3	43.6	36.7	21.5	24.4	107.7	70.9	29.6	41.2	36.8	8.2
1964	115.4	91.4	50.2	41.2	24.0	26.6	112.9	75.6	32.8	42.8	37.3	9.1
1965	118.1	92.1	52.2	39.9	25.9	28.3	124.5	86.5	40.5	46.0	37.9	9.9
1966	125.7	98.4	56.1	42.3	27.3	28.0	143.7	100.2	50.6	49.6	43.5	11.0
1967	130.0	100.1	63.8	36.3	29.9	29.2	153.7	105.2	53.1	52.1	48.6	11.8
1968	140.2	108.8	70.0	38.7	31.5	32.3	177.7	128.1	68.7	59.4	49.6	13.5
1969	147.8	114.4	75.2	39.2	33.3	35.7	189.2	137.0	74.1	62.8	52.3	17.8
1970	161.3	125.2	80.4	44.7	36.1	36.8	196.4	142.1	75.4	66.7	54.4	19.2
1971	161.9	124.1	79.3	44.9	37.8	37.9	207.8	156.1	84.4	71.7	51.7	17.9
1972	173.7	136.5	87.1	49.5	37.2	42.2	230.2	177.5	95.7	81.7	52.8	20.5
1973	210.3	166.9	108.0	58.9	43.4	57.5	244.4	194.7	100.9	93.9	49.7	27.6
1974	234.4	183.4	123.5	59.9	51.0	67.5	238.4	189.3	101.3	87.9	49.2	33.2
1975	232.9	178.5	121.3	57.2	54.4	57.4	209.8	163.3	82.1	81.2	46.5	31.6
1976	243.4	183.9	121.8	62.1	59.5	63.0	249.7	200.4	100.9	99.5	49.3	31.5
1977	246.9	183.9	119.5	64.4	63.0	67.9	274.7	223.2	112.9	110.3	51.5	32.2
1978	270.2	203.0	132.1	70.9	67.2	78.7	300.1	245.2	130.0	115.3	54.8	43.2
1979	293.5	225.7	148.1	77.6	67.8	107.1	304.1	248.7	132.1	116.7	55.3	58.6
1980	320.5	248.2	161.0	87.3	72.3	113.7	289.9	235.6	133.6	102.0	54.2	66.6
1981	326.1	244.0	154.2	89.7	82.2	120.7	304.1	246.1	143.4	102.7	58.0	79.4
1982	296.7	217.7	130.5	87.2	79.0	117.9	304.1	243.1	143.0	100.1	61.1	82.1
1983	285.9	208.3	124.6	83.8	77.6	111.0	342.1	276.5	167.6	108.9	65.6	78.0
1984	305.7	221.3	133.8	87.5	84.4	119.4	427.7	346.1	219.9	126.2	81.6	93.5
1985	309.2	224.8	139.3	85.6	84.4	103.4	454.6	366.5	237.2	129.3	88.1	88.2
1986	329.6	234.3	144.8	89.6	95.3	99.2	484.7	398.0	254.6	143.4	86.7	90.2
1987	364.0	257.7	163.0	94.7	106.2	105.1	507.1	414.8	264.2	150.6	92.3	100.5
1988	421.6	307.4	202.8	104.6	114.2	123.8	525.7	431.3	274.7	156.7	94.3	116.1
1989	471.8	343.8	230.9	112.9	128.0	144.7	545.4	450.4	287.1	163.3	95.0	130.1
1990	510.5	368.9	249.4	119.5	141.6	148.0	565.1	461.4	292.5	168.9	103.7	128.8
1991	542.6	397.1	269.4	127.7	145.5	131.3	562.1	464.4	297.2	167.2	97.7	116.7
1992	578.8	426.5	291.4	135.2	152.3	109.2	611.2	512.8	333.4	179.4	98.4	102.8
1993	602.5	446.0	312.5	133.4	156.5	109.1	676.3	572.7	380.9	191.8	103.6	103.4
1994	654.8	495.0	355.1	139.9	159.8	___	769.0	660.0	454.6	205.3	109.0	___

Source: *Economic Report of the President* (Washington, D.C.: U.S. Government Printing Office, 1995), Table B-22.

TABLE 7
Relation of gross domestic product, gross national product, net national product, and national income, 1959–94 [billions of dollars]

Year or quarter	Gross domestic product	Plus: Receipts of factor income from rest of the world	Less: Payments of factor income to rest of the world	Equals: Gross national product	Less: Consumption of fixed capital	Equals: Net national product	Less Indirect business tax and nontax liability	Business transfer payments	Statistical-discrepancy	Plus: Subsidies less current surplus of government enterprises	Equals: National income
1959	492.2	4.3	1.5	497.0	44.6	452.5	41.9	1.4	−1.8	−0.9	410.1
1960	513.3	5.0	1.8	516.6	46.3	470.2	45.5	1.4	−3.1	−.8	425.7
1961	531.8	5.4	1.8	535.4	47.7	487.7	48.1	1.5	−2.2	.2	440.5
1962	571.6	6.1	1.8	575.8	49.3	526.5	51.7	1.6	−1.0	.3	474.5
1963	603.1	6.6	2.1	607.7	51.3	556.4	54.7	1.8	−2.0	−.3	501.5
1964	648.0	7.4	2.4	653.0	53.9	599.2	58.8	2.0	−.7	.1	539.1
1965	702.7	8.1	2.7	708.1	57.3	650.7	62.7	2.2	−.7	.3	586.9
1966	769.8	8.3	3.1	774.9	62.1	712.8	65.4	2.3	2.8	1.4	643.7
1967	814.3	8.9	3.4	819.8	67.4	752.4	70.4	2.5	.8	1.2	679.9
1968	889.3	10.3	4.1	895.5	73.9	821.5	79.0	2.8	−.1	1.2	741.0
1969	959.5	11.9	5.8	965.6	81.5	884.2	86.6	3.1	−2.6	1.5	798.6
1970	1,010.7	13.0	6.6	1,017.1	88.8	928.3	94.3	3.2	.0	2.6	833.5
1971	1,097.2	14.1	6.4	1,104.9	97.6	1,007.3	103.6	3.4	3.1	2.4	899.5
1972	1,207.0	16.4	7.7	1,215.7	109.9	1,105.7	111.4	3.9	1.1	3.4	992.9
1973	1,349.6	23.8	11.1	1,362.3	120.4	1,241.9	121.0	4.5	−.5	2.6	1,119.5
1974	1,458.6	30.3	14.6	1,474.3	140.2	1,334.1	129.3	5.0	1.4	.4	1,198.8
1975	1,585.9	28.2	14.9	1,599.1	165.2	1,433.9	140.0	5.2	6.0	2.6	1,285.3
1976	1,768.4	32.8	15.7	1,785.5	182.8	1,602.7	151.6	6.5	10.4	1.4	1,435.5
1977	1,974.1	37.7	17.2	1,994.6	205.2	1,789.4	165.5	7.3	10.9	3.3	1,609.1
1978	2,232.7	47.1	25.3	2,254.5	234.8	2,019.8	177.8	8.2	7.6	3.6	1,829.8
1979	2,488.6	69.7	37.5	2,520.8	272.4	2,248.4	188.7	9.9	13.8	2.9	2,038.9
1980	2,708.0	80.6	46.5	2,742.1	311.9	2,430.2	212.0	11.2	13.6	4.8	2,198.2
1981	3,030.6	94.1	60.9	3,063.8	362.4	2,701.4	249.3	13.4	10.9	4.7	2,432.5
1982	3,149.6	97.3	67.1	3,179.8	399.1	2,780.8	256.4	15.4	−7.4	6.2	2,522.5
1983	3,405.0	95.8	66.5	3,434.4	418.4	3,016.0	280.1	16.6	10.2	11.7	2,720.8
1984	3,777.2	108.1	83.8	3,801.5	433.2	3,368.3	309.5	19.0	−9.0	9.5	3,058.3
1985	4,038.7	97.3	82.4	4,053.6	454.5	3,599.1	329.9	21.0	−13.9	6.4	3,268.4
1986	4,268.6	96.0	86.9	4,277.7	478.6	3,799.2	345.5	24.2	1.2	9.7	3,437.9
1987	4,539.9	105.1	100.5	4,544.5	502.2	4,042.4	365.0	24.0	−24.8	14.1	3,692.3
1988	4,900.4	128.7	120.8	4,908.2	534.0	4,374.2	385.3	25.6	−28.4	10.9	4,002.6
1989	5,250.8	157.5	141.5	5,266.8	580.4	4,686.4	414.7	26.6	1.1	5.4	4,249.5
1990	5,546.1	168.6	146.9	5,567.8	602.7	4,965.1	444.0	26.8	7.8	4.5	4,491.0
1991	5,724.8	155.7	139.7	5,740.8	626.5	5,114.3	478.3	26.3	1.5	−.1	4,608.2
1992	6,020.2	133.5	127.9	6,025.8	658.5	5,367.3	504.4	28.1	8.8	3.5	4,829.5
1993	6,343.3	136.6	132.1	6,347.8	669.1	5,678.7	525.3	28.7	2.3	9.0	5,131.4
1994	6,736.9	—	—	—	715.5	—	553.7	30.6	—	1.0	—

Source: Economic Report of the President (Washington, D.C.: U.S. Government Printing Office, 1995), Table B-23.

TABLE 8
Relation of national income and personal income, 1959–94 [billions of dollars]]

Year or quarter	National income	Less: Corporate profits with inventory valuation and capital consumption adjustments	Net interest	Contributions for social insurance	Wage accruals less disbursements	Plus: Personal interest income	Personal dividend income	Government transfer payments to persons	Business transfer payments to persons	Equals: Personal income
1959	410.1	52.3	10.2	18.8	0.0	22.7	12.7	25.7	1.3	391.2
1960	425.7	50.7	11.2	21.9	.0	25.0	13.4	27.5	1.3	409.2
1961	440.5	51.6	13.1	22.9	.0	26.9	14.0	31.5	1.4	426.5
1962	474.5	59.6	14.6	25.4	.0	29.3	15.0	32.6	1.5	453.4
1963	501.5	65.1	16.1	28.5	.0	32.4	16.1	34.5	1.7	476.4
1964	539.1	72.1	18.2	30.1	.0	36.1	18.0	36.0	1.8	510.7
1965	586.9	82.9	21.1	31.6	.0	40.3	20.2	39.1	2.0	552.9
1966	643.7	88.6	24.3	40.6	.0	44.9	20.9	43.6	2.1	601.7
1967	679.9	86.0	28.1	45.5	.0	49.5	22.1	52.3	2.3	646.5
1968	741.0	92.6	30.4	50.4	.0	54.6	24.5	60.6	2.5	709.9
1969	798.6	89.6	33.6	57.9	.0	60.8	25.1	67.5	2.8	773.7
1970	833.5	77.5	40.0	62.2	.0	69.2	23.5	81.8	2.8	831.0
1971	899.5	90.3	45.4	68.9	.6	75.7	23.5	97.0	3.0	893.5
1972	992.9	103.2	49.3	79.0	.0	81.8	25.5	108.4	3.4	980.5
1973	1,119.5	116.4	56.5	97.6	−.1	94.1	27.7	124.1	3.8	1,098.7
1974	1,198.8	104.5	71.8	110.5	−.5	112.4	29.6	147.4	4.0	1,205.7
1975	1,285.3	121.9	80.0	118.5	.1	123.0	29.2	185.7	4.5	1,307.3
1976	1,435.5	147.1	85.1	134.5	.1	134.6	34.7	202.8	5.5	1,446.3
1977	1,609.1	175.7	100.7	149.8	.1	155.7	39.4	217.5	5.9	1,601.3
1978	1,829.8	199.7	120.5	171.8	.3	184.5	44.2	234.8	6.8	1,807.9
1979	2,038.9	202.5	149.9	197.8	−.2	223.2	50.4	262.8	7.9	2,033.1
1980	2,198.2	177.7	191.2	216.6	.0	274.0	57.1	312.6	8.8	2,265.4
1981	2,432.5	182.0	233.4	251.3	.1	336.1	66.9	355.7	10.2	2,534.7
1982	2,522.5	151.5	262.4	269.6	.0	376.8	67.1	396.3	11.8	2,690.9
1983	2,720.8	212.7	270.0	290.2	−.4	397.5	77.8	426.1	12.8	2,862.5
1984	3,058.3	264.2	307.9	325.0	.2	461.9	78.8	437.8	15.1	3,154.6
1985	3,268.4	280.8	326.2	353.8	−.2	498.1	87.9	468.1	17.8	3,379.8
1986	3,437.9	271.6	350.2	379.8	.0	531.7	104.7	497.1	20.7	3,590.4
1987	3,692.3	319.8	360.4	400.7	.0	548.1	100.4	521.3	20.8	3,802.0
1988	4,002.6	365.0	387.7	442.3	.0	583.2	108.4	555.9	20.8	4,075.9
1989	4,249.5	362.8	452.7	473.2	.0	668.2	126.5	603.8	21.1	4,380.3
1990	4,491.0	380.6	463.7	503.1	.1	698.2	144.4	666.3	21.3	4,673.8
1991	4,608.2	390.3	447.4	525.9	−.1	695.1	150.5	749.2	20.8	4,860.3
1992	4,829.5	405.1	420.0	556.4	−20.0	665.2	161.0	837.9	22.3	5,154.3
1993	5,131.4	485.8	399.5	585.6	20.0	637.9	181.3	892.6	22.8	5,375.1
1994	—	—	—	626.3	.0	664.3	194.3	940.2	23.5	5,701.9

Source: *Economic Report of the President* (Washington, D.C.: U.S. Government Printing Office, 1995), Table B-24.

National income by type of income, 1959–94 [billions of dollars]

Year or quarter	National income	Compensation of employees			Proprietors' income with inventory valuation and capital consumption adjustments							
		Total	Wages and salaries	Supplements to wages and salaries	Total	Farm			Nonfarm			
						Total	Proprietors' income	Capital consumption adjustment	Total	Proprietors' income	Inventory valuation adjustment	Capital consumption adjustment
1959	410.1	281.2	259.8	21.4	51.7	10.7	11.6	-0.9	41.1	40.2	0.0	0.9
1960	425.7	296.7	272.8	23.8	51.9	11.2	12.1	-.8	40.6	39.8	.0	.8
1961	440.5	305.6	280.5	25.1	54.3	11.9	12.7	-.8	42.4	41.8	.0	.6
1962	474.5	327.4	299.3	28.1	56.4	11.9	12.7	-.8	44.5	43.9	.0	.6
1963	501.5	345.5	314.8	30.7	57.7	11.8	12.5	-.7	45.9	45.2	.0	.7
1964	539.1	371.0	337.7	33.2	60.5	10.6	11.3	-.7	49.8	49.2	-.1	.7
1965	586.9	399.8	363.7	36.1	65.0	12.9	13.7	-.7	52.1	51.9	-.2	.4
1966	643.7	443.0	400.3	42.7	69.4	14.0	14.8	-.8	55.3	55.4	-.2	.2
1967	679.9	465.5	428.9	46.6	70.9	12.7	13.5	-.8	58.2	58.3	-.2	.1
1968	741.0	524.7	471.9	52.8	75.1	12.7	13.6	-.9	62.4	63.0	-.4	-.2
1969	798.6	578.4	518.3	60.1	78.9	14.4	15.6	-1.1	64.5	65.0	-.5	.0
1970	833.5	618.3	551.5	66.8	79.9	14.6	15.9	-1.3	65.3	66.0	-.5	-.2
1971	899.5	659.4	584.5	74.9	86.2	15.2	16.6	-1.4	70.9	72.0	-.6	-.5
1972	992.9	726.2	638.7	87.6	97.4	19.1	20.9	-1.8	78.3	79.3	-.7	-.2
1973	1,119.5	812.8	708.6	104.2	116.5	32.2	34.3	-2.0	84.3	86.5	-2.0	-.2
1974	1,198.8	891.3	772.2	119.1	115.3	25.5	28.2	-2.8	89.8	94.2	-3.8	-.6
1975	1,285.3	948.7	814.7	134.0	121.2	23.7	27.5	-3.8	97.5	100.2	-1.2	-1.4
1976	1,435.5	1,058.3	899.6	158.7	132.9	18.3	22.5	-4.2	114.6	117.6	-1.3	-1.7
1977	1,609.1	1,177.3	994.0	183.3	146.4	17.1	21.8	-4.8	129.4	132.5	-1.3	-1.8
1978	1,829.8	1,333.0	1,120.9	212.1	167.7	21.5	27.0	-5.5	146.2	150.2	-2.1	-2.0
1979	2,038.9	1,496.4	1,255.3	241.1	181.8	24.7	31.2	-6.4	157.0	161.8	-2.9	-1.9
1980	2,198.2	1,644.4	1,376.6	267.8	171.8	11.5	19.4	-7.9	160.3	165.8	-3.0	-2.5
1981	2,432.5	1,815.5	1,515.6	299.8	180.8	21.2	30.2	-9.0	159.6	160.9	-1.4	.0
1982	2,522.5	1,916.0	1,593.3	322.7	170.7	13.5	23.1	-9.7	157.3	157.8	-.6	.0
1983	2,720.8	2,029.4	1,684.2	345.2	186.7	2.4	12.1	-9.7	184.3	176.1	-.6	8.7
1984	3,058.3	2,226.9	1,850.0	376.9	236.0	21.3	30.8	-9.4	214.7	197.1	-.6	18.1
1985	3,268.4	2,382.8	1,986.3	396.5	259.9	21.5	30.5	-9.0	238.4	212.4	-.5	26.1
1986	3,437.9	2,523.8	2,105.4	418.4	283.7	22.3	31.0	-8.7	261.5	230.6	-.2	30.9
1987	3,692.3	2,698.7	2,261.2	437.4	310.2	31.3	39.6	-8.3	279.0	252.4	-.1	27.4
1988	4,002.6	2,921.3	2,443.0	478.3	324.3	30.9	38.8	-8.0	293.4	266.8	-.8	28.1
1989	4,249.5	3,100.2	2,586.4	513.8	347.3	40.2	48.3	-8.1	307.0	281.1	-1.5	27.2
1990	4,491.0	3,297.6	2,745.0	552.5	363.3	41.9	49.8	-7.8	321.4	305.6	-1.2	16.2
1991	4,608.2	3,404.8	2,816.0	588.8	376.2	36.7	44.3	-7.6	339.5	328.3	-.4	11.4
1992	4,829.5	3,591.2	2,954.8	636.4	418.7	44.4	51.9	-7.5	374.4	362.0	-.2	12.9
1993	5,131.4	3,780.4	3,100.8	679.6	441.6	37.3	44.5	-7.2	404.3	390.2	-.5	14.9
1994	—	4,005.1	3,279.2	725.9	473.1	39.2	46.6	-7.3	433.9	419.8	-1.2	15.2

Source: *Economic Report of the President* (Washington, D.C.: U.S. Government Printing Office, 1995), Table B-25.

TABLE 9 (continued)

National income by type of income, 1959–94 [billions of dollars]

Year or quarter	Rental income of persons with capital consumption adjustment			Corporate profits with inventory valuation and capital consumption adjustments									Net interest
					Profits with inventory valuation adjustment and without capital consumption adjustment								
								Profits					
								Profits after tax					
	Total	Rental income of persons	Capital consumption adjustment	Total	Total	Profits before tax	Profits tax liability	Total	Dividends	Undistributed profits	Inventory valuation adjustment	Capital consumption adjustment	
1959	14.7	18.0	-3.4	52.3	53.1	53.4	23.6	29.7	12.7	17.0	-0.3	-0.8	10.2
1960	15.3	18.7	-3.4	50.7	51.0	51.1	22.7	28.4	13.4	15.0	-.2	-.3	11.2
1961	15.8	19.2	-3.3	51.6	51.3	51.0	22.8	28.2	14.0	14.2	.3	.3	14.6
1962	16.5	19.8	-3.3	59.6	56.4	56.4	24.0	32.4	15.0	17.4	.0	3.2	16.1
1963	17.1	20.3	-3.2	65.1	61.2	61.2	26.2	34.9	16.1	18.8	.1	3.9	18.2
1964	17.3	20.5	-3.2	72.1	67.5	68.0	28.0	40.0	18.0	22.0	-.5	4.6	21.1
1965	18.0	21.3	-3.3	82.9	77.6	78.8	30.9	47.9	20.2	27.8	-1.2	5.3	24.3
1966	18.5	22.1	-3.6	88.6	83.0	85.1	33.7	51.4	20.9	30.5	-2.1	5.6	28.1
1967	19.4	23.4	-3.9	86.0	80.3	81.8	32.7	49.2	22.1	27.1	-1.6	5.7	30.4
1968	18.2	22.8	-4.6	92.6	86.9	90.6	39.4	51.2	24.6	26.6	-3.7	5.6	33.6
1969	18.0	23.9	-5.9	89.6	83.2	89.0	39.7	49.4	25.2	24.1	-5.9	6.4	40.0
1970	17.8	24.2	-6.4	77.5	71.8	78.4	34.4	44.0	23.7	20.3	-6.6	5.6	45.4
1971	18.2	25.6	-7.4	90.3	85.5	90.1	37.7	52.4	23.7	28.6	-4.6	4.8	49.3
1972	16.8	26.1	-9.3	103.2	97.9	104.5	41.9	62.6	25.8	36.9	-6.6	5.3	49.3
1973	17.3	28.2	-10.9	116.4	110.9	130.9	49.3	81.6	28.1	53.5	-20.0	5.5	
1974	15.8	29.3	-13.5	104.5	103.4	142.8	51.8	91.0	30.4	60.6	-39.5	1.2	71.8
1975	13.5	29.5	-15.9	121.9	129.4	140.4	50.9	89.5	30.1	59.4	-11.0	-7.6	80.0
1976	12.1	29.9	-17.8	147.1	158.8	173.7	64.2	109.5	35.6	73.9	-14.9	-11.7	85.1
1977	9.0	30.0	-21.0	175.7	186.7	203.3	73.0	130.3	40.7	89.5	-16.6	-11.0	100.7
1978	8.9	34.4	-25.5	199.7	212.8	237.9	83.5	154.4	45.9	108.5	-25.0	-13.1	120.5
1979	8.4	39.1	-30.8	202.5	219.8	261.4	88.0	173.4	52.4	121.0	-41.6	-17.3	149.9
1980	13.2	49.0	-35.8	177.7	197.8	240.9	84.8	156.1	59.0	97.1	-43.0	-20.2	191.2
1981	20.8	61.1	-40.2	182.0	203.2	228.9	81.1	147.8	69.2	78.6	-25.7	-21.2	233.4
1982	21.9	64.4	-42.4	151.5	166.4	176.3	63.1	113.2	70.0	43.2	-9.9	-14.9	262.4
1983	22.1	64.8	-42.8	212.7	202.2	210.7	77.2	133.5	81.2	52.3	-8.5	10.4	270.0
1984	23.3	66.5	-43.2	264.2	236.4	240.5	94.0	146.4	82.7	63.8	-4.1	27.8	307.9
1985	18.7	63.4	-44.6	280.8	225.3	225.0	96.5	128.5	92.4	36.1	.2	55.5	326.2
1986	8.7	53.4	-44.7	271.6	227.6	217.8	106.5	111.3	109.9	1.6	9.7	44.1	350.2
1987	3.2	50.0	-46.8	319.8	273.4	287.9	127.1	160.8	106.2	54.6	-14.5	46.4	360.4
1988	4.3	53.4	-49.1	365.0	320.3	347.5	137.0	210.5	115.3	95.2	-27.3	44.7	387.7
1989	-13.5	44.2	-57.7	362.8	325.4	342.9	141.3	201.6	134.6	67.1	-17.5	37.4	452.7
1990	-14.2	42.7	-56.9	380.6	354.7	365.7	138.7	227.1	153.5	73.6	-11.0	25.9	463.7
1991	-10.5	47.4	-58.0	390.3	370.9	365.2	131.1	234.1	160.0	74.1	5.8	19.4	447.4
1992	-5.5	61.2	-66.7	405.1	389.4	395.9	139.7	256.2	171.1	85.1	-6.4	15.7	420.0
1993	24.1	86.3	-62.2	485.8	456.2	462.4	173.2	289.2	191.7	97.5	-6.2	29.5	399.5
1994	27.7	98.8	-71.2						205.2		-18.7	37.7	—

TABLE 10

Total and per capita disposable personal income and personal consumption expenditures in current and 1987 dollars, 1959–94

| Year or quarter | Disposable personal income | | | | Personal consumption expenditures | | | | Population (thousands) |
| | Total (billions of dollars) | | Per capita (dollars) | | Total (billions of dollars) | | Per capita (dollars) | | |
	Current dollars	1987 dollars	Current dollars	1987 dollars	Current dollars	1987 dollars	Current dollars	1987 dollars	
1959	1346.7	1,284.9	1,958	7,256	318.1	1,178.9	1,796	6,658	177,073
1960	360.5	1,313.0	1,994	7,264	332.4	1,210.8	1,839	6,698	180,760
1961	376.2	1,356.4	2,048	7,382	343.5	1,238.4	1,869	6,740	183,742
1962	398.7	1,414.8	2,137	7,583	364.4	1,293.3	1,953	6,931	186,590
1963	418.4	1,461.1	2,210	7,718	384.2	1,341.9	2,030	7,089	189,300
1964	454.7	1,562.2	2,369	8,140	412.5	1,417.2	2,149	7,384	191,927
1965	491.0	1,653.5	2,527	8,508	444.6	1,497.0	2,287	7,703	194,347
1966	530.7	1,734.3	2,699	8,822	481.6	1,573.8	2,450	8,005	196,599
1967	568.6	1,811.4	2,861	9,114	509.3	1,622.4	2,562	8,163	198,752
1968	617.8	1,886.8	3,977	9,399	559.1	1,707.5	2,785	8,506	200,745
1969	663.8	1,947.4	3,274	9,606	603.7	1,771.2	2,978	8,737	202,736
1970	722.0	2,025.3	3,521	9,875	646.5	1,813.5	3,152	8,842	205,089
1971	784.9	2,099.9	3,779	10,111	700.3	1,873.7	3,372	9,022	207,692
1972	848.5	2,186.2	4,042	10,414	767.8	1,978.4	3,658	9,425	209,924
1973	958.1	2,334.1	4,521	11,013	848.1	2,066.7	4,002	9,752	211,939
1974	1,046.5	2,317.0	4,893	10,832	927.7	2,053.8	4,337	9,602	213,898
1975	1,150.9	2,355.4	5,329	10,906	1,024.9	2,097.5	4,745	9,711	215,981
1976	1,264.0	2,440.9	5,796	11,192	1,143.1	2,207.3	5,241	10,121	218,086
1977	1,391.3	2,512.6	6,316	11,406	1,271.5	2,296.6	5,772	10,425	220,289
1978	1,567.8	2,638.4	7,042	11,851	1,421.2	2,391.8	6,384	10,744	222,629
1979	1,753.0	2,710.1	7,787	12,039	1,583.7	2,448.4	7,035	10,876	225,106
1980	1,952.9	2,733.6	8,576	12,005	1,748.1	2,447.1	7,677	10,746	227,715
1981	2,174.5	2,795.8	9,455	12,156	1,926.2	2,476.9	8,375	10,770	229,989
1982	2,319.6	2,820.4	9,989	12,146	2,059.2	2,503.7	8,868	10,782	232,201
1983	2,493.7	2,893.6	10,642	12,349	2,257.5	2,619.4	9,634	11,179	234,326
1984	2,759.5	3,080.1	11,673	13,029	2,460.3	2,746.1	10,408	11,617	236,393
1985	2,943.0	3,162.1	12,339	13,258	2,667.4	2,865.8	11,184	12,015	238,510
1986	3,131.5	3,261.9	13,010	13,552	2,850.6	2,969.1	11,843	12,336	240,691
1987	3,289.5	3,289.5	13,545	13,545	3,052.2	3,052.2	12,568	12,568	242,860
1988	3,542.2	3,404.3	14,477	13,890	3,296.1	3,162.4	13,448	12,903	245,093
1989	3,787.0	3,464.9	15,307	14,005	3,523.1	3,223.3	14,241	13,029	247,397
1990	4,050.5	3,524.5	16,205	14,101	3,761.2	3,272.6	15,048	13,093	249,951
1991	4,236.6	3,538.5	16,766	14,003	3,902.4	3,259.4	15,444	12,899	252,688
1992	4,505.8	3,648.1	17,636	14,279	4,136.9	3,349.5	16,192	13,110	255,484
1993	4,688.7	3,704.1	18,183	14,341	4,378.2	3,458.7	16,951	13,391	258,290
1994	4,959.3	3,835.4	19,002	14,696	4,627.0	3,578.5	17,728	13,711	260,991

Source: Economic Report of the President (Washington, D.C.: U.S. Government Prinitng Office, 1995), Table B-28.

TABLE 11
Civilian population and the labor force, 1929–94
[monthly data seasonally adjusted, except as noted]

Year or month	Civilian non-institu-tional population[1]	Civilian labor force	Employment			Un-employment	Not in labor force	Civilian labor force partici-pation rate[2]	Civilian / employment population ratio[3]	Unemployment rate civilian workers[4]
		Total	Total	Agri-cultural	Non-agri-cultural					
	Thousands of persons 14 years of age and over									Percent
1929	—	49,180	47,630	10,450	37,180	1,550	—	—	—	3.2
1933	—	51,590	38,760	10,090	28,670	12,830	—	—	—	24.9
1939	—	55,230	45,750	9,610	36,140	9,480	—	—	—	17.2
1940	99,840	55,640	47,520	9,540	37,980	8,120	44,200	55.7	47.6	14.6
1941	99,900	55,910	50,350	9,100	41,250	5,560	43,990	56.0	50.4	9.9
1942	98,640	56,410	53,750	9,250	44,500	2,660	42,230	57.2	54.5	4.7
1943	94,640	55,540	54,470	9,080	45,390	1,070	39,100	58.7	57.6	1.9
1944	93,220	54,630	53,960	8,950	45,010	670	38,590	58.6	57.9	1.2
1945	94,090	53,860	52,820	8,580	44,240	1,040	40,230	57.2	56.1	1.9
1946	103,070	57,520	55,250	8,320	46,930	2,270	45,550	55.8	53.6	3.9
1947	106,018	60,168	57,812	8,256	49,557	2,356	45,850	56.8	54.5	3.9
	Thousands of persons 16 years of age and over									
1947	101,827	59,350	57,038	7,890	49,148	2,311	42,477	58.3	56.0	3.9
1948	103,068	60,621	58,343	7,629	50,714	2,276	42,477	58.8	56.6	3.8
1949	103,994	61,286	57,651	7,658	49,993	3,637	42,708	58.9	55.4	5.9
1950	104,995	62,208	58,918	7,160	51,758	3,288	42,787	59.2	56.1	5.3
1951	104,621	62,017	59,961	6,726	53,235	2,055	42,604	59.2	57.3	3.3
1952	105,231	62,138	60,250	6,500	53,749	1,883	43,093	59.0	57.3	3.0
1953	107,056	63,015	61,179	6,260	54,919	1,834	44,041	58.9	57.1	2.9
1954	108,321	63,643	60,109	6,205	53,904	3,532	44,678	58.8	55.5	5.5
1955	109,683	65,023	62,170	6,450	55,722	2,852	44,660	59.3	56.7	4.4
1956	110,954	66,552	63,799	6,283	57,514	2,750	44,402	60.0	57.5	4.1
1957	112,265	66,929	64,071	5,947	58,123	2,859	45,336	59.6	57.1	4.3
1958	113,727	67,639	63,036	5,586	57,450	4,602	46,088	59.5	55.4	6.8
1959	115,329	68,369	64,630	5,565	59,065	3,740	46,960	59.3	56.0	5.5
1960	117,245	69,628	65,778	5,458	60,318	3,852	47,617	59.4	56.1	5.5
1961	118,771	70,459	65,746	5,200	60,546	4,714	48,312	59.3	55.4	6.7
1962	120,153	70,614	66,702	4,944	61,759	3,911	49,539	58.8	55.5	5.5
1963	122,416	71,833	67,762	4,687	63,076	4,070	50,583	58.7	55.4	5.7
1964	124,485	73,091	69,305	4,523	64,782	3,786	51,394	58.7	55.7	5.2
1965	126,513	74,455	71,088	4,361	66,726	3,366	52,058	58.9	56.2	4.5
1966	128,058	75,770	72,895	3,979	68,915	2,875	52,228	59.2	56.9	3.8
1967	129,874	77,347	74,372	3,844	70,527	2,975	52,527	59.6	57.3	3.8
1968	132,028	78,737	75,920	3,817	72,103	2,817	53,291	59.6	57.5	3.6
1969	134,335	80,734	77,902	3,606	74,296	2,832	53,602	60.1	58.0	3.5
1970	137,085	82,771	78,678	3,463	75,215	4,093	54,315	60.4	57.4	4.9
1971	140,216	84,382	79,367	3,394	75,972	5,016	55,834	60.2	56.6	5.9
1972	144,126	87,034	82,153	3,484	78,669	4,882	57,091	60.4	57.0	5.6
1973	147,096	89,429	85,064	3,470	81,594	4,365	57,667	60.8	57.8	4.9
1974	150,120	91,949	86,794	3,515	83,279	5,156	58,171	61.3	57.8	5.6
1975	153,153	93,775	85,846	3,408	82,438	7,929	59,377	61.2	56.1	8.5
1976	156,150	96,158	88,752	3,331	85,421	7,406	59,991	61.6	56.8	7.7
1977	159,033	99,009	92,017	3,283	88,734	6,991	60,025	62.3	57.9	7.1
1978	161,910	102,251	96,048	3,387	92,661	6,202	59,659	63.2	59.3	6.1
1979	164,863	104,962	98,824	3,347	95,477	6,137	59,900	63.7	59.9	5.8
1980	167,745	106,940	99,303	3,364	95,938	7,637	60,806	63.8	59.2	7.1
1981	170,130	108,670	100,397	3,368	97,030	8,273	61,460	63.9	59.0	7.6
1982	172,271	110,204	99,526	3,401	96,125	10,678	62,067	64.0	57.8	9.7
1983	174,215	111,550	100,834	3,383	97,450	10,717	62,665	64.0	57.9	9.6
1984	176,383	113,544	105,005	3,321	101,685	8,539	62,839	64.4	59.5	7.5
1985	178,206	115,461	107,150	3,179	103,971	8,312	62,744	64.8	60.1	7.2
1986	180,587	117,834	109,597	3,163	106,434	8,237	62,752	65.3	60.7	7.0
1987	182,753	119,865	112,440	3,208	109,232	7,425	62,888	65.6	61.5	6.2
1988	184,613	121,669	114,968	3,169	111,800	6,701	62,944	65.9	62.3	5.5
1989	186,393	123,869	117,342	3,199	114,142	6,528	62,523	66.5	63.0	5.3
1990	188,049	124,787	117,914	3,186	114,728	6,874	63,262	66.4	62.7	5.5
1991	189,765	125,303	116,877	3,233	113,644	8,426	64,462	66.0	61.6	6.7
1992	191,576	126,982	117,598	3,207	114,391	9,384	64,593	66.3	61.4	7.4
1993	193,550	128,040	119,306	3,074	116,232	8,734	65,509	66.2	61.6	6.8
1994	196,814	131,056	123,060	3,409	119,651	7,996	65,758	66.6	62.5	6.1

Source: *Economic Report of the President* (Washington, D.C.: U.S. Government Printing Office, 1995), Table B-33.
[1] Not seasonally adjusted.
[2] Civilian labor force as percent of civilian noninstitutional population.
[3] Civilian employment as percent of civilian noninstitutional population.
[4] Unemployed as percent of civilian labor force.

[for all urban consumers; 1982–84 = 100, except as noted]

Year or month	All items (CPI-U)	Commodities			Services			All items less food	Special indexes			
		All commodities	Food	Commodities less food	All services	Medical care services	Services less medical care services		All items less energy	All items less food and energy	All items less medical care	CPU-U-X1 (all items) (Dec. 1982 =97.6)
1950	24.1	29.0	25.4	31.4	16.9	12.8	—	23.8	—	—	—	26.2
1951	26.0	31.6	28.2	33.8	17.8	13.4	—	25.3	—	—	—	28.3
1952	26.5	32.0	28.7	34.1	18.6	14.3	—	25.9	—	—	—	28.8
1953	26.7	31.9	28.3	34.2	19.4	14.8	—	26.4	—	—	—	29.0
1954	26.9	31.6	28.2	33.8	20.0	15.3	—	26.6	—	—	—	29.2
1955	26.8	31.3	27.8	33.6	20.4	15.7	—	26.6	—	—	—	29.1
1956	27.2	31.6	28.0	33.9	20.9	16.3	—	27.1	—	—	—	29.6
1957	28.1	32.6	28.9	34.9	21.8	17.0	22.8	28.0	28.9	28.9	28.7	30.5
1958	28.9	33.3	30.2	35.3	22.6	17.9	23.6	28.6	29.7	29.6	29.5	31.4
1959	29.1	33.3	29.7	35.8	23.3	18.7	24.2	29.2	29.9	30.2	29.8	31.6
1960	29.6	33.6	30.0	36.0	24.1	19.5	25.0	29.7	30.4	30.6	30.2	32.2
1961	29.9	33.8	30.4	36.1	24.5	20.2	25.4	30.0	30.7	31.0	30.5	32.5
1962	30.2	34.1	30.6	36.3	25.0	20.9	25.9	30.3	31.1	31.4	30.8	32.8
1963	30.6	34.4	31.1	36.6	25.5	21.5	26.3	30.7	31.5	31.8	31.1	33.7
1964	31.0	34.8	31.5	36.9	26.0	22.0	26.8	31.1	32.0	32.3	31.5	33.7
1965	31.5	35.2	32.2	37.2	26.6	22.7	27.4	31.6	32.5	32.7	32.0	34.2
1966	32.4	36.1	33.8	37.7	27.6	23.9	28.3	32.3	33.5	33.5	33.0	35.2
1967	33.4	36.8	34.1	38.6	28.8	26.0	29.3	33.4	34.4	34.7	33.7	36.3
1968	34.8	38.1	35.3	40.0	30.3	27.9	30.8	34.9	35.9	36.3	35.1	37.7
1969	36.7	39.9	37.1	41.7	32.4	30.2	32.9	36.8	38.0	38.4	37.0	39.4
1970	38.8	41.7	39.2	43.4	35.0	32.3	35.6	39.0	40.3	40.8	39.2	41.3
1971	40.5	43.2	40.4	45.1	37.0	34.7	37.5	40.8	42.0	42.7	40.8	43.1
1972	41.8	44.5	42.1	46.1	38.4	35.9	38.9	42.0	43.4	44.0	42.1	44.4
1973	44.4	47.8	48.2	47.7	40.1	37.5	40.6	43.7	46.1	45.6	44.8	47.2
1974	49.3	53.5	55.1	52.8	43.8	41.4	44.3	48.0	50.6	49.4	49.8	51.9
1975	53.8	58.2	59.8	57.6	48.0	46.6	48.3	52.5	55.1	53.9	54.3	56.2
1976	56.9	60.7	61.6	60.5	52.0	51.3	52.2	56.0	58.2	57.4	57.2	59.4
1977	60.6	64.2	65.5	63.8	56.0	56.4	55.9	59.6	61.9	61.0	60.8	63.2
1978	65.2	68.8	72.0	67.5	60.8	61.2	60.7	63.9	66.7	65.5	65.4	67.5
1979	72.6	76.6	79.9	75.3	67.5	67.2	67.5	71.2	73.4	71.9	72.9	74.0
1980	82.4	86.0	86.8	85.7	77.9	74.8	78.2	81.5	81.9	80.8	82.8	82.3
1981	90.9	93.2	93.6	93.1	88.1	82.8	88.7	90.4	90.1	89.2	91.4	90.1
1982	96.5	97.0	97.4	96.9	96.0	92.6	96.4	96.3	96.1	95.8	96.8	95.6
1983	99.6	99.8	99.4	100.0	99.4	100.7	99.2	99.7	99.6	99.6	99.6	99.6
1984	103.9	103.2	103.2	103.1	104.6	106.7	104.4	104.0	104.3	104.6	103.7	103.9
1985	107.6	105.4	105.6	105.2	109.9	113.2	109.6	108.0	108.4	109.1	107.2	107.6
1986	109.6	104.4	109.0	101.7	115.4	121.9	114.6	109.8	112.6	113.5	108.8	109.6
1987	113.6	107.7	113.5	104.3	120.2	130.0	119.1	113.6	117.2	118.2	112.6	113.6
1988	118.3	111.5	118.2	107.7	125.7	138.3	124.3	118.3	122.3	123.4	117.0	118.3
1989	124.0	116.7	125.1	112.0	131.9	148.9	130.1	123.7	128.1	129.0	122.4	124.0
1990	130.7	122.8	132.4	117.4	139.2	162.7	136.8	130.3	134.7	135.5	128.8	130.7
1991	136.2	126.6	136.3	121.3	146.3	177.1	143.3	136.1	140.9	142.1	133.8	136.2
1992	140.3	129.1	137.9	124.2	152.0	190.5	148.4	140.8	145.4	147.3	137.5	140.3
1993	144.5	131.5	140.9	126.3	157.9	202.9	153.6	145.1	150.0	152.2	141.2	144.5
1994	148.2	133.8	144.3	127.9	163.1	213.4	158.4	149.0	154.1	156.5	144.7	148.2

Source: Economic Report of the President (Washington, D.C.: U.S. Government Printing Office, 1995), Table B-61.

TABLE 13
Changes inspecial consumer price indexes, 1958–94
[for all urban consumers; percent change]

Year or month	All items (CPU–U)		All items less food		All items less energy		All items less food and energy		All items less medical care	
	Dec. to Dec.	Year to year	Dec. to Dec.	Year to year	Dec. to Dec.	Year to year	Dec. to Dec.	Year to year	Dec. to Dec.	Year to year
1958	1.8	2.8	1.8	2.1	2.1	2.8	1.7	2.4	1.7	2.8
1959	1.7	.7	2.1	2.1	1.3	.7	2.0	2.0	1.4	1.0
1960	1.4	1.7	1.0	1.7	1.3	1.7	1.0	1.3	1.3	1.3
1961	.7	1.0	1.3	1.0	.7	1.0	1.3	1.3	.3	1.0
1962	1.3	1.0	1.0	1.0	1.3	1.3	1.3	1.3	1.3	1.0
1963	1.6	1.3	1.6	1.3	1.9	1.3	1.6	1.3	1.6	1.0
1964	1.0	1.3	1.0	1.3	1.3	1.6	1.2	1.6	1.0	1.3
1965	1.9	1.6	1.6	1.6	1.9	1.6	1.5	1.2	1.9	1.6
1966	3.5	2.9	3.5	2.2	3.4	3.1	3.3	2.4	3.4	3.1
1967	3.0	3.1	3.3	3.4	3.2	2.7	3.8	3.6	2.7	2.1
1968	4.7	4.2	5.0	4.5	4.9	4.4	5.1	4.6	4.7	4.2
1969	6.2	5.5	5.6	5.4	6.5	5.8	6.2	5.8	6.1	5.4
1970	5.6	5.7	6.6	6.0	5.4	6.1	6.6	6.3	5.2	5.9
1971	3.3	4.4	3.0	4.6	3.4	4.2	3.1	4.7	3.2	4.1
1972	3.4	3.2	2.9	2.9	3.5	3.3	3.0	3.0	3.4	3.2
1973	8.7	6.2	5.6	4.0	8.2	6.2	4.7	3.6	9.1	6.4
1974	12.3	11.0	12.2	9.8	11.7	9.8	11.1	8.3	12.2	11.2
1975	6.9	9.1	7.3	9.4	6.6	8.9	6.7	9.1	6.7	9.0
1976	4.9	5.8	6.1	6.7	4.8	5.6	6.1	6.5	4.5	5.3
1977	6.7	6.5	6.4	6.4	6.7	6.4	6.5	6.3	6.7	6.3
1978	9.0	7.6	8.3	7.2	9.1	7.8	8.5	7.4	9.1	7.6
1979	13.3	11.3	14.0	11.4	11.1	10.0	11.3	9.8	13.4	11.5
1980	12.5	13.5	13.0	14.5	11.7	11.6	12.2	12.4	12.5	13.6
1981	8.9	10.3	9.8	10.9	8.5	10.0	9.5	10.4	8.8	10.4
1982	3.8	6.2	4.1	6.5	4.2	6.7	4.5	7.4	3.6	5.9
1983	3.8	3.2	4.1	3.5	4.5	3.6	4.8	4.0	3.6	2.9
1984	3.9	4.3	3.9	4.3	4.4	4.7	4.7	5.0	3.9	4.1
1985	3.8	3.6	4.1	3.8	4.0	3.9	4.3	4.3	3.5	3.4
1986	1.1	1.9	.5	1.7	3.8	3.9	3.8	4.0	.7	1.5
1987	4.4	3.6	4.6	3.5	4.1	4.1	4.2	4.1	4.3	3.5
1988	4.4	4.1	4.2	4.1	4.7	4.4	4.7	4.4	4.2	3.9
1989	4.6	4.8	4.5	4.6	4.6	4.7	4.4	4.5	4.5	4.6
1990	6.1	5.4	6.3	5.3	5.2	5.2	5.2	5.0	5.9	5.2
1991	3.1	4.2	3.3	4.5	3.9	4.6	4.4	4.9	2.7	3.9
1992	2.9	3.0	3.2	3.5	3.0	3.2	3.3	3.7	2.7	2.8
1993	2.7	3.0	2.7	3.1	3.1	3.2	3.2	3.3	2.6	2.7
1994	2.7	2.6	2.6	2.7	2.6	2.7	2.6	2.8	2.5	2.5

Source: *Economic Report of the President* (Washington, D.C.: U.S. Government Printing Office, 1995), Table B-62.

TABLE 14
Changes in producer price indexes for finished goods, 1958–94
[percent change]

Year or month	Total finished goods		Finished consumer foods		Finished goods excluding consumer foods						Finished energy goods		Finished goods excluding foods and energy	
					Total		Consumer goods		Capital equipment					
	Dec. to Dec.	Year to year	Dec. to Dec.	Year to year	Dec. to Dec.	Year to year	Dec. to Dec.	Year to year	Dec. to Dec.	Year to year	Dec. to Dec.	Year to year	Dec. to Dec.	Year to year
1958	0.3	2.2	0.6	6.1	—	—	0.3	0	1.2	2.6	—	—	—	—
1959	-.3	-.3	-3.7	-4.7	—	—	.9	1.2	.9	1.9	—	—	—	—
1960	1.8	.9	5.3	2.0	—	—	.3	.6	.3	.3	—	—	—	—
1961	-.6	0	-1.9	-.3	—	—	-.3	-.3	0	.3	—	—	—	—
1962	.3	.3	.6	.8	—	—	0	0	.3	.3	—	—	—	—
1963	-.3	-.3	-1.4	-1.1	—	—	0	0	.6	.3	—	—	—	—
1964	.6	.3	.6	.3	—	—	.3	-.3	.9	.9	—	—	—	—
1965	3.3	1.8	9.1	4.0	—	—	.9	.9	1.5	1.2	—	—	—	—
1966	2.0	3.2	1.3	6.5	—	—	1.8	1.5	3.8	2.4	—	—	—	—
1967	1.7	1.1	-.3	-1.8	—	—	2.0	1.8	3.1	3.5	—	—	—	—
1968	3.1	2.8	4.6	3.9	2.5	2.6	2.0	2.3	3.0	3.4	—	—	—	—
1969	4.9	3.8	8.1	6.0	3.3	2.8	2.8	2.3	4.8	3.5	—	—	—	—
1970	2.1	3.4	-2.3	3.3	4.3	3.5	3.8	3.0	4.8	4.7	—	—	—	—
1971	3.3	3.1	5.8	1.6	2.0	3.7	2.1	3.5	2.4	4.0	—	—	—	—
1972	3.9	3.2	7.9	5.4	2.3	2.0	2.1	1.8	2.1	2.6	—	—	—	—
1973	11.7	9.1	22.7	20.5	6.6	4.0	7.5	4.6	5.1	3.3	—	—	—	—
1974	18.3	15.4	12.8	14.0	21.1	16.2	20.3	17.0	22.7	14.3	—	—	17.7	11.4
1975	6.6	10.6	5.6	8.4	7.2	12.1	6.8	10.4	8.1	15.2	16.3	17.2	6.0	11.4
1976	3.8	4.5	-2.5	-.3	6.2	6.2	6.0	6.2	6.5	6.7	11.6	11.7	5.7	5.7
1977	6.7	6.4	6.9	5.3	6.8	7.1	6.7	7.3	7.2	6.4	12.0	15.7	6.2	6.0
1978	9.3	7.9	11.7	9.0	8.3	7.2	8.5	7.1	8.0	7.9	8.5	6.5	8.4	7.5
1979	12.8	11.2	7.4	9.3	14.8	11.8	17.6	13.3	8.8	8.7	58.1	35.0	9.4	8.9
1980	11.8	13.4	7.5	5.8	13.4	16.2	14.1	18.5	11.4	10.7	27.9	49.2	10.8	11.2
1981	7.1	9.2	1.5	5.8	8.7	10.3	8.6	13.3	9.2	10.3	14.1	19.1	7.7	8.6
1982	3.6	4.1	2.0	2.2	4.2	4.6	4.2	4.1	3.9	5.7	-.1	-1.5	4.9	5.7
1983	.6	1.6	2.3	1.0	0	1.8	-.9	1.2	2.0	2.8	-9.2	-4.8	1.9	3.0
1984	1.7	2.1	3.5	4.4	1.1	1.4	.8	1.0	1.8	2.3	-4.2	-4.2	2.0	2.4
1985	1.8	1.0	.6	-.8	2.2	1.4	2.1	1.1	2.7	2.2	-.2	-3.9	2.7	2.5
1986	-2.3	-1.4	2.8	2.6	-4.0	-2.6	-6.6	-4.6	2.1	2.0	-38.1	-28.1	2.7	2.3
1987	2.2	2.1	-.2	2.1	3.2	2.1	4.1	2.2	1.3	1.8	11.2	-1.9	2.1	2.4
1988	4.0	2.5	5.7	2.8	3.2	2.4	3.1	2.4	3.6	2.3	-3.6	-3.2	4.3	3.3
1989	4.9	5.2	5.2	5.4	4.8	5.0	5.3	5.6	3.8	3.9	9.5	9.9	4.2	4.4
1990	5.7	4.9	2.6	4.8	6.9	5.0	8.7	5.9	3.4	3.5	30.7	14.2	3.5	3.7
1991	-.1	2.1	-1.5	-.2	.3	3.0	-.7	2.9	2.5	3.1	-9.6	4.1	3.1	3.6
1992	1.6	1.2	1.6	-.6	1.6	1.8	1.6	1.8	1.7	1.9	-.3	-.4	2.0	2.4
1993	.2	1.2	2.4	1.9	-.4	1.1	-1.4	.7	1.8	1.8	-4.1	.3	.4	1.2
1994	1.7	.6	1.0	.9	1.9	.6	1.9	-.1	2.0	2.1	3.4	-1.3	1.6	1.0

Source: *Economic Report of the President* (Washington, D.C.: U.S. Government Printing Office, 1995), Table B-67.

TABLE 15
Money stock, liquid assets, and debt measures, 1959–94
[averages of daily figures; billions of dollars]

Year and month	M1 — Sum of currency, demand deposits, travelers checks, and other checkable deposits (OCDs)	M2 — M1 plus overnight RPs and Eurodollars MMMF balances (general purpose and broker/dealer), MMDAs, and savings and small time deposits	M3 — M2 plus large time deposits, term RPs, term Eurodollars and institution-only MMMF balances	L — M3 plus other liquid assets	Debt — Debt of domestic nonfinancial sectors (monthly average)	Percent change from year or 6 months earlier M1	M2	M3	Debt
December:									
1959	140.0	297.8	299.8	388.6	687.7	—	—	—	7.6
1960	140.7	312.3	315.3	403.6	723.1	0.5	4.9	5.2	5.1
1961	145.2	335.5	341.0	430.8	765.8	3.2	7.4	8.2	5.9
1962	147.8	362.7	371.4	466.1	818.6	1.9	8.1	8.9	6.9
1963	153.3	393.2	406.0	503.8	873.5	3.7	8.4	9.3	6.7
1964	160.3	424.8	442.5	540.4	937.0	4.6	8.0	9.0	7.3
1965	167.9	459.3	482.2	584.4	1,003.8	4.7	8.1	9.0	7.1
1966	172.0	480.0	505.1	614.5	1,071.2	2.4	4.5	4.7	6.7
1967	183.3	524.3	557.1	666.5	1,145.4	6.6	9.2	10.3	6.9
1968	197.4	566.3	606.2	728.9	1,236.8	7.7	8.0	8.8	8.0
1969	203.9	589.5	615.0	763.5	1,326.9	3.3	4.1	1.5	7.3
1970	214.4	628.1	677.4	816.2	1,416.0	5.1	6.5	10.1	6.7
1971	228.3	712.7	776.1	902.9	1,549.5	6.5	13.5	14.6	9.4
1972	249.2	805.2	886.0	1,022.9	1,704.4	9.2	13.0	14.2	10.0
1973	262.8	861.0	984.9	1,142.4	1,890.7	5.5	6.9	11.2	10.9
1974	274.3	908.5	1,070.3	1,250.2	2,064.0	4.4	5.5	8.7	9.2
1975	287.5	1,023.2	1,172.2	1,366.9	2,251.5	4.8	12.6	9.5	9.1
1976	306.3	1,163.6	1,311.7	1,516.5	2,496.3	6.5	13.7	11.9	10.9
1977	331.1	1,286.5	1,472.5	1,705.3	2,813.7	8.1	10.6	12.3	12.7
1978	358.2	1,388.6	1,646.4	1,910.7	3,192.2	8.2	8.0	11.8	13.5
1979	382.5	1,497.0	1,803.9	2,117.1	3,568.1	6.8	7.8	9.6	11.8
1980	408.5	1,629.3	1,988.8	2,325.8	3,896.9	6.8	8.9	10.3	9.2
1981	436.3	1,793.3	2,235.9	2,598.7	4,279.3	6.8	10.0	12.4	9.8
1982	474.3	1,953.2	2,443.2	2,853.1	4,692.2	8.7	8.9	9.3	9.6
1983	521.0	2,187.6	2,696.2	3,157.6	5,244.3	9.8	12.0	10.4	11.8
1984	552.1	2,377.9	2,994.6	3,536.0	6,011.4	6.0	8.5	11.1	14.6
1985	619.9	2,575.0	3,211.6	3,838.9	6,902.1	12.3	8.4	7.2	14.8
1986	724.5	2,818.2	3,497.3	4,137.5	7,785.2	16.9	9.5	8.9	12.8
1987	750.1	2,920.1	3,681.3	4,340.2	8,544.6	3.5	3.5	5.3	9.8
1988	787.4	3,081.4	3,920.4	4,674.6	9,315.0	5.0	5.5	6.5	9.0
1989	794.7	3,239.8	4,067.3	4,897.3	10,045.1	0.9	4.9	3.7	7.8
1990	826.4	3,353.0	4,125.7	4,974.8	10,690.2	4.0	3.2	1.4	6.4
1991	897.7	3,455.2	4,180.4	4,992.9	11,171.1	8.6	3.5	1.3	4.5
1992	1,024.8	3,509.0	4,183.0	5,057.1	11,706.1	14.2	3.0	.1	4.8
1993	1,128.4	3,567.9	4,232.0	5,135.0	12,335.4	10.1	1.6	1.2	5.4
1994	1,147.6	3,600.0	4,282.4	—	—	1.7	.9	1.2	—

Source: Economic Report of the President (Washington, D.C.: U.S. Government Printing Office, 1995), Table B-68.

TABLE 16
Bond yields and interest rates, 1929–94 [percent per annum]

| U.S. Treasury securities | | | | | Corporate bonds (Moody's) | | | | | | | |
| Bills (new issues)[1] | | Constant maturities[2] | | | | | High grade municipal bonds (Standard & Poor's) | New-home mortgage yields[3] | Commercial paper, 6 months[4] | Prime rate charged by banks[5] | Discount rate, Federal Reserve Bank of New York[6] | Federal funds rate[6] |
3-month	6-month	3-year	10-year	30-year	Aaa	Baa						
—	—	—	—	—	4.73	5.90	4.27	—	5.85	5.50–6.00	5.16	—
0.515	—	—	—	—	4.49	7.76	4.71	—	1.73	1.50–4.00	2.56	—
.023	—	—	—	—	3.01	4.96	2.76	—	.59	1.50	1.00	—
.014	—	—	—	—	2.84	4.75	2.50	—	.56	1.50	1.00	—
.130	—	—	—	—	2.77	4.33	2.10	—	.53	1.50	1.00	—
.326	—	—	—	—	2.83	4.28	2.36	—	.66	1.50	[7]1.00	—
.373	—	—	—	—	2.73	3.91	2.06	—	.69	1.50	[7]1.00	—
.375	—	—	—	—	2.72	3.61	1.86	—	.73	1.50	[7]1.00	—
.375	—	—	—	—	2.62	3.29	1.67	—	.75	1.50	[7]1.00	—
.375	—	—	—	—	2.53	3.05	1.64	—	.81	1.50	[7]1.00	—
.594	—	—	—	—	2.61	3.24	2.01	—	1.03	1.50–1.75	1.00	—
1.040	—	—	—	—	2.82	3.47	2.40	—	1.44	1.75–2.00	1.34	—
1.102	—	—	—	—	2.66	3.42	2.21	—	1.49	2.00	1.50	—
1.218	—	—	—	—	2.62	3.24	1.98	—	1.45	2.07	1.59	—
1.552	—	—	—	—	2.86	3.41	2.00	—	2.16	2.56	1.75	—
1.766	—	—	—	—	2.96	3.52	2.19	—	2.33	3.00	1.75	—
1.931	—	2.47	2.85	—	3.20	3.74	2.72	—	2.52	3.17	1.99	—
.953	—	1.63	2.40	—	2.90	3.51	2.37	—	1.58	3.05	1.60	—
1.753	—	2.47	2.82	—	3.06	3.53	2.53	—	2.18	3.16	1.89	1.78
2.658	—	3.19	3.18	—	3.36	3.88	2.93	—	3.31	3.77	2.77	2.73
3.267	—	3.98	3.65	—	3.89	4.71	3.60	—	3.81	4.20	3.12	3.11
1.839	—	2.84	3.32	—	3.79	4.73	3.56	—	2.46	3.83	2.15	1.57
3.405	3.832	4.46	4.33	—	4.38	5.05	3.95	—	3.97	4.48	3.36	3.30
2.928	3.247	3.98	4.12	—	4.41	5.19	3.73	—	3.85	4.82	3.53	3.22
2.378	2.605	3.54	3.88	—	4.35	5.08	3.46	—	2.97	4.50	3.00	1.96
2.778	2.908	3.47	3.95	—	4.33	5.02	3.18	—	3.26	4.50	3.00	2.68
3.157	3.253	3.67	4.00	—	4.26	4.86	3.23	5.89	3.55	4.50	3.23	3.18
3.549	3.686	4.03	4.19	—	4.40	4.83	3.22	5.83	3.97	4.50	3.55	3.50
3.954	4.055	4.22	4.28	—	4.49	4.87	3.27	5.81	4.38	4.54	4.04	4.07
4.881	5.082	5.23	4.92	—	5.13	5.67	3.82	6.25	5.55	5.63	4.50	5.11
4.321	4.630	5.03	5.07	—	5.51	6.23	3.98	6.46	5.10	5.61	4.19	4.22
5.339	5.470	5.68	5.65	—	6.18	6.94	4.51	6.97	5.90	6.30	5.16	5.66
6.677	6.853	7.02	6.67	—	7.03	7.81	5.81	7.81	7.83	7.96	5.87	8.20
6.458	6.562	7.29	7.35	—	8.04	9.11	6.51	8.45	7.71	7.91	5.95	7.18
4.348	4.511	5.65	6.16	—	7.39	8.56	5.70	7.74	5.11	5.72	4.88	4.66
4.071	4.466	5.72	6.21	—	7.21	8.16	5.27	7.60	4.73	5.25	4.50	4.43
7.041	7.178	6.95	6.84	—	7.44	8.24	5.18	7.96	8.15	8.03	6.44	8.73
7.886	7.926	7.82	7.56	—	8.57	9.50	6.09	8.92	9.84	10.81	7.83	10.50
5.838	6.122	7.49	7.99	—	8.83	10.61	6.89	9.00	6.32	7.86	6.25	5.82
4.989	5.266	6.77	7.61	—	8.43	9.75	6.49	9.00	5.34	6.84	5.50	5.04
5.265	5.510	6.69	7.42	7.75	8.02	8.97	5.56	9.02	5.61	6.83	5.46	5.54
7.221	7.572	8.29	8.41	8.49	8.73	9.49	5.90	9.56	7.99	9.06	7.46	7.93
10.041	10.017	9.71	9.44	9.28	9.63	10.69	6.39	10.78	10.91	12.67	10.28	11.19
11.506	11.374	11.55	11.46	11.27	11.94	13.67	8.51	12.66	12.29	15.27	11.77	13.36
14.029	13.776	14.44	13.91	13.45	14.17	19.04	11.23	14.70	14.76	18.87	13.42	16.38
10.686	11.084	12.92	13.00	12.76	13.79	16.11	11.57	15.14	11.89	14.86	11.02	12.26
8.63	8.75	10.45	11.10	11.18	12.04	13.55	9.47	12.57	8.89	10.79	8.50	9.09
9.58	9.80	11.89	12.44	12.41	12.71	14.19	10.15	12.38	10.16	12.04	8.80	10.23
7.48	7.66	9.64	10.62	10.79	11.37	12.72	9.18	11.55	8.01	9.93	7.69	8.10
5.98	6.03	7.06	7.68	7.78	9.02	10.39	7.38	10.17	6.39	8.33	6.33	6.81
5.82	6.05	7.68	8.39	8.59	9.38	10.58	7.73	9.31	6.85	8.21	5.66	6.66
6.69	6.92	8.26	8.85	8.96	9.71	10.83	7.76	9.19	7.68	9.32	6.20	7.57
8.12	8.04	8.55	8.49	8.45	9.26	10.18	7.24	10.13	8.80	10.87	6.93	9.21
7.51	7.47	8.26	8.55	8.61	9.32	10.36	7.25	10.05	7.95	10.01	6.98	8.10
5.42	5.49	6.82	7.86	8.14	8.77	9.80	6.89	9.32	5.85	8.46	5.45	5.69
3.45	3.57	5.30	7.01	7.67	8.14	8.98	6.41	8.24	3.80	6.25	3.25	3.52
3.02	3.14	4.44	5.87	6.59	7.22	7.93	5.63	7.20	3.80	6.00	3.00	3.02
4.29	4.66	6.27	7.09	7.37	7.97	8.63	6.19	7.49	4.93	7.15	3.60	4.21

Economic Report of the President (Washington, D.C.: U.S. Government Printing Office, 1995), Table B-72.
n new issues within period; bank-discount basis.
on the more actively traded issues adjusted to constant maturities by the Treasury Department.
ve rate (in the primary market) on conventional mortgages, reflecting fees and charges as well as contract rate and assuming, on the
, repayment at end of 10 years. Rates beginning January 1973 not strictly comparable with prior rates.
iscount basis; prior to November 1979, data are for 4–6 months paper.
onthly data, high and low for the period. Prime rate for 1929–33 and 1947–48 are ranges of the rate in effect during the period.
uly 19, 1975, the daily effective rate is an average of the rates on a given day weighted by the volume of transactions at these rates.
that date, the daily effective rate was the rate considered most representative of the day's transactions, usually the one at which most
ions occurred.
ctober 30, 1942, to April 24, 1946, a preferential rate of 0.50 percent was in effect for advances secured by Government securities
g in 1 year or less.

TABLE 17
Federal receipts, outlays, surplus or deficit, and debt, selected fiscal years, 1929–94
[billions of dollars; fiscal years]

Fiscal year or period	Total			On-budget			Off-budget			Gross Federal debt (end of period)		Addendum: Gross domestic product
	Receipts	Outlays	Surplus or deficit (−)	Receipts	Outlays	Surplus or deficit (−)	Receipts	Outlays	Surplus or deficit (−)	Total	Held by the public	
1929	3.9	3.1	0.7	3.9	3.1	0.7	—	—	—	¹16.9	—	—
1933	2.0	4.6	−2.6	2.0	4.6	−2.6	—	—	—	¹22.5	—	56.8
1939	6.3	9.1	−2.8	5.8	9.2	−3.4	0.5	0.0	0.5	48.2	41.4	87.8
1940	6.5	9.5	−2.9	6.0	9.5	−3.5	0.6	0.0	0.6	50.7	42.8	95.4
1941	8.7	13.7	−4.9	8.0	13.6	−5.6	0.7	0.0	0.7	57.5	48.2	112.5
1942	14.6	35.1	−20.5	13.7	35.1	−21.3	0.9	0.1	0.8	79.2	67.8	141.8
1943	24.0	78.6	−54.6	22.9	78.5	−55.6	1.1	0.1	1.0	142.6	127.8	175.4
1944	43.7	91.3	−47.6	42.5	91.2	−48.7	1.3	0.1	1.2	204.1	184.8	201.7
1945	45.2	92.7	−47.6	43.8	92.6	−48.7	1.3	0.1	1.2	260.1	235.2	212.0
1946	39.3	55.2	−15.9	38.1	55.0	−17.0	1.2	0.2	1.0	271.0	241.9	212.5
1947	38.5	34.5	4.0	37.1	34.2	2.9	1.5	0.3	1.2	257.1	224.3	222.9
1948	41.6	29.8	11.8	39.9	29.4	10.5	1.6	0.4	1.2	252.0	216.3	246.7
1949	39.4	38.8	0.6	37.7	38.4	−0.7	1.7	0.4	1.3	252.6	214.3	262.7
1950	39.4	42.6	−3.1	37.3	42.0	−4.7	2.1	0.5	1.6	256.9	219.0	265.8
1951	51.6	45.5	6.1	48.5	44.2	4.3	3.1	1.3	1.8	255.3	214.3	315.5
1952	66.2	67.7	−1.5	62.6	66.0	−3.4	3.6	1.7	1.9	259.1	214.8	340.5
1953	69.6	76.1	−6.5	65.5	73.8	−8.3	4.1	2.3	1.8	266.0	218.4	363.8
1954	69.7	70.9	−1.2	65.1	67.9	−2.8	4.6	2.9	1.7	270.8	224.5	368.0
1955	65.5	68.4	−3.0	60.4	64.5	−4.1	5.1	4.0	1.1	274.4	226.6	384.7
1956	74.6	70.6	3.9	68.2	65.7	2.5	6.4	5.0	1.5	272.7	222.2	416.3
1957	80.0	76.6	3.4	73.2	70.6	2.6	6.8	6.0	0.8	272.3	219.3	438.3
1958	79.6	82.4	−2.8	71.6	74.9	−3.3	8.0	7.5	0.5	279.7	226.3	448.1
1959	79.2	92.1	−12.8	71.0	83.1	−12.1	8.3	9.0	−0.7	287.5	234.7	480.2
1960	92.5	92.2	0.3	81.9	81.3	0.5	10.6	10.9	−0.2	290.5	236.8	504.6
1961	94.4	97.7	−3.3	82.3	86.0	−3.8	12.1	11.7	0.4	292.6	238.4	517.0
1962	99.7	106.8	−7.1	87.4	93.3	−5.9	12.3	13.5	−1.3	302.9	248.0	555.2
1963	106.6	111.3	−4.8	92.4	96.4	−4.0	14.2	15.0	−0.8	310.3	254.0	584.5
1964	112.6	118.5	−5.9	96.2	102.8	−6.5	16.4	15.7	0.6	316.1	256.8	625.3
1965	116.8	118.2	−1.4	100.1	101.7	−1.6	16.7	16.5	0.2	322.3	260.8	671.0
1966	130.8	134.5	−3.7	111.7	114.8	−3.1	19.1	19.7	−0.6	328.5	263.7	735.4
1967	148.8	157.5	−8.6	124.4	137.0	−12.6	24.4	20.4	4.0	340.4	266.6	793.3
1968	153.0	178.1	−25.2	128.1	155.8	−27.7	24.9	22.3	2.6	368.7	289.5	847.2
1969	186.9	183.6	3.2	157.9	158.4	−0.5	29.0	25.2	3.7	365.8	278.1	925.7
1970	192.8	195.6	−2.8	159.3	168.0	−8.7	33.5	27.6	5.9	380.9	283.2	985.4
1971	187.1	210.2	−23.0	151.3	177.3	−26.1	35.8	32.8	3.0	408.2	303.0	1,050.9
1972	207.3	230.7	−23.4	167.4	193.8	−26.4	39.9	36.9	3.1	435.9	322.4	1,147.8
1973	230.8	245.7	−14.9	184.7	200.1	−15.4	46.1	45.6	0.5	466.3	340.9	1,274.0
1974	263.2	269.4	−6.1	209.3	217.3	−8.0	53.9	52.1	1.8	483.9	343.7	1,403.6
1975	279.1	332.3	−53.2	216.6	271.9	−55.3	62.5	60.4	2.0	544.9	394.7	1,509.8
1976	298.1	371.8	−73.7	231.7	302.2	−70.5	66.4	69.6	−3.2	629.0	477.4	1,684.2
Transition quarter	81.2	96.0	−14.7	63.2	76.6	−13.3	18.0	19.4	−1.4	643.6	495.5	445.0
1977	355.6	409.2	−53.7	278.7	328.5	−49.8	76.8	80.7	−3.9	706.4	549.1	1,917.2
1978	399.6	458.7	−59.2	314.2	369.1	−54.9	85.4	89.7	−4.3	776.6	607.1	2,155.0
1979	463.3	504.0	−40.7	365.3	404.1	−38.7	98.0	100.0	−2.0	829.5	640.3	2,429.5
1980	517.1	590.9	−73.8	403.9	476.6	−72.7	113.2	114.3	−1.1	909.1	709.8	2,644.1
1981	599.3	678.2	−79.0	469.1	543.1	−74.0	130.2	135.2	−5.0	994.8	785.3	2,964.4
1982	617.8	745.8	−128.0	474.3	594.4	−120.1	143.5	151.4	−7.9	1,137.3	919.8	3,122.2
1983	600.6	808.4	−207.8	453.2	661.2	−208.0	147.3	147.1	0.2	1,371.7	1,131.6	3,316.5
1984	666.5	851.8	−185.4	500.4	686.0	−185.7	166.1	165.8	0.3	1,564.7	1,300.5	3,695.0
1985	734.1	946.4	−212.3	547.9	769.6	−221.7	186.2	176.8	9.4	1,817.5	1,499.9	3,967.7
1986	769.1	990.3	−221.2	568.9	806.8	−238.0	200.2	183.5	16.7	2,120.6	1,736.7	4,219.0
1987	854.1	1,003.9	−149.8	640.7	810.1	−169.3	213.4	193.8	19.6	2,346.1	1,888.7	4,452.4
1988	909.0	1,064.1	−155.2	667.5	861.4	−194.0	241.5	202.7	38.8	2,601.3	2,050.8	4,808.4
1989	990.7	1,143.2	−152.5	727.0	933.3	−205.2	263.7	210.9	52.8	2,868.0	2,189.9	5,173.3
1990	1,031.3	1,252.7	−221.4	749.7	1,027.6	−278.0	281.7	225.1	56.6	3,206.6	2,410.7	5,481.5
1991	1,054.3	1,323.4	−269.2	760.4	1,081.8	−321.4	293.9	241.7	52.2	3,598.5	2,688.1	5,676.4
1992	1,090.5	1,380.9	−290.4	788.0	1,128.5	−340.5	302.4	252.3	50.1	4,002.1	2,998.8	5,921.5
1993	1,153.5	1,408.7	−255.1	841.6	1,142.1	−300.5	311.9	266.6	45.3	4,351.4	3,247.5	6,258.6
1994	1,257.7	1,460.9	−203.2	922.7	1,181.5	−258.8	335.0	279.4	55.7	4,643.7	3,432.2	6,633.6

Source: *Economic Report of the President* (Washington, D.C.: U.S. Government Printing Office, 1995), Table B-77.
¹Not strictly comparable
NOTE: Through fiscal year 1976, the fiscal year was on a July 1–June 30 basis: beginning October 1976 (fiscal year 1977), the fiscal year is on an October 1–September 30 basis. The 3-month period from July 1, 1976 through September 30, 1976 is a separate fiscal period known as the transition quarter. Refunds of receipts are excluded from receipts and outlays.

TABLE 18

International investment position of the United States at year-end, 1985–93
[billions of dollars]

Type of investment	1985	1986	1987	1988	1989	1990	1991	1992	1993
Net International Investment Position of the United States:									
With direct investment at current cost	125.3	34.6	−22.8	−144.8	−251.4	−251.4	−349.5	−507.9	−555.7
With direct investment at market value	128.5	125.1	58.1	.9	−91.8	−224.1	−368.7	−590.0	−507.7
U.S. assets abroad:									
With direct investment at current cost	1,296.4	1,468.8	1,625.4	1,773.0	1,976.0	2,066.9	3,137.0	2,149.6	2,370.4
With direct investment at market value	1,288.3	1,566.4	1,709.0	1,935.9	2,236.7	2,165.7	2,300.2	2,267.3	2,647.4
U.S. official reserve assets	117.9	139.9	162.4	144.2	168.7	174.7	159.2	147.4	164.9
Gold[1]	85.8	102.4	127.6	107.4	105.2	102.4	92.6	87.2	102.6
Special drawing rights	7.3	8.4	10.3	9.6	10.0	11.0	11.2	8.5	9.0
Reserve position in the International Monetary Fund	11.9	11.7	11.3	9.7	9.0	9.1	9.5	11.8	11.8
Foreign currencies	12.9	17.3	13.1	17.4	44.6	52.2	45.9	40.0	41.5
U.S. government assets, other than official reserve assets	87.8	89.6	88.9	86.1	84.5	82.0	79.0	80.6	80.9
U.S. credits and other long-term assets	85.8	88.7	88.1	85.4	83.9	81.4	77.4	79.0	79.0
Repayable in dollars	84.1	87.1	86.5	83.9	82.4	80.0	76.2	77.9	78.0
Other	1.7	1.6	1.6	1.5	1.5	1.3	1.2	1.1	1.0
U.S. foreign currency holdings and U.S. short-term assets	1.9	.9	.9	.7	.6	.6	1.6	1.6	1.9
U.S. private assets:									
With direct investment at current cost	1,090.7	1,239.3	1,374.1	1,542.7	1,725.8	1,810.2	1,898.8	1,921.5	2,124.6
With direct investment at market value	1,082.6	1,336.9	1,457.7	1,705.6	1,983.5	1,909.1	2,061.9	2,039.2	2,401.6
Direct investment abroad:									
At current cost	387.2	421.2	493.3	515.7	560.0	620.5	650.6	668.2	716.2
At market value	379.1	518.7	577.0	678.6	817.8	719.4	813.8	785.9	993.2
Foreign securities	114.3	143.4	154.0	176.0	217.6	228.7	301.5	331.4	518.5
Bonds	73.3	80.4	84.3	90.0	97.8	118.7	142.7	153.4	220.8
Corporate stocks	41.0	63.0	69.6	86.0	119.9	110.0	158.8	178.1	297.7
U.S. claims on unaffiliated foreigners reported by U.S. nonbanking concerns	141.9	167.4	177.4	197.8	234.3	265.3	256.3	253.9	254.5
U.S. claims reported by U.S. banks, not included elsewhere	447.4	507.3	549.5	653.2	713.8	695.7	690.4	668.0	635.5
Foreign assets in the United States:									
With direct investment at current cost	1,171.1	1,434.2	1,648.2	1,917.8	2,230.4	2,318.3	2,486.5	2,657.5	2,926.2
With direct investment at market value	1,159.8	1,441.3	1,650.9	1,935.0	2,328.5	2,389.8	2,668.9	2,857.3	3,155.1
Foreign official assets in the United States	202.5	241.2	283.1	322.0	341.9	375.3	401.5	442.9	516.9
U.S. government securities	145.1	178.9	220.5	260.9	263.7	295.0	315.9	335.7	388.5
U.S. Treasury securities	138.4	173.3	213.7	253.0	257.3	287.9	307.1	323.0	370.9
Other	6.6	5.6	6.8	8.0	6.4	7.1	8.8	12.7	17.6
Other U.S. Government liabilities	15.8	18.0	15.7	15.2	15.4	17.2	18.4	21.0	22.7
U.S. liabilities reported by U.S. banks, not included elsewhere	26.7	27.9	31.8	31.5	36.5	39.9	38.4	55.0	69.6
Other foreign official assets	14.9	16.4	15.0	14.4	26.3	23.2	28.7	31.3	36.1
Other foreign assets in the United States:									
With direct investment at current cost	968.6	1,193.0	1,365.1	1,595.7	1,888.5	1,943.0	2,085.0	2,214.6	2,409.3
With direct investment at market value	957.3	1,200.1	1,367.9	1,612.9	1,986.6	2,014.4	2,267.4	2,414.4	2,638.2
Direct investment in the United States									
At current cost	231.3	265.8	313.5	374.3	436.6	468.1	491.9	497.1	516.7
At market value	220.0	273.0	316.2	391.5	534.7	539.6	674.2	696.8	745.6
U.S. Treasury securites	88.0	96.1	82.6	100.9	166.5	162.4	189.5	224.8	254.1
U.S. securities other than U.S. Treasury securities	207.9	309.8	341.7	392.3	482.9	467.4	559.2	621.0	733.2
Corporate and other bonds	82.3	140.9	166.1	191.3	231.7	245.7	287.3	320.8	393.2
Corporate stocks	125.6	168.9	175.6	201.0	251.2	221.7	271.9	300.2	340.0
U.S. liabilities to unaffiliated foreigners reported by U.S. nonbanking concerns	87.0	90.7	110.2	144.5	167.1	213.4	208.9	220.7	233.3
U.S. liabilities reported by U.S. banks, not included elsewhere	354.5	430.6	517.2	583.7	635.5	631.6	635.6	651.0	672.0

Source: *Economic Report of the President* (Washington, D.C.: U.S. Government Printing Office, 1995), Table B-102.
[1]Valued at market price.

TABLE 19
U.S. international transactions, 1946–93
[millions of dollars; credits (+); debits (–)]

Year or quarter	Merchandise			Services			Balance on goods and services	Investment income			Unilateral transfers, net	Balance on current account
	Exports	Imports	Net	Net military transactions	Net travel and transportation receipts	Other services, net		Receipts on U.S. assets abroad	Payments on foreign assets in U.S.	Net		
1946	11,764	–5,067	6,697	–424	733	310	7,316	772	–212	560	–2,991	4,8
1947	16,097	–5,973	10,124	–358	946	145	10,857	1,102	–245	857	–2,722	8,9
1948	13,265	–7,557	5,708	–351	374	175	5,906	1,921	–437	1,484	–4,973	2,4
1949	12,213	–6,874	5,339	–410	230	208	5,367	1,831	–476	1,355	–5,849	8
1950	10,203	–9,081	1,122	–56	–120	242	1,188	2,068	–559	1,509	–4,537	–1,8
1951	14,243	–11,176	3,067	169	298	254	3,788	2,633	–583	2,050	–4,954	8
1952	13,449	–10,838	2,611	528	83	309	3,531	2,751	–555	2,196	–5,113	6
1953	12,412	–10,975	1,437	1,753	–238	307	3,259	2,736	–624	2,112	–6,657	–1,2
1954	12,929	–10,353	2,576	902	–269	305	3,514	2,929	–582	2,347	–5,642	2
1955	14,424	–11,527	2,897	–113	–297	299	2,786	3,406	–676	2,730	–5,086	4
1956	17,556	–12,803	4,753	–221	–361	447	4,618	3,837	–735	3,102	–4,990	2,7
1957	19,562	–13,291	6,271	–423	–189	482	6,141	4,180	–796	3,384	–4,763	4,7
1958	16,414	–12,952	3,462	–849	–633	486	2,466	3,790	–825	2,965	–4,647	7
1959	16,458	–15,310	1,148	–831	–821	573	69	4,132	–1,061	3,071	–4,422	–1,2
1960	19,650	–14,758	4,892	–1,057	–964	639	3,598	4,616	–1,238	3,379	–4,062	2,8
1961	20,108	–14,537	5,571	–1,131	–978	732	4,195	4,999	–1,245	3,755	–4,127	3,9
1962	20,781	–16,260	4,521	–912	–1,152	912	3.370	5,618	–1,324	4,294	–4,277	3,3
1963	22,272	–17,048	5,224	–742	–1,309	1,036	4,210	6,157	–1,560	4,596	–4,392	4,
1964	25,501	–18,700	6,801	–794	–1,146	1,161	6,022	6,824	–1,783	5,041	–4,240	6,8
1965	26,461	–21,510	4,951	–487	–1,280	1,480	4,664	7,437	–2,088	5,350	–4,583	5,
1966	29,310	–25,493	3,817	–1,043	–1,331	1,497	2,940	7,528	–2,481	5,047	–4,955	3,0
1967	30,666	–26,866	3,800	–1,187	–1,750	1,742	2,604	8,021	–2,747	5,274	–5,294	2,
1968	33,626	–32,991	635	–596	–1,548	1,759	250	9,367	–3,378	5,990	–5,629	
1969	36,414	–35,807	607	–718	–1,763	1,964	91	10,913	–4,869	6,044	–5,735	
1970	42,469	–39,866	2,603	–641	–2,038	2,330	2,224	11,748	–5,515	6,233	–6,156	2,
1971	43,319	–45,579	–2,260	653	–2,345	2,649	–1,303	12,707	–5,435	7,272	–7,402	–1,
1972	49,381	–55,797	–6,416	1,072	–3,063	2,965	–5,443	14,765	–6,572	8,192	–8,544	–5,
1973	71,410	–70,499	911	740	–3,158	3,406	1,900	21,808	–9,655	12,153	–6,913	7,
1974	98,306	–103,811	–5,505	165	–3,184	4,231	–4,292	27,587	–12,084	15,503	–9,249	1,
1975	107,088	–98,185	8,903	1,461	–2,812	4,854	12,404	25,351	–12,564	12,787	–7,075	18,
1976	114,745	–124,228	–9,483	931	–2,558	5,027	–6,082	29,375	–13,311	16,063	–5,686	4,
1977	120,816	–151,907	–31,091	1,731	–3,565	5,680	–27,246	32,354	–14,217	18,137	–5,226	–14,
1978	142,075	–176,002	–33,927	857	–3,573	6,879	–29,763	42,088	–21,680	20,408	–5,788	–15,
1979	184,439	–212,007	–27,568	1,313	–2,935	7,251	–24,565	63,834	–32,961	30,873	–6,593	–
1980	224,250	–249,750	–25,500	–1,822	–997	8,912	–19,407	72,606	–42,532	30,073	–8,349	2
1981	237,044	–265,067	–28,023	–844	144	12,552	–16,172	86,529	–53,626	32,903	–11,702	5
1982	211,157	–247,642	–36,485	112	–992	13,209	–24,156	86,200	–56,412	29,788	–17,075	–11
1983	201,799	–268,901	–67,102	–563	–4,227	14,095	–57,796	84,778	–53,700	31,078	–17,741	–44
1984	219,926	–332,418	–112,492	–2,547	–8,438	14,277	–109,200	104,075	–74,068	30,038	–20,612	–99
1985	215,915	–338,088	–122,173	–4,390	–9,798	14,266	–122,095	92,760	–73,087	19,673	–22,950	–12°
1986	223,344	–368,425	–145,081	–5,181	–7,321	18,855	–138,789	90,858	–79,095	11,763	–24,176	–151
1987	250,208	–409,765	–159,557	–3,844	–6,481	17,900	–151,981	99,239	–91,302	7,937	–23,052	–167
1988	320,230	–447,189	–126,959	–6,315	–1,511	19,961	–114,824	127,414	–115,806	11,607	–24,977	–128
1989	362,116	–477,365	–115,249	–6,726	5,071	26,558	–90,345	152,517	–138,858	13,659	–26,134	–102
1990	389,303	–498,336	–109,033	–7,567	8,978	28,811	–78,810	160,300	–139,574	20,725	–33,663	–9¹
1991	416,913	–490,981	–74,068	–5,485	17,957	33,124	–28,472	136,914	–122,081	14,833	6,687	–€
1992	440,361	–536,458	–96,097	–3,034	20,885	37,862	–40,384	114,449	–109,909	4,540	–32,042	–6°
1993	456,866	–589,441	–132,575	–763	20,840	36,773	–75,725	113,856	–109,910	3,946	–32,117	–10³

Source: Economic Report of the President (Washington, D.C.: U.S. Government Printing Office, 1995), Table B-103.

TABLE 19 (continued)

U.S. international transactions, 1946–93 [millions of dollars]

| Year or quarter | U.S. assets abroad, net [increase/capital outflow (−)] | | | | Foreign assets in the U.S., net [increase/capital inflow (+)] | | | Allocations of special drawing rights (SDRs) | Statistical discrepancy | |
	Total	U.S. official reserve assets	Other U.S. government assets	U.S. private assets	Total	Foreign official assets	Other foreign assets		Total (sum of the items with sign reversed)	Of which: Seasonal adjustment discrepancy
1946	—	−623	—	—	—	—	—	—	—	—
1947	—	−3,315	—	—	—	—	—	—	—	—
1948	—	−1,736	—	—	—	—	—	—	—	—
1949	—	−266	—	—	—	—	—	—	—	—
1950	—	1,758	—	—	—	—	—	—	—	—
1951	—	−33	—	—	—	—	—	—	—	—
1952	—	−415	—	—	—	—	—	—	—	—
1953	—	1,256	—	—	—	—	—	—	—	—
1954	—	480	—	—	—	—	—	—	—	—
1955	—	182	—	—	—	—	—	—	—	—
1956	—	−869	—	—	—	—	—	—	—	—
1957	—	−1,165	—	—	—	—	—	—	—	—
1958	—	2,292	—	—	—	—	—	—	—	—
1959	—	1,035	—	—	—	—	—	—	—	—
1960	−4,099	2,145	−1,100	−5,144	2,294	1,473	821	—	−1,019	—
1961	−5,538	607	−910	−5,235	2,705	765	1,939	—	−989	—
1962	−4,174	1,535	−1,085	−4,623	1,911	1,270	641	—	−1,124	—
1963	−7,270	378	−1,662	−5,986	3,217	1,986	1,231	—	−360	—
1964	−9,560	171	−1,680	−8,050	3,643	1,660	1,983	—	−907	—
1965	−5,716	1,225	−1,605	−5,336	742	134	607	—	−457	—
1966	−7,321	570	−1,543	−6,347	3,661	−672	4,333	—	629	—
1967	−9,757	53	−2,423	−7,386	7,379	3,451	3,928	—	−205	—
1968	−10,977	−870	−2,274	−7,833	9,928	−774	10,703	—	438	—
1969	−11,585	−1,179	−2,200	−8,206	12,702	−1,301	14,002	—	−1,516	—
1970	−9,337	2,481	−1,589	−10,229	6,359	6,908	−550	867	−219	—
1971	−12,475	2,349	−1,884	−12,940	22,970	26,879	−3,909	717	−9,779	—
1972	−14,497	−4	−1,568	−12,925	21,461	10,475	10,986	710	−1,879	—
1973	−22,874	158	−2,644	−20,388	18,388	6,026	12,362	—	−2,654	—
1974	−34,745	−1,467	366	−33,643	34,241	10,546	23,696	—	−1,458	—
1975	−39,703	−849	−3,474	−35,380	15,670	7,027	8,643	—	5,917	—
1976	−51,269	−2,558	−4,214	−44,498	36,518	17,693	18,826	—	10,455	—
1977	−34,785	−375	−3,693	−30,717	51,319	36,816	14,503	—	−2,199	—
1978	−61,130	732	−4,660	−57,202	64,036	33,678	30,358	—	12,236	—
1979	−66,054	−1,133	−3,746	−61,176	38,752	−13,665	52,416	1,139	26,449	—
1980	−86,967	−8,155	−5,162	−73,651	58,112	15,497	42,615	1,152	25,386	—
1981	−114,147	−5,175	−5,097	−103,875	83,032	4,960	78,072	1,093	24,992	—
1982	−122,335	−4,965	−6,131	−111,239	92,418	3,593	88,836	—	41,359	—
1983	−58,735	−1,196	−5,006	−52,533	83,380	5,845	77,534	—	19,815	—
1984	−34,917	−3,131	−5,489	−26,298	113,932	3,140	110,792	—	20,758	—
1985	−39,225	−3,858	−2,821	−32,547	141,183	−1,119	142,301	—	23,415	—
1986	−104,818	312	−2,022	−103,109	226,111	35,648	190,463	—	29,908	—
1987	−71,443	9,149	1,006	−81,597	242,983	45,387	197,596	—	−4,443	—
1988	−99,360	−3,912	2,967	−98,414	240,265	39,758	200,507	—	−12,712	—
1989	−168,744	−25,293	1,259	−144,710	218,490	8,503	209,987	—	53,075	—
1990	−70,363	−2,158	2,307	−70,512	122,192	33,910	88,282	—	39,919	—
1991	−51,512	5,763	2,900	−60,175	98,134	17,199	80,935	—	−39,670	—
1992	−61,510	3,901	−1,652	−63,759	146,504	40,858	105,646	—	−17,108	—
1993	−147,898	−1,379	−306	−146,213	230,698	71,681	159,017	—	21,096	—

Source: *Economic Report of the President* (Washington, D.C.: U.S. Government Printing Office, 1995), Table B-103.

TABLE 20
U.S. merchandise exports and imports by area, 1985–94
[billions of dollars]

Item	1985	1986	1987	1988	1989	1990	1991	1992	1993	1994 first 3 quarters at annual rate[1]
Exports	215.9	223.4	250.2	320.2	362.1	389.3	416.9	440.4	456.9	491.4
Industrial countries	140.5	150.3	165.6	207.3	234.2	253.8	261.3	265.1	270.7	289.0
Canada	55.4	56.5	62.0	74.3	81.1	83.5	85.9	91.4	101.2	112.0
Japan	22.1	26.4	27.6	37.2	43.9	47.8	47.2	46.9	46.7	51.7
Western Europe[2]	56.0	60.4	68.6	86.4	98.4	111.4	116.8	114.5	111.3	112.4
Australia, New Zealand, and South Africa	7.0	7.1	7.4	9.4	10.9	11.2	11.4	12.4	11.5	12.9
Australia	5.1	5.1	5.3	6.8	8.1	8.3	8.3	8.7	8.1	9.4
Other countries, except Eastern Europe	71.9	71.0	83.2	109.1	122.2	130.6	150.4	169.5	179.8	197.0
OPEC[3]	11.4	10.4	10.7	13.8	13.3	13.4	18.4	20.7	18.7	16.6
Other[4]	60.5	60.6	71.6	95.3	108.9	117.2	132.0	148.8	161.1	180.4
Eastern Europe	3.2	2.1	2.3	3.8	5.5	4.3	4.8	5.6	6.2	5.4
International organizations and unallocated	.2	—	—	.1	.2	.6	.4	.1	.2	.0
Imports	338.1	368.4	409.8	447.2	477.4	498.3	491.0	536.5	589.4	655.7
Industrial countries	219.0	245.4	259.7	283.2	292.5	299.9	294.3	316.3	347.8	382.5
Canada	70.2	69.7	73.6	84.6	89.9	93.1	93.0	100.9	113.3	127.7
Japan	65.7	80.8	84.6	89.8	93.5	90.4	92.3	97.4	107.2	117.1
Western Europe	77.5	89.0	96.1	102.6	102.4	109.2	102.0	111.4	120.9	131.0
Australia, New Zealand, and South Africa	5.6	5.9	5.4	6.2	6.6	7.3	7.0	6.6	6.4	6.7
Australia	2.7	2.6	3.0	3.5	3.9	4.4	4.1	3.7	3.3	3.2
Other countries, except Eastern Europe	117.3	121.1	148.2	161.8	182.8	196.1	194.9	218.2	238.1	267.9
OPEC[3]	22.8	18.9	24.4	23.0	30.7	38.2	33.4	33.7	32.6	31.1
Other[4]	94.5	102.2	123.8	138.8	152.1	157.9	161.5	184.5	205.4	236.7
Eastern Europe	1.8	2.0	1.9	2.2	2.1	2.3	1.8	2.0	3.5	5.3
International organizations and unallocated	—	—	—	—	—	—	—	—	—	—
Balance (excess of exports +)	−122.2	−145.1	−159.6	−127.0	−115.2	−109.0	−74.1	−96.1	−132.6	−164.3
Industrial countries	−78.4	−95.1	−94.1	−75.9	−58.3	−46.1	−33.0	−51.2	−77.2	−93.5
Canada	−14.8	−13.2	−11.6	−10.3	−8.9	−9.6	−7.1	−9.5	−12.1	−15.6
Japan	−43.5	−54.4	−56.9	−52.6	−49.7	−42.6	−45.0	−50.5	−60.5	−65.4
Western Europe[2]	−21.4	−28.6	−27.5	−16.2	−4.0	2.2	14.8	3.1	−9.7	−18.6
Australia, New Zealand, and South Africa	1.4	1.1	2.0	3.2	4.2	3.9	4.4	5.8	5.2	6.2
Australia	2.4	2.5	2.3	3.3	4.2	3.9	4.2	5.0	4.8	6.3
Other countries, except Eastern Europe	−45.3	−50.1	−65.8	−52.7	−60.6	−65.6	−44.5	−48.7	−58.3	−70.9
OPEC[3]	−11.4	−8.5	−13.7	−9.2	−17.4	−24.8	−15.0	−13.0	−14.0	−14.5
Other[4]	33.9	−41.6	−52.1	−43.5	−43.2	−40.7	−29.5	−35.7	−44.3	−56.4
Eastern Europe[2]	1.4	.1	.3	1.6	3.5	2.1	3.0	3.7	2.7	.1
International organizations and unallocated	.2	—	—	.1	.2	.6	.4	.1	.2	.0

Source: *Economic Report of the President* (Washington, D.C.: U.S. Government Printing Office, 1995), Table B-105.
[1] Preliminary; seasonally adjusted.
[2] The former German Democratic Republic (East Germany) included in Western Europe beginning fourth quarter 1990 and in Eastern Europe prior to that time.
[3] Organizations of Petroleum Exporting Countries, consisting of Algeria, Ecuador (thorugh 1992), Gabon, Indonesia, Iran, Iraq, Kuwait, Libya, Nigeria, Qatar, Saudi Arabia, United Arab Emirates, and Venezuela.
[4] Latin American Republics, other Western Hemisphere, and other countries in Asia and Africa, less members of OPEC.
NOTE: Data are on an international transactions basis and exclude military.

TABLE 21
Industrial production and consumer prices, major industrial countries, 1969–94

Year or quarter	United States	Canada	Japan	European Union[1]	France	Germany[2]	Italy	United Kingdom
	Industrial production (1987 = 100)[3]							
1969	65.3	59.9	48.3	69.6	69	70.9	64.2	78.5
1970	61.4	59.0	55.0	73.1	72	75.5	68.3	78.9
1971	62.2	62.3	56.5	74.7	77	77.0	68.0	78.5
1972	68.3	67.8	59.6	78.0	81	79.9	70.8	79.9
1973	73.8	75.8	69.0	83.7	87	85.0	77.7	87.0
1974	72.7	77.3	66.3	84.3	90	84.8	81.2	85.4
1975	66.3	71.6	59.3	78.7	83	79.6	73.7	80.8
1976	72.4	76.5	65.9	84.5	90	86.8	82.9	83.4
1977	78.2	79.0	68.6	86.6	92	88.0	83.8	87.6
1978	82.6	81.8	73.0	89.0	94	90.4	85.4	90.1
1979	85.7	85.7	78.2	93.1	99	94.7	91.1	93.6
1980	84.1	82.8	81.8	92.8	98.9	95.0	96.2	87.0
1981	85.7	84.5	82.6	91.1	98.3	93.2	94.7	84.2
1982	81.9	76.2	83.0	89.9	97.3	90.3	91.7	85.8
1983	84.9	81.2	85.5	90.8	96.5	90.9	88.9	88.9
1984	92.8	91.0	93.5	92.8	97.1	93.5	91.8	89.0
1985	94.4	96.1	96.9	95.8	97.2	97.7	92.9	93.9
1986	95.3	95.4	96.7	98.0	98.0	99.6	96.2	96.2
1987	100.0	100.0	100.0	100.0	100.0	100.0	100.0	100.0
1988	104.4	105.3	109.4	104.2	104.6	103.9	105.9	104.8
1989	106.0	105.2	115.7	108.2	108.9	108.8	109.2	107.0
1990	106.0	101.7	120.6	110.4	111.0	114.5	109.4	106.7
1991	104.3	97.5	122.9	110.3	111.0	117.9	108.4	102.5
1992	107.6	98.4	115.8	109.3	109.7	115.6	108.2	102.0
1993	112.0	103.2	111.0	105.6	105.6	107.2	105.4	104.5
1994	118.1	—	—	—	—	—	—	—
	Consumer prices (1982–84 = 100)							
1969	36.7	34.0	35.8	25.3	27.4	51.0	16.6	20.4
1970	38.8	35.1	35.8	26.6	28.7	52.9	16.8	21.8
1971	40.5	36.1	40.9	28.3	30.3	55.6	17.6	23.8
1972	41.8	37.9	42.9	30.1	32.2	58.7	18.7	25.5
1973	44.4	40.7	47.9	32.7	34.5	62.8	20.6	27.9
1974	49.3	45.2	59.0	37.4	39.3	67.2	24.6	32.3
1975	53.8	50.1	65.9	42.8	43.9	71.2	28.8	40.2
1976	56.9	53.8	72.2	47.9	48.1	74.2	33.6	46.8
1977	60.6	58.1	78.1	53.8	52.7	76.9	40.1	54.2
1978	65.2	63.3	81.4	58.7	57.5	79.0	45.1	58.7
1979	72.6	69.1	84.4	65.1	63.6	82.3	52.1	66.6
1980	82.4	76.1	91.0	74.0	72.3	86.8	63.5	78.5
1981	90.9	85.6	95.3	83.2	82.0	92.2	75.3	87.9
1982	96.5	94.9	98.0	92.2	91.6	97.0	87.7	95.4
1983	99.6	100.4	99.8	100.2	100.5	100.3	100.8	99.8
1984	103.9	104.8	102.1	107.4	107.9	102.7	111.5	104.8
1985	107.6	108.9	104.1	114.0	114.2	104.8	121.1	111.1
1986	109.6	113.4	104.8	118.2	117.2	104.7	128.5	114.9
1987	113.6	118.4	104.9	122.2	120.9	104.9	134.4	119.7
1988	118.3	123.2	105.7	126.7	124.2	106.3	141.1	125.6
1989	124.0	129.3	108.0	133.3	128.6	109.2	150.4	135.4
1990	130.7	135.5	111.4	140.8	133.0	112.1	159.5	148.2
1991	136.2	143.1	115.0	148.0	137.2	116.0	169.8	156.9
1992	140.3	145.2	116.9	154.3	140.6	120.6	178.8	162.7
1993	144.5	147.9	118.5	159.4	143.5	125.6	186.3	165.3
1994	148.2	148.2	119.3	—	145.8	129.4	193.6	169.3

Source: Economic Report of the President (Washington, D.C.: U.S. Government Printing Office, 1995), Table B-108.

[1] Consists of Belgium-Luxembourg, Denmark, France, Greece, Ireland, Italy, Netherlands, United Kingdom, Germany, Portugal, and Spain. Industrial production includes data for Greece beginning 1981; data for Portugal and Spain are included beginning 1982.

[2] Data are for West Germany only.

[3] All data exclude construction. Quarterly data are seasonally adjusted.

TABLE 22
Civilian unemployment rate and hourly compensation, major industrial countries, 1969–94 [quarterly data seasonally adjusted]

Year or quarter	United States	Canada	Japan	France	Germany[1]	Italy	United Kingdom
	Civilian unemployment rate (percent)[2]						
1969	3.5	4.4	1.1	2.3	0.6	3.5	3.1
1970	4.9	5.7	1.2	2.5	.5	3.2	3.1
1971	5.9	6.2	1.3	2.8	.6	3.3	3.9
1972	5.6	6.2	1.4	2.9	.7	3.8	4.2
1973	4.9	5.5	1.3	2.8	.7	3.7	3.2
1974	5.6	5.3	1.4	2.9	1.6	3.1	3.1
1975	8.5	6.9	1.9	4.2	3.4	3.4	4.6
1976	7.7	7.1	2.0	4.6	3.4	3.9	5.9
1977	7.1	8.1	2.0	5.2	3.4	4.1	6.4
1978	6.1	8.3	2.3	5.4	3.3	4.1	6.3
1979	5.8	7.4	2.1	6.1	2.9	4.4	5.4
1980	7.1	7.5	2.0	6.5	2.8	4.4	7.0
1981	7.6	7.5	2.2	7.6	4.0	4.9	10.5
1982	9.7	11.0	2.4	8.3	5.6	5.4	11.3
1983	9.6	11.8	2.7	8.6	[3]6.9	5.9	11.8
1984	7.5	11.2	2.8	10.0	7.1	5.9	11.8
1985	7.2	10.5	2.6	10.5	7.2	6.0	11.2
1986	7.0	9.5	2.8	10.6	6.6	[3]7.5	11.2
1987	6.2	8.8	2.9	10.8	6.3	7.9	10.3
1988	5.5	7.8	2.5	10.3	6.3	7.9	8.6
1989	5.3	7.5	2.3	9.6	5.7	7.8	7.3
1990	5.5	8.1	2.1	9.1	5.0	7.0	6.9
1991	6.7	10.3	2.1	9.6	4.3	[3]6.9	8.8
1992	7.4	11.3	2.2	10.4	4.6	7.3	10.0
1993	6.8	11.2	2.5	11.8	5.8	[3]10.5	10.4
1994	[3]6.1	10.3	—	—	—	11.6	9.5
	Manufacturing hourly compensation in U.S. dollars (1982 = 100)[4]						
1969	—	30.4	14.6	20.5	18.1	20.6	17.4
1970	—	33.9	17.4	21.6	22.9	25.1	20.1
1971	—	37.7	20.7	24.4	27.0	29.4	23.7
1972	—	41.3	27.3	29.4	32.5	34.9	28.3
1973	—	44.3	37.4	38.4	44.2	41.2	31.6
1974	—	52.2	45.6	42.1	51.6	48.1	36.1
1975	—	57.3	52.1	58.2	59.7	60.5	45.8
1976	—	67.7	56.2	59.9	62.9	59.0	43.1
1977	62.8	69.5	68.6	66.1	74.5	65.7	46.9
1978	67.9	69.8	94.0	81.4	92.8	78.8	60.0
1979	74.4	74.8	95.5	97.5	109.1	97.4	78.7
1980	83.3	83.0	98.3	113.3	119.3	111.1	104.4
1981	91.5	93.1	107.6	101.8	102.2	100.9	105.1
1982	100.0	100.0	100.0	100.0	100.0	100.0	100.0
1983	102.7	106.2	107.7	95.3	99.9	104.3	92.9
1984	106.0	105.9	111.0	90.2	93.9	103.5	88.2
1985	111.3	105.6	115.0	95.0	96.0	107.0	93.8
1986	115.8	107.8	171.2	128.4	135.6	142.7	112.3
1987	118.4	116.3	204.2	153.4	171.4	173.3	136.9
1988	123.1	130.9	234.4	160.6	182.1	179.3	156.0
1989	127.9	141.2	231.2	158.1	178.4	187.0	162.8
1990	134.7	151.3	237.5	195.1	222.2	238.1	183.3
1991	141.9	163.4	270.6	196.3	230.5	254.3	201.8
1992	147.9	161.5	300.5	216.6	256.7	274.4	218.1
1993	152.8	152.1	352.2	209.5	259.6	230.5	195.4

Source: Economic Report of the President (Washington, D.C.: U.S. Government Printing Office, 1995), Table B-109.
[1]Data are for West Germany only.
[2]Civilian unemployment rates, approximating U.S. concepts. Quarterly data for France and Germany should be viewed as less precise indicators of unemployment under U.S. concepts than the annual data.
[3]There are breaks in the series for Germany (1983), Italy (1986, 1991, and 1993), and United States (1994). Based on the prior series, the rate for Germany was 7.2 percent in 1983, and the rate for Italy was 6.3 percent in 1986 and 6.6 in 1991. The break in 1993 raised Italy's rate by approximately 1.1 percentage points. For details on break in series in 1994 for United States, see footnote 5, Table B-33.
[4]Hourly compensation in manufacturing, U.S. dollar basis. Data relate to all employed persons (wage and salary earners and the self-employed) in the United States and Canada, and to all employees (wage and salary earners) in the other countries. For France and United Kingdom, compensation adjusted to include changes in employment taxes that are not compensation to employees, but are labor costs to employers.

TABLE 23
Growth rates in real gross domestic product, 1976–94
[percent change at annual rate]

Area and country	1976–85	1986	1987	1988	1989	1990	1991	1992	1993	1994[1]
World	3.4	3.6	4.0	4.7	3.4	2.2	0.9	1.7	2.3	3.1
Industrial countries	2.8	2.9	3.2	4.4	3.3	2.4	.8	1.5	1.3	2.7
United States	2.9	2.9	3.1	3.9	2.5	1.2	−.6	2.3	3.1	3.7
Canada	3.4	3.3	4.2	5.0	2.4	−.2	−1.8	.6	2.2	4.1
Japan	4.2	2.6	4.1	6.2	4.7	4.8	4.3	1.1	.1	.9
European Union	2.3	2.9	2.9	4.3	3.5	3.0	1.2	1.1	−.3	2.1
France	2.3	2.5	2.3	4.4	4.3	2.5	.8	1.2	−1.0	1.9
Germany[2]	2.2	2.3	1.5	3.7	3.6	5.7	2.9	2.2	−1.1	2.3
Italy	3.1	2.9	3.1	4.1	2.9	2.1	1.2	.7	−.7	1.5
United Kingdom[3]	1.9	4.3	4.8	5.0	2.2	.4	−2.0	−.5	2.0	3.3
Developing countries	4.5	4.8	5.7	5.3	4.2	3.8	4.5	5.9	6.1	5.6
Africa	2.4	2.4	1.4	3.9	3.6	1.9	1.4	.2	1.0	3.3
Asia	6.4	6.7	8.0	9.2	5.7	5.8	6.2	8.2	8.5	8.0
Middle East and Europe	3.5	2.5	6.0	.3	3.7	4.0	1.9	7.0	4.8	1.4
Western Hemisphere	3.3	4.1	3.3	1.0	1.6	.3	3.4	2.5	3.4	2.8
Countries in transition[4]	3.7	3.6	2.8	4.3	2.2	−3.5	−11.8	−15.5	−9.0	−8.3
Central and eastern Europe	—	—	—	—	—	—	−11.5	−11.7	−5.7	−5.4
Russia	—	—	—	—	—	—	−13.0	−19.0	−12.0	−12.0

Source: *Economic Report of the President* (Washington, D.C.: U.S. Government Printing Office, 1995), Table B-111.
[1] All figures are forecats. For United States, preliminary estimates by the Department of Commerce show that real GDP grew at a 4.0 percent annual rate in 1994.
[2] Through 1990 data are for West Germany only.
[3] Average of expenditure, income, and output estimates of GDP at market prices.
[4] For most countries included in the group, total output is measured by real net material product (NMP) or by NMP-based estimates of GDP.